SPE Petroleum Engineering Certification and PE License Exam Reference Guide

SPE Petroleum Engineering Certification and PE License Exam Reference Guide

Ali Ghalambor, PhD, PE

Society of Petroleum Engineers

Disclaimer

This book was prepared by members of the Society of Petroleum Engineers and their well-qualified colleagues from material published in the recognized technical literature and from their own individual experience and expertise. While the material presented is believed to be based on sound technical knowledge, neither the Society of Petroleum Engineers nor any of the authors or editors herein provide a warranty either expressed or implied in its application. Correspondingly, the discussion of materials, methods, or techniques that may be covered by letters patents implies no freedom to use such materials, methods, or techniques without permission through appropriate licensing. Nothing described within this book should be construed to lessen the need to apply sound engineering judgment nor to carefully apply accepted engineering practices in the design, implementation, or application of the techniques described herein.

ISBN 978-1-61399-410-8

14 15 16 17 18 19/ 9 8 7 6 5 4 3 2 1

Society of Petroleum Engineers
222 Palisades Creek Drive
Richardson, TX 75080-2040 USA

http://www.spe.org/store
service@spe.org
1.972.952.9393

Table of Contents

Foreword vii

Acknowledgments ix

1. Reservoir Engineering 1
   1.1 Volume Calculations 1
   1.2 Drive Mechanisms 5
   1.3 Stages of Production 6
   1.4 Well Performance 9
   1.5 Secondary Recovery Processes 11
   1.6 Tertiary Recovery Processes 17
   1.7 Reserves Estimations 18
   1.8 Reservoir Simulation 21

2. Drilling Engineering 27
   2.1 Geomechanics 27
   2.2 Drilling Fluids 30
   2.3 Fluid Mechanics 38
   2.4 Well Control 45
   2.5 Drilling Mechanics 52
   2.6 Tubular Mechanics 61
   2.7 Casing Design 67
   2.8 Cementing 71
   2.9 Well Planning 74
   2.10 Drilling Problems 81

3. Formation Evaluation 99
   3.1 Archie's Water Saturation 99
   3.2 Formation Resistivity Factor 99
   3.3 Flushed Zone Water Saturation 100
   3.4 Porosity Calculations From Sonic Data 100
   3.5 Young's Modulus 100
   3.6 Bulk Modulus 101
   3.7 Shear Modulus 101
   3.8 Poisson's Ratio 101
   3.9 D-exponent 101
   3.10 Porosity/Bulk Density 102
   3.11 Saturation 102
   3.12 Skin Calculations 104
   3.13 Horizontal Flow Influx Equations 107

4. Production Engineering 117
   4.1 Inflow/Outflow Performance 117
   4.2 Impact of Length and Force Changes to the Tubing String 121
   4.3 Tubing Design 122
   4.4 Perforating 125
   4.5 Acidizing 132
   4.6 Fracturing 135
   4.7 Sand Control 143
   4.8 Well Production Problems 145
   4.9 Artificial Lift 149

5. Facilities 159
   5.1 Separation Units 159
   5.2 Treating and Processing Units 161
   5.3 Pumps 166

5.4   Compressors 168

5.5   Pipelines 172

5.6   Flow Measurement Units 178

5.7   Storage Facilities 181

5.8   Electrical Systems 186

6. Petroleum Economics **195**

6.1   Valuation of Oil and Gas Reserves 195

6.2   Reservoir Management 196

6.3   Investment Decision Analysis 198

6.4   Risk Analysis 199

7. Conversion Factors **203**

References **205**

Foreword

The Society of Petroleum Engineers has a vision to "enable the global oil and gas E&P industry to share technical knowledge needed to meet the world's energy needs in a safe and environmentally responsible manner." One way of achieving this vision is by sustaining the competency, professionalism, impartiality, and integrity of the personnel within the industry. SPE has responded to this challenge by establishing the SPE Professional Certification (SPEC), which offers members a vehicle to develop their technical competencies and skills across the entire field of petroleum engineering. The SPEC is internationally recognized and represents a high standard of knowledge in different areas of petroleum engineering via an exam that includes engineering fundamentals and complex practical problems.

The SPE Certification Exam has been offered internationally for 8 years and is complemented by an SPE short course that gives candidates insight into the range of topics that the exam will cover and the style of questions that they will face. Initially, no specific course manual existed; in most cases, the SPE *Petroleum Engineering Handbook* series was the main source of reference for the course.

In the summer of 2008, the SPE Engineering Professionalism Committee discussed the idea of writing a book that could be used as a single reference for the SPE Certification Exam and Exam Review Course. The initial concept of the book was that it would be the one-stop, go-to reference for future oil and gas industry professionals, with all major concepts, equations, charts, tables, and formulas between its covers. The initial idea of the reference book soon evolved into a "Quick Reference Guide for Petroleum Engineers," but because the primary intended use for the book was as a reference for the SPE Certification and US PE exams, it finally evolved into the *SPE Petroleum Engineering Certification and PE License Exam Reference Guide* that you are holding today.

The guide has been written for a wide range of audiences and, therefore, will have many applications and uses. It will be of value to university students, recent graduates, and young professionals within the oil and gas industry and academia. However, it is also intended specifically for use by experienced professionals who are working on day-to-day projects and require access to a broader appreciation of petroleum engineering immediately outside of their specific areas of expertise.

Along with being of great value before and during examinations, the guide will also be of great use in the workplace. This guide complements the *Petroleum Engineering Handbook* series by summarizing all of the concepts in a single volume. As a result, there is no need to carry a suitcase full of books on every assignment. The book is expected to become commonplace in every department and on every desk, platform, or rig in the oil and gas industry. Additionally, the book is anticipated to be the first-stop reference when oil industry professionals are faced with any upstream or downstream problem.

With this in mind, the *SPE Petroleum Engineering Certification and PE License Exam Reference Guide* was written in a way that will allow oil industry professionals to apply a formula or an equation that may not be at the forefront of their minds to their daily processes and procedures without having to cross-reference other texts. The fact that the book is aimed at professionals who have been in the industry for some time allows the user to be familiar with the concepts behind the procedures, so there is no need for a real textbook-style explanation behind their derivation.

In tune with the SPE vision, daily use of the guide by working engineers will increase professional standards and knowledge sharing, therefore creating an industry that "meets the world's energy needs in a safe and environmentally responsible manner."

Dr. Mohammed Razik Shaikh, SPEC

Acknowledgments

The SPE Petroleum Professional Certification Subcommittee gratefully acknowledges the contributions of the author of the *SPE Petroleum Engineering Certification and PE License Exam Reference Guide*, Prof. Ali Ghalambor, and the SPE Engineering Professionalism Committee. Additionally, the Subcommittee recognizes past and present committee members for their encouragement in preparing this guide. The Subcommittee also recognizes the review effort by the SPE Petroleum Engineering Certification and US Engineering Registration subcommittees. The Author acknowledges the assistance of Mr. Foad Haeri in literature search and gathering of information. Finally, the Author welcomes suggestions for improvements and communicating any discovery of errors and omissions for correction.

Chapter 1

Reservoir Engineering

This chapter contains equations to help study and analyze various aspects of reservoir engineering, including the estimation of original oil in place in saturated and undersaturated oil reservoirs, and the original gas in place in dry gas, wet gas, and retrograde gas condensate reservoirs using both volumetric and material balance methods. The chapter also includes relationships for many reservoir drive mechanisms, such as depletion, segregation, and water drive production stages, by considering reservoir flow behavior, geometry, and fluid compressibility, and pressure drawdown and buildup analysis. Furthermore, the chapter provides the equations for enhanced oil recovery methods using water, gas, and polymer injection, and parameters considering such issues as interfacial tension, capillary pressure, mobility ratio, oil recovery efficiency, waterflood patterns, and polymer retention measurements. Finally, the chapter includes methods to estimate reserves, such as exponential, hyperbolic, and harmonic decline methods, and numerical calculations of reservoir simulation.

1.1 Volume Calculations

Original Oil in Place in Volumetric Undersaturated Oil Reservoirs

Volume Method

Above bubblepoint pressure

$$N = \frac{7758 \times A \times h \times \phi \times (1 - S_{wi})}{B_{oi}}$$

N Original oil in place, STB
A Area of the zone, acres
h Thickness of the zone, ft
ϕ Porosity, unitless
B_{oi} Oil formation volume factor at initial reservoir pressure, bbl/STB
S_{wi} Water saturation at initial reservoir pressure, unitless

Below bubblepoint pressure

$$N = \frac{7758 \times A \times h \times \phi \times (1 - S_{wi} - S_g)}{B_o}$$

N Original oil in place, STB
A Area of the zone, acres
h Thickness of the zone, ft
ϕ Porosity, unitless
B_o Oil formation volume factor, bbl/STB
S_{wi} Water saturation at initial reservoir pressure, unitless
S_g Gas saturation, unitless

Material Balance Method

Above bubblepoint pressure

$$N = \frac{N_p B_o}{B_{oi}\left[\dfrac{c_o S_o + c_w S_{wi} + c_f}{1 - S_{wi}}\right]\Delta p}$$

N Original oil in place, STB
N_p Cumulative oil produced, STB
B_o Oil formation volume factor, bbl/STB
B_{oi} Oil formation volume factor at initial reservoir pressure, bbl/STB
Δp Change in volumetric reservoir pressure, psia
c_o Oil compressibility, psi^{-1}
c_w Water compressibility, psi^{-1}
c_f Formation compressibility, psi^{-1}
S_o Oil saturation, unitless
S_{wi} Water saturation at initial reservoir pressure, unitless

Below bubblepoint pressure

$$N_r = \frac{N_p[B_t + (R_p - R_{si})B_g]}{B_t - B_{ti}}$$

N_r Original oil remaining, STB
N_p Cumulative oil produced, STB
B_t Two-phase oil formation volume factor, bbl/STB
B_{ti} Two-phase oil formation volume factor at initial reservoir pressure, bbl/STB
B_g Gas formation volume factor, bbl/scf
R_p Cumulative produced gas/oil ratio, scf/STB
R_{si} Solution gas/oil ratio at initial reservoir pressure, scf/STB

Oil Remaining in the Reservoir After a Period of Production in Undersaturated Oil Reservoirs With Water Influx

Volume Method

$$N_r = \frac{7758 \times A \times h \times \phi \times (1 - S_{wi} - S_{or})}{B_{oi}}$$

N_r Oil remaining in place, STB
A Area of the zone, acres
h Thickness of the zone, ft
ϕ Porosity, unitless
B_{oi} Oil formation volume factor at initial reservoir pressure, bbl
S_{wi} Water saturation at initial reservoir pressure, unitless
S_{or} Residual oil saturation, unitless

Original Oil in Place in Undersaturated Oil Reservoirs With Water Influx

Material Balance Method

$$N = \frac{N_p\left[B_t + \left(R_p - R_{si}\right)B_g\right] - W_e + B_w W_p}{B_t - B_{ti}}$$

N Initial oil in place, STB
N_p Cumulative oil produced, STB
B_t Two-phase oil formation volume factor, bbl/STB

B_{ti} Two-phase oil formation volume factor at initial reservoir pressure, bbl/STB
B_w Water formation volume factor, bbl/STB
B_g Gas formation volume factor, bbl/scf
W_p Cumulative produced water, STB
W_e Water influx, bbl
R_p Cumulative produced gas/oil ratio, scf/STB
R_{si} Solution gas/oil ratio at initial reservoir pressure, scf/STB

Original Oil in Place in Saturated Oil Reservoirs

Volume Method

$$N = \frac{7758 \times A_{oz} \times h_{oz} \times \phi_{oz} \times (1 - S_{wioz})}{B_{oi}}$$

N Original oil in place, STB
A_{oz} Area of the oil zone, acres
h_{oz} Average net thickness of the oil zone, ft
ϕ_{oz} Average porosity in the oil zone, unitless
B_{oi} Oil formation volume factor at initial reservoir pressure, bbl/STB
S_{wioz} Initial average connate water saturation in the oil zone, unitless

Material Balance Method: (With Water Influx)

$$N = \frac{N_p \left[B_t + \left(R_p - R_{si} \right) B_g \right] - W_e + B_w W_p}{B_t - B_{ti} + \dfrac{m B_{ti}}{B_{gi}} \left(B_g - B_{gi} \right)}$$

N Initial oil in place, STB
N_p Cumulative oil produced, STB
B_t Two-phase oil formation volume factor, bbl/STB
B_{ti} Two-phase oil formation volume factor at initial reservoir pressure, bbl/STB
B_w Water formation volume factor, bbl/STB
B_g Gas formation volume factor, bbl/scf
B_{gi} Gas formation volume factor at initial reservoir pressure, bbl/scf
W_p Cumulative produced water, STB
W_e Water influx, bbl
R_p Cumulative produced gas/oil ratio, scf/STB
R_{si} Solution gas/oil ratio at initial reservoir pressure, scf/STB
m Ratio of initial reservoir free gas volume to initial reservoir oil volume, unitless

Original Gas in Place in Volumetric Dry Gas, Wet Gas, and Retrograde Gas Condensate Reservoirs

Volume Method

$$G = \frac{7758 \times A \times h \times \phi \times (1 - S_{wi})}{B_{gi}}$$

G Original gas in place, scf
A Area of the zone, acres
h Thickness of the zone, ft
ϕ Porosity, unitless
B_{gi} Gas formation volume factor at initial reservoir pressure, bbl/scf
S_{wi} Water saturation at initial reservoir pressure, unitless

Material Balance Method

$$\frac{p}{z} = \frac{p_i}{z_i} \left(1 - \frac{G_p}{G} \right)$$

Recovery Factor

$$RF = \frac{G_p}{G} = \frac{B_g}{\left(B_g - B_{gi}\right)}$$

G Original gas in place, scf
G_p Cumulative gas produced, scf
p Pressure, psi
z Gas compressibility factor, unitless
B_{gi} Initial gas formation volume factor, bbl/scf
B_g Gas formation volume factor, bbl/scf

Specific gravity of a reservoir gas

$$\gamma_r = \frac{R\gamma_g + 4584\gamma_o}{R + 132800\gamma_o / M_o}$$

R Gas liquid ratio, scf/STB
γ_g Gas specific gravity
γ_o Oil specific gravity
M_o Molecular weight of oil (condensate)

Original Gas in Place in Gas Reservoirs With Water Influx

Material Balance Method

$$G = \frac{G_p B_g - W_e + B_w W_p}{B_g - B_{gi}}$$

G Initial gas in place, scf
G_p Cumulative gas produced, scf
B_w Water formation volume factor, bbl/STB
B_g Gas formation volume factor, bbl/scf
B_{gi} Gas formation volume factor at initial reservoir pressure, bbl/scf
W_p Cumulative produced water, STB
W_e Water influx, bbl

Material Balance Expressed as a Linear Equation (by Havlena and Odeh)

$$F = N\left(E_o + mE_g + E_{f,w}\right) + W_e B_w$$

$$F = N_p\left[B_o + \left(R_p - R_{so}\right)B_g\right] + W_p B_w$$

$$E_o = \left(B_o - B_{oi}\right) + \left(R_{soi} - R_{so}\right)B_g$$

$$E_g = B_{oi}\left(\frac{B_g}{B_{gi}} - 1\right)$$

$$E_{f,w} = \left(1 + m\right)B_{oi}\left(\frac{c_w S_{wi} + c_f}{1 - S_{wi}}\right)\Delta p$$

N Initial oil in place, STB
N_p Cumulative oil produced, STB
B_o Oil formation volume factor, bbl/STB
B_g Gas formation volume factor, bbl/scf
B_{oi} Initial oil formation volume factor, bbl/STB
B_{gi} Initial gas formation volume factor, bbl/scf

Δp Change in volumetric reservoir pressure, psia
c_o Oil compressibility, psi^{-1}
c_w Water compressibility, psi^{-1}
c_f Formation compressibility, psi^{-1}
S_{wi} Water saturation at initial reservoir pressure, unitless
S_o Oil saturation, unitless
R_p Cumulative produced gas/oil ratio, scf/STB
R_{soi} Initial solution gas/oil ratio, scf/STB
R_{so} Solution gas/oil ratio, scf/STB
m Ratio, $= GB_{gi}/NB_{oi}$

1.2 Drive Mechanisms

Depletion Drive Index (DDI)

$$DDI = \frac{N\left(B_t - B_{ti}\right)}{N_p\left[B_t + \left(R_p - R_{soi}\right)B_g\right]}$$

Segregation Drive Index (SDI)

$$SDI = \frac{G\left(B_g - B_{gi}\right)}{N_p\left[B_t + \left(R_p - R_{soi}\right)B_g\right]}$$

Water Drive Index (WDI)

$$WDI = \frac{W_e - W_p B_w}{N_p\left[B_t + \left(R_p - R_{soi}\right)B_g\right]}$$

Expansion Drive Index (EDI)

$$EDI = \frac{NB_{oi}(1+m)\left[\dfrac{c_w S_{wi} + c_f}{1 - S_{wi}}\right]\Delta p}{N_p\left[B_t + (R_p - R_{soi})B_g\right]}$$

$$DDI + SDI + WDI + EDI = 1$$

N Initial oil in place, STB
N_p Cumulative oil produced, STB
G Initial gas in place, scf
W_e Water influx into reservoir, bbl
W_p Cumulative water produced, STB
B_t Two-phase formation volume factor, bbl/STB, $= B_o + \left(R_{soi} - R_{so}\right)B_g$
B_o Oil formation volume factor, bbl/STB
R_p Cumulative produced gas/oil ratio, scf/STB
R_{soi} Initial solution gas/oil ratio, scf/STB
R_{so} Solution gas/oil ratio, scf/STB
B_{ti} Initial two-phase formation volume factor, bbl/STB, $= B_{oi}$
B_{oi} Initial oil formation volume factor, bbl/STB
B_g Gas formation volume factor, bbl/scf
B_{gi} Initial gas formation volume factor, bbl/scf
B_w Water formation volume factor, bbl/STB
c_w Water compressibility, psi^{-1}
c_f Formation compressibility, psi^{-1}
S_{wi} Water saturation at initial reservoir pressure, unitless
Δp Change in volumetric reservoir pressure, psia
m Ratio, $= GB_{gi}/NB_{oi}$

Solution Gas Drive Mechanism

Above the Bubblepoint Pressure

$$N_p B_o = N B_{oi} \left(\frac{(B_o - B_{oi})}{B_{oi}} + \frac{(c_o S_o + c_w S_{wi} + c_f)}{1 - S_{wi}} \Delta p \right)$$

Below the Bubblepoint Pressure

$$N_p \left[B_o + (R_p - R_{so}) B_g \right] = N \left[(B_o - B_{oi}) + (R_{soi} - R_{so}) B_g \right]$$

Gas-Cap Drive Mechanism

$$N_p \left[B_o + (R_p - R_{so}) B_g \right] = N B_{oi} \left[\frac{(B_o - B_{oi}) + (R_{soi} - R_{so}) B_g}{B_{oi}} + m \left(\frac{B_g}{B_{gi}} - 1 \right) \right]$$

Water Drive Mechanism

$$W_e = (c_w + c_f) W_i \Delta p$$

N Initial oil in place, STB
N_p Cumulative oil produced, STB
B_o Oil formation volume factor, bbl/STB
B_g Gas formation volume factor, bbl/scf
B_{oi} Initial oil formation volume factor, bbl/STB
B_{gi} Initial gas formation volume factor, bbl/scf
Δp Change in volumetric reservoir pressure, psia
c_o Oil compressibility, psi^{-1}
c_w Water compressibility, psi^{-1}
c_f Formation compressibility, psi^{-1}
S_{wi} Water saturation at initial reservoir pressure, unitless
S_o Oil saturation, unitless
R_p Cumulative produced gas/oil ratio, scf/STB
R_{soi} Initial solution gas/oil ratio, scf/STB
R_{so} Solution gas/oil ratio, scf/STB
W_e Water influx into reservoir, bbl
W_i Initial volume of water, bbl
m Ratio, $= G B_{gi} / N B_{oi}$

1.3 Stages of Production

Darcy's Law

$$u = -\frac{k}{\mu} \frac{dp}{dL}$$

u Velocity, ft/sec
k Permeability, md
μ Viscosity, cp
P Pressure, psia
L Distance, ft

Steady-State Linear Flow of Incompressible Fluids

$$q = \frac{0.001127 \, k \, A \, (p_1 - p_2)}{\mu \, L}$$

q Flow rate, B/D
k Absolute permeability, md
p Pressure, psia
μ Viscosity, cp
L Distance, ft
A Cross-sectional area, ft^2

Steady-State Linear Flow of Slightly Compressible Fluids

$$q_{\text{ref}} = \left[\frac{0.001127\,k\,A}{\mu\,c\,L}\right]\ln\left[\frac{1+c\left(p_{\text{ref}}-p_2\right)}{1+c\left(p_{\text{ref}}-p_1\right)}\right]$$

q_{ref} Flow rate at a reference pressure, p_{ref}, B/D
p_1 Upstream pressure, psi
p_2 Upstream pressure, psi
k Absolute permeability, md
μ Viscosity, cp
c Average liquid compressibility, psi^{-1}

Steady-State Linear Flow of Compressible Fluids

$$Q_{sc} = \frac{0.003164\,T_{sc}\,A\,k\left(p_1^{\,2}-p_2^{\,2}\right)}{p_{sc}\,T\,L\,z\,\mu_g}$$

Q_{sc} Gas flow rate at standard conditions, scf/D
k Permeability, md
T Temperature, °R
μ_g Gas viscosity, cp
A Cross-sectional area, ft^2
L Total length of the linear system, ft

Steady-State Radial Flow of Incompressible Fluids

$$Q_o = \frac{0.00708\,k\,h\left(p_e - p_{wf}\right)}{\mu_o\,B_o\left[\ln\left(r_e/r_w\right)+s\right]}$$

Q_o Oil flow rate, STB/D
p_e External pressure, psi
p_{wf} Bottomhole flowing pressure, psi
k Permeability, md
μ_o Oil viscosity, cp
B_o Oil formation volume factor, bbl/STB
h Thickness, ft
r_e External or drainage radius, ft
r_w Wellbore radius, ft
s Skin factor, unitless

Steady-State Radial Flow of Slightly Compressible Fluids

$$Q_o = \left[\frac{0.00708\,k\,h}{\mu_o\,B_o\,c_o\left[\ln\left(r_e/r_w\right)+s\right]}\right]\ln\left[1+c_o\left(p_e - p_{wf}\right)\right]$$

Q_o Oil flow rate, STB/D
p_e External pressure, psi
p_{wf} Bottomhole flowing pressure, psi
k Permeability, md
μ_o Oil viscosity, cp

B_o Oil formation volume factor, bbl/STB
h Thickness, ft
r_e External or drainage radius, ft
r_w Wellbore radius, ft
c_o Isothermal compressibility coefficient, psi^{-1}
s Skin factor, unitless

Steady-State Radial Flow of Compressible Fluids

$$Q_g = \frac{0.703\,k\,h\,(\psi_e - \psi_w)}{T \ln(r_e/r_w)}$$

$$Q_{g(P<2000)} = \frac{k\,h\,(p_e^2 - p_{wf}^2)}{1422\,T(\mu_g z)_{avg} \ln(r_e/r_w)}$$

Qg Gas flow rate, scf/D
k Permeability, md
h Thickness, ft
T Temperature, °R
r_e External or drainage radius, ft
r_w Wellbore radius, ft
μ_g Gas viscosity, cp
z Gas compressibility factor
ψ_e Real gas pseudopressure as evaluated from 0 to p_e, psi^2/cp
ψ_w Real gas pseudopressure as evaluated from 0 to p_{wf}, psi^2/cp
p_e External pressure, psi
p_{wf} Bottomhole flowing pressure, psi

Unsteady-State (Transient) Radial Flow of Slightly Compressible Fluids (Diffusivity Equation)

$$\frac{\partial^2 p}{\partial r^2} + \frac{1}{r}\frac{\partial p}{\partial r} = \frac{\phi\mu c_t}{0.006328\,k}\frac{\partial p}{\partial t}$$

k Permeability, md
r Radial position, ft
p Pressure, psia
c_t Total compressibility, psi^{-1} $c_t = c_o S_o + c_w S_w + c_g S_g + c_f$
t Time, days
ϕ Porosity, unitless
μ Viscosity, cp

Unsteady-State (Transient) Radial Flow of Compressible Fluids (Diffusivity Equation)

$$\frac{\partial^2 m(p)}{\partial r^2} + \frac{1}{r}\frac{\partial m(p)}{\partial r} = \frac{\phi\mu c_t}{0.000264\,k}\frac{\partial m(p)}{\partial t}$$

$$m(p_{wf}) = m(p_i) - 57895.3\left(\frac{p_{sc}}{T_{sc}}\right)\left(\frac{Q_g T}{kh}\right)\left[\log\left(\frac{kt}{\phi\mu_i c_{ti} r_w^2}\right) - 3.23\right]$$

p_e Initial reservoir pressure, psi
p_{wf} Bottomhole flowing pressure, psi
Q_g Gas flow rate, Mscf/D
t Time, hr
k Permeability, md
p_{sc} Standard pressure, psi
T_{sc} Standard temperature, °R
T Reservoir temperature, °R
r_w Wellbore radius, ft

h Thickness, ft
μ_i Gas viscosity at the initial pressure, cp
c_{ti} Total compressibility coefficient at p_i, psi^{-1}
ϕ Porosity

Pseudosteady-State Radial Flow of Slightly Compressible Fluids

$$Q = \frac{0.00708\,k\,h\,(\bar{p}_r - p_{wf})}{\mu B\left[\ln\left(r_e/r_w\right) - 0.75 + s\right]}$$

Q Flow rate, STB/D
$\bar{p}_r$ Average reservoir pressure, psi
p_{wf} Bottomhole flowing pressure, psi
k Permeability, md
h Thickness, ft
μ Oil viscosity, cp
B Formation volume factor, bbl/STB
r_e External or drainage radius, ft
r_w Wellbore radius, ft
s Skin factor, unitless

Pseudosteady-State Radial Flow of Compressible Fluids

$$Q_g = \frac{k\,h\left[\bar{p}_r^{\,2} - p_{wf}^{\,2}\right]}{1422\,T\,\bar{\mu}\,\bar{z}\left[\ln\left(r_e/r_w\right) - 0.75 + s\right]}$$

Q_g Flow rate, STB/D
$\bar{p}_r$ Average reservoir pressure, psi, $= \sqrt{\left(p_r^{\,2} + p_{wf}^{\,2}\right)/2}$ for $p < 2000$
p_{wf} Bottomhole flowing pressure, psi
k Permeability, md
h Thickness, ft
T Temperature, °R
$\bar{\mu}$ Oil viscosity, cp
$\bar{z}$ Gas compressibility factor
r_e External or drainage radius, ft
r_w Wellbore radius, ft
s Skin factor, unitless
ϕ Porosity, unitless

The E$_i$-Function Solution to Diffusivity Equation (Constant Rate)

$$p_{wf} = p_i - \frac{162.6\,Q_o\,B_o\,\mu_o}{k\,h}\left[\log\left(\frac{kt}{\phi\mu_o c_t r_w^2}\right) - 3.23 + 0.87s\right]$$

p_{wf} Bottomhole flowing pressure, psi
p_i Initial reservoir pressure, psi
k Permeability, md
t Time, hr $t > 9.48 \times 10^4 \left(\phi\mu_o c_t r^2/k\right)$
h Thickness, ft
μ_o Oil viscosity, cp
B_o Oil formation volume factor, bbl/STB
Q_o Oil flow rate, STB/D
r_w Wellbore radius, ft
c_t Total compressibility, psi^{-1}

1.4 Well Performance

Pressure Drawdown Analysis (or Constant Terminal Rate Solutions)

$$k = \frac{162.6q\mu\beta}{mh}$$

$$s = 1.151\left[\frac{P_i - P_{1hr}}{m} - \log\frac{k}{\phi\mu c_t r_w^2} + 3.23\right]$$

$$t_{wbs} \cong \frac{(200,000 + 12,000s)C_s}{(kh/\mu)}$$

$$C_s = \frac{q\beta}{24}\frac{\Delta t}{\Delta p}$$

Δt and Δp are values read from a point on the unit-slope line on log-log plot. Less acceptable alternative is to use the actual mechanical properties of the well:

For a Well With Rising Liquid/Gas Interface in the Wellbore

$$C_s = 25.65\frac{A_{wb}}{\rho}$$

For a Wellbore Containing Only Single-Phase Fluid

$$C_s = c_{wb}V_{wb}$$

Reservoir Pore Volume

$$V_p = \frac{-0.234qB}{c_t\left(\dfrac{\partial p_{wf}}{\partial p_t}\right)}, \quad \text{ft}^3$$

$\left(\dfrac{\partial p_{wf}}{\partial p_t}\right)$ is the slope of the straight line p_{wf} vs. t plot on Cartesian graph paper.

Transient Period

E_i form (at any r):

$$p(r,t) = p_i + \frac{70.6Q\,B\,\mu}{k\,h}E_i\left[-\frac{948\phi\mu c_t r^2}{kt}\right]$$

Log form valid for $\dfrac{948\phi\mu_o c_t r^2}{kt} < 0.01$:

$$p(r,t) = p_i - m\left[\log\left(\frac{kt}{\phi\mu c_t r^2}\right) - 3.23\right]$$

Pseudosteady State

$$p_{wf}(t) = p_i - m\left[\log\left(\frac{4A}{\gamma C_A r_w^2}\right) - 0.87S\right] - \frac{0.2339QBt}{c_t Ah\phi}$$

Time (hours) when pseudosteady state begins:

$$t = \frac{\phi\mu c_t At_{DA}}{0.000264k}$$

t_{DA} Dependent on reservoir shape factor C_A, which could be read from the table, "Exact for t_{DA}" column

Pressure Buildup Analysis

Horner Equation

$$p_{ws}\left(\Delta t\right) = p_i - m \log\left(\frac{t_p + \Delta t}{\Delta t}\right)$$

$$k = \frac{162.6 q \mu B}{m h}$$

$$r_i = \left(\frac{kt}{948 \phi \mu c_t}\right)^{1/2}$$

$$S = 1.151\left[\frac{\left(p_{1hr} - p_{w\Delta t=0}\right)}{m} - \log\left(\frac{k}{\mu c_t \phi r_w^2}\right) + 3.23\right]$$

$$t_{wbs} \cong \frac{170,000 C_s e^{0.14s}}{\left(kh/\mu\right)}$$

$$C_s = \frac{q\beta}{24}\frac{\Delta t}{\Delta p}$$

Δt and Δp are values read from a point on the unit-slope line on log-log plot. Less acceptable alternative is to use the actual mechanical properties of the well:

For a Well With Rising Liquid/Gas Interface in the Wellbore

$$C_s = 25.65\frac{A_{wb}}{\rho}$$

For a Wellbore Containing Only Single-Phase Fluid

$$C_s = c_{wb}V_{wb}$$

p_{wf}	Wellbore flowing pressure, psi
p_{ws}	Wellbore pressure during buildup, psi
$p_{w\Delta t=0}$	Wellbore pressure at instant of shut-in, psi
p_{1hr}	Horner shut-in pressure, psi, at $\Delta t = 1$hr
t_p	Effective producing time, hr
ϕ	Porosity, unitless
h	Thickness, ft
μ	Oil viscosity, cp
B	Oil formation volume factor, bbl/STB
k	Permeability, md
c_t	Total compressibility, psi^{-1}
r_w	Wellbore radius, ft
Δt	Shut-in time, hr
Q	Oil flow rate, STB/D
r_w	Wellbore radius, ft
c_t	Total compressibility, psi^{-1}
γ	Euler's constant = 1.781
A	Drainage area, ft^2
C_A	Dietz shape factor, unitless = 31.62 for a circular reservoir
m	Slope, psi/log cycle = $\dfrac{162.6 QB\mu}{kh}$
C_s	Wellbore storage constant, bbl/psi
A_{wb}	Wellbore area, ft^2
ρ	Density of liquid in wellbore, lbm/ft^3
c_{wb}	Compressibility of liquid in wellbore, psi^{-1}
V_{wb}	Wellbore volume, bbl
t_{wbs}	Wellbore storage duration, hr

1.5 Secondary Recovery Processes

Interfacial tension (IFT)

$$\sigma = \frac{rh(\rho_w - \rho_a)g}{2\cos\theta}$$

σ Interfacial tension, dynes/cm
r Capillary tube radius, cm
h Height of water rise in the capillary, cm
ρ_w Water density, g/cm³
ρ_a Air density, g/cm³
g Gravity acceleration constant, 980 cm/s²
θ Contact angle between water and capillary tube, degree

Capillary Pressure in a Tube

$$p_c = \frac{2\sigma\cos\theta}{r}$$

p_c Capillary pressure, dynes/cm²
σ Interfacial tension between two immiscible phases, dynes/cm
θ Contact angle, degree
r Radius of the capillary tube, cm

Mobility Ratio of Water to Oil

$$M_{w,o} = \frac{(\lambda_w)_{S_{or}}}{(\lambda_o)_{S_{wc}}} = \left(\frac{k_{rw}}{\mu_w}\right)_{S_{or}} \left(\frac{\mu_o}{k_{ro}}\right)_{S_{wc}}$$

λ_w Mobility of displacing fluid or water behind the front
λ_o Mobility of displaced fluid or oil ahead of the front
S_{or} Residual oil saturation
S_{wc} Connate water saturation
k_{rw} Relative permeability to water evaluated at residual oil saturation S_{or}
k_{ro} Relative permeability to oil evaluated at connate water saturation S_{wc}
μ_o Oil viscosity, cp
μ_w Water viscosity, cp

Fractional Flow Equation for Water Displacing Oil in a Linear Horizontal System

$$f_w = \frac{1}{1 + \left(\dfrac{k_o}{k_w}\right)\left(\dfrac{\mu_w}{\mu_o}\right)}$$

k_w Permeability to water, darcies
k_o Permeability to oil, darcies
μ_w Viscosity of water, cp
μ_o Viscosity of oil, cp

General Form of Fractional Flow Equation

$$f_w = \frac{1 + \left(\dfrac{0.001127k_o A}{\mu_o q_t}\right)\left[\dfrac{\partial p_c}{\partial x} - 0.433\Delta\rho\sin\alpha\right]}{1 + \left(\dfrac{k_o}{k_w}\right)\left(\dfrac{\mu_w}{\mu_o}\right)}$$

f_w Fraction of water (water cut), bbl/bbl
k_w Effective permeability of water, md

k_o Effective permeability of oil, md
μ_w Viscosity of water, cp
μ_o Viscosity of oil, cp
A Cross-sectional area, ft^2
$\Delta\rho$ Water-oil density differences, g/cm^3
q_t Total flow rate, B/D
α Dip angle
x Distance
p_c Capillary pressure, psi

Frontal Advanced Equation (Buckley-Leverett)

$$x = \frac{5.615q_t t}{\phi A}\left(\frac{df_w}{dS_w}\right)_{S_w}$$

x Distance traveled by a fixed saturation in time t, ft
q_t Total flow rate, B/D
t Time interval, days
ϕ Porosity, fraction
A Cross-sectional area of flow, ft^2

$\left(\dfrac{df_w}{dS_w}\right)_{S_w}$ Slope of fractional flow curve at S_w

Breakthrough Time

$$t_{bt} = \frac{LA\phi}{q_i\left(\dfrac{df_w}{dS_w}\right)_{S_{wf}}}$$

Δt Time to water breakthrough at the producer, days
q_i Injection rate, B/D
L Linear distance from injection well to production well, ft
A Cross-sectional area, ft^2
ϕ Porosity
S_{wf} Water saturation at the producing well

$\left(\dfrac{df_w}{dS_w}\right)_{S_{wf}}$ Slope of the main tangent line at S_{wf}

Hall Plot Equation for Monitoring the Performance of the Injector

$$\sum\Delta\left(p_{inj} - \bar{p}\right)\times\Delta t = m_H W_i$$

Δt Injection time, days
p_{inj} Bottomhole injection pressure, psia
$\bar{p}$ Average reservoir pressure, psia
W_i Cumulative water injection volume, bbl
m_H Slope, $= \dfrac{141.2\,\mu_w\left[\ln\left(r_e/r_w\right)\right]}{k_w h}$
k_w Effective permeability to water, md
r_e External radius, ft
r_w Wellbore radius, ft
μ_w Water viscosity, cp
h Formation thickness, ft

To predict the critical velocity required to propagate a stable interface through a linear system in which gravity forces dominate, with piston-like displacement and neglected P_c effects:

$$q_c = \frac{\left(4.9 \times 10^{-1}\right) k k_{rw} A (\rho_w - \rho_o) \sin \alpha}{\mu_w (M-1)}$$

ρ_o Oil density, lbm/ft^3
ρ_w Water density, lbm/ft^3
α Dip angle, degree
k_{rw} Relative permeability to water, fraction
k Absolute permeability, darcies
A Cross-sectional area, ft^2
μ_w Water viscosity, cp
M Mobility ratio

Displacement Efficiency of a Waterflood

$$E_D = 1 - \frac{S_{or}/B_{oa}}{S_{oi}/B_{oi}}$$

S_{or} Residual oil saturation
S_{oi} Initial oil saturation
B_{oa} Oil formation volume factor at the beginning of waterflood
B_{oi} Oil formation volume factor at the waterflood pressure

Overall Waterflood Oil Recovery Efficiency

$$E_R = E_D E_I E_A$$

E_D Unit displacement efficiency
E_I Vertical displacement efficiency
E_A Areal displacement efficiency

Displacement Efficiency

$$E_D = \frac{\overline{S}_w - S_{wi} - S_{gi}}{1 - S_{wi} - S_{gi}}$$

$\overline{S}_w$ verage water saturation in the swept area
S_{wi} Initial water saturation at the start of the flood
S_{gi} Initial gas saturation at the start of the flood

Areal Sweep Efficiency

Before Breakthrough

$$E_A = \frac{W_{inj}}{(PV)(\overline{S}_{wBT} - S_{wi})}$$

$\overline{S}_{wBT}$ Average water saturation at breakthrough
W_{inj} Cumulative water injected, bbl
(PV) Flood pattern pore volume, bbl

At Breakthrough

$$E_{ABT} = 0.54602036 + \frac{0.03170817}{M} + \frac{0.30222997}{e^M} - 0.00509693M$$

E_{ABT} Areal sweep efficiency at breakthrough
M Mobility ratio

After Breakthrough

$$E_A = E_{ABT} + 0.633 \log\left(\frac{W_{inj}}{W_{iBT}}\right)$$

Water Injectivity Equation (Five-Spot Pattern Filled With Oil)

$$\left(\frac{i}{\Delta P}\right)_{base} = \frac{0.003541 h k k_{ro}}{\mu_o \left[\ln\dfrac{d}{r_w} - 0.619\right]}$$

i_{base} Base (initial) water injection rate, B/D
Δp_{base} Base (initial) pressure difference, psi
h Net thickness, ft
k Absolute permeability, md
k_{ro} Oil relative permeability as evaluated at S_{wi}
d Distance between injector and producer, ft
r_w Wellbore radius, ft
μ_o Oil viscosity, cp

Dimensionless Gravity Number

$$G = \frac{7.853 \times 10^{-6} k k_{rw} A (\rho_w - \rho_o)\sin\theta}{i_w \mu_w}$$

k Absolute permeability, md
k_{rw} Water relative permeability as evaluated at S_{or}
A Cross-sectional area, ft^2
ρ_w Water density, lbm/ft^3
ρ_o Oil density, lbm/ft^3
μ_w Water viscosity, cp
i_w Water injection rate, B/D
θ Dip angle, degree

Vertical sweep efficiency (Stiles' Method)

$$E_V = \frac{k_i \sum_{j=1}^{i} h_j + \sum_{j=i+1}^{i} (kh)_j}{k_i h_t}$$

i Breakthrough layer, i.e., $i = 1,2,3, \ldots n$
n Total number of layers
h_t Total thickness, ft
h_i Layer thickness, ft
k_i Layer permeability, md

Fill-Up Water Volume

$$V_w = S_g V_p / B_w$$

V_w Fill-up water volume, STB
V_p Reservoir pore volume, bbl, $= 7758 Ah\phi$
A Cross-sectional area, ft^2
h Thickness, ft
ϕ Porosity
B_w Water formation volume factor, bbl/STB

Recoverable Oil From Waterflooding

$$\text{STB} = \left[(S_o - S_{or}) \times V_p\right]/B_o$$

S_o Oil saturation
S_{or} Residual oil saturation
V_p Reservoir pore volume, bbl
B_o Oil formation volume factor, bbl/STB

Flood Front Map

$$r_{ob} = \left(\frac{5.615 I_{cw} E}{\pi \phi h S_g} \right)^{1/2}$$

r_{ob} Outer radius of the banked oil, ft
I_{cw} Cumulative water injected, bbl
S_g Gas saturation at start of injection, fraction
E Layer injection efficiency (fraction of water volume that enters the layer where effective waterflood is taking place)
h Thickness, ft

$$r_{wb} = r_{ob} \left(\frac{S_g}{\overline{S}_{wbt} - S_{iw}} \right)^{\frac{1}{2}}$$

r_{wb} Water bank radius, ft
$\overline{S}_{wbt}$ Average water saturation behind front, fraction
S_{iw} Connate water saturation, fraction
S_g Gas saturation, fraction

Waterflood Patterns
Direct Line Drive

$$q_i = \frac{3.541 kh \Delta p}{\mu \left(\ln \frac{a}{r_w} + 1.571 \frac{d}{a} - 1.838 \right)} \qquad \frac{d}{a} \geq 1$$

Staggered Line Drive

$$q_i = \frac{3.541 kh \Delta p}{\mu \left(\ln \frac{a}{r_w} + 1.571 \frac{d}{a} - 1.838 \right)}$$

Five-Spot

$$q_i = \frac{3.541 kh \Delta p}{\mu \left(\ln \frac{d}{r_w} - 0.619 \right)}$$

q Injection rate, B/D
k Permeability, md
h Thickness, ft
Δp Pressure difference, psi
μ Viscosity, cp
r_w Wellbore radius, ft
d Distance between a producer well and an injector well
a Distance between two producer wells or two injector wells

Reservoir Water Cut and the Water/Oil Ratio (WOR) Relationships

Reservoir f_w/Reservoir WOR_r Relationship

$$WOR_r = \frac{f_w}{1 - f_w}$$

Reservoir f_w/Surface WOR_s Relationship

$$WOR_s = \frac{B_o f_w}{B_w(1-f_w)}$$

Reservoir WOR_r/Surface WOR_s Relationship

$$WOR_s = WOR_r \left(\frac{B_o}{B_w} \right)$$

Surface f_{ws}/Surface WOR_s Relationship

$$f_{ws} = \frac{WOR_s}{WOR_s + 1}$$

Surface f_{ws}/Reservoir f_w Relationship

$$f_{ws} = \frac{B_o}{B_w \left(\dfrac{1}{f_w} - 1 \right) + B_o}$$

WOR_s	Surface water/oil ratio, STB/STB
WOR_r	Reservoir water/oil ration, bbl/bbl
f_{ws}	Surface water cut, STB/STB
f_w	Reservoir water cut, bbl/bbl
B_w	Water formation volume factor, bbl/STB
B_o	Oil formation volume factor, bbl/STB

1.6 Tertiary Recovery Processes

Welge Equation for the Fractional Flow of Gas

$$f_g = \frac{1 + \left(0.044 k k_{ro} \Delta\rho A \sin\alpha \middle/ q_t \mu_o \right)}{1 + 1/M}$$

A	Area of cross section normal to the bedding plane, ft^2
f_g	Fraction of flowing
k	Permeability, darcies
k_{ro}	Relative permeability to oil, fraction
k_{rg}	Relative permeability to gas, fraction
M	Mobility ratio, $= \dfrac{k_{rg}}{\mu_g} \dfrac{\mu_o}{\mu_{ro}}$
q_T	Total flow rate through the area, res ft^3/D
α	Angle of dip, positive downdip, degree
$\Delta\rho$	Density difference, lbm/ft^3, $= \rho_g - \rho_o$
μ_o	Viscosity of oil, cp
μ_g	Viscosity of gas, cp

Critical Rate in Displacing the Oil by Gas:

$$\left(\frac{q_T}{A} \right)_{critical} = \frac{0.044 k \Delta\rho \sin\alpha}{\dfrac{\mu_o}{k_{ro}} - \dfrac{\mu_g}{k_{rg}}}$$

q_T	Total volumetric flow rate through area, ft^3/D
k	Permeability, darcies
k_{ro}	Relative permeability to oil, fraction

k_{rg} Relative permeability to gas, fraction
α Angle of dip, positive downdip, degree
$\Delta\rho$ Density difference, lbm/ft³, $= \rho_g - \rho_o$
μ_o Viscosity of oil, cp
μ_g Viscosity of gas, cp
A Area of cross section normal to the bedding plane, ft²

Empirical Flory Equation for Polymers

$$d_p = 8\left(M_p[\eta]\right)^{\frac{1}{3}}$$

d_p Mean end-to-end distance of a polymer in solution, Angstroms (10^{-10} m)
$[\eta]$ Polymer's intrinsic viscosity, dL/g
M_p Polymer molecular weight

Resistant Factor of the Polymer Solution (Mobility Reduction)

$$R_f = \frac{\lambda_w}{\lambda_p}$$

λ_w Mobility of the solvent of the polymer solution
λ_p Mobility of the polymer solution

Resistant Factor of the Polymer Solution (Permeability Reduction)

$$R_{rf} = \frac{k_b}{k_a}$$

k_b Brine permeability measured before polymer flooding
k_a Brine permeability measured after polymer flooding

Polymer Retention Measurements

$$\Gamma_v = 2.7194 \ \ (1-\phi)\rho_{RG}$$

ϕ Porosity
ρ_{RG} Density of the reservoir rock grains (no porosity included)
Γ Mass of polymer absorbed onto reservoir rock, µg/g
Γ_v Mass of polymer absorbed per unit volume of reservoir rock, lbm/acre-ft

Prediction of MMP for Nitrogen or Lean Gas Injection (Firoozabadi and Aziz Correlation)

$$MMP = 9433 - 188 \times 10^3 \left(\frac{C_{2-5}}{M_{C7+}T^{0.25}}\right) + 1430 \times 10^3 \left(\frac{C_{2-5}}{M_{C7+}T^{0.25}}\right)^2$$

MMP Minimum miscibility pressure, psia
M_{C7+} Molecular weight of C_{7+}, lbm/lbm-mole
C_{2-5} Percent of C_2 through C_5 including CO_2 and H_2S in the reservoir fluid
T Reservoir temperature, °F

1.7 Reserves Estimations

Exponential Decline Method for Rate

$$q = q_i e^{-Dt}$$

Exponential Decline Method for Cumulative Oil Production

$$N_p = \frac{q_i - q}{D}$$

Exponential Decline Method for Nominal Decline Rate

$$D = -\ln\left(1 - D_e\right)$$

$$D_e = \frac{q_i - q}{q_i}$$

Exponential Decline Method for Effective Decline Rate

$$D_e = 1 - e^{-D}$$

Exponential Decline Method for Life

$$t = \frac{\ln\left(q_i/q\right)}{D}$$

q Well production rate at time t, STB/D
q_i Well production rate at time 0, STB/D
D Nominal exponential decline rate, 1/day
D_e Effective decline rate, 1/day
N_p Cumulative oil production, STB
t Time, day

Hyperbolic Decline Method for Rate

$$q = q_i \left(1 + bD_i t\right)^{-\frac{1}{b}}$$

Hyperbolic Decline Method for Cumulative Oil Production

$$N_p = \frac{q_i^{b}}{D_i \left(1 - b\right)} \left(q_i^{1-b} - q^{1-b}\right)$$

Hyperbolic Decline Method for Nominal Decline Rate

$$D_i = \frac{1}{b}\left[\left(1 - D_{ei}\right)^{-b} - 1\right]$$

$$D_{ei} = \frac{q_i - q}{q_i}$$

Hyperbolic Decline Method for Effective Decline Rate

$$D_e = 1 - e^{-D}$$

Hyperbolic Decline Method for Life

$$t = \frac{\left(q_i/q\right)^{b} - 1}{bD_i}$$

q Well production rate at time t, STB/D
q_i Well production rate at time 0, STB/D
D_i Initial nominal exponential decline rate ($t = 0$), 1/day
D_e Effective decline rate, 1/day
N_p Cumulative oil production, STB
b Hyperbolic exponent, $b > 0$, $b \neq 1$
t Time, day

Harmonic Decline Method for Rate

$$q = \frac{q_i}{1 + bD_i t}$$

Harmonic Decline Method for Cumulative Oil Production

$$N_p = \frac{q_i}{D_i} \ln \frac{q_i}{q}$$

Harmonic Decline Method for Nominal Decline Rate

$$D_i = \frac{D_{ei}}{1 - D_{ei}}$$

Harmonic Decline Method for Effective Decline Rate

$$D_{ei} = \frac{q_i - q}{q_i}$$

Harmonic Decline Method for Life

$$t = \frac{(q_i/q) - 1}{D_i}$$

q Well production rate at time t, STB/D
q_i Well production rate at time 0, STB/D
D_i Initial nominal exponential decline rate ($t = 0$), 1/day
D_{ei} Effective decline rate, 1/day
N_p Cumulative oil production, STB
b Hyperbolic exponent, =1
t Time, day

Analogy Method

$$F_{RS} = F_{RA} (\phi S_{hi})_S / (\phi S_{hi})_A$$

F_{RS} Recovery factor, subject reservoir
F_{RA} Recovery factor, analogous reservoir
ϕ Porosity
S_{hi} Initial hydrocarbon saturation, fraction

Volumetric Method

Initial Reserves of Oil

$$N_{Ri} = N_i E_{Ro} = \left[7758 \phi_o (1 - S_{wo}) A_o h_{no} / B_{oi} \right] E_{Ro}$$

N_{Ri} Initial oil reserves, STB
N_i Initial oil in place, STB
E_{Ro} Recovery efficiency of oil, fraction
ϕ_o Porosity
S_{wo} Water saturation in the oil zone, fraction
A_o Area of the oil zone, acres
h_{no} Average net oil pay, ft
B_{oi} Initial oil formation volume factor, bbl/STB

Initial Reserves of Solution Gas

$$G_{RSi} = G_{Si} E_{Rg} = N_i R_{si} E_{Rg}$$

G_{RSi} Initial solution gas reserves, scf
G_{Si} Initial solution gas in place, scf
E_{Rg} Recovery efficiency of gas, fraction
N_i Initial oil in place, STB
R_{si} Initial solution gas/oil ratio, scf/STB

The Volumetric Estimate of Gas in Place (GIP) in Coalbed Reservoirs

$$G_i = Ah \left[\frac{43560 \phi_f \left(1 - S_{wfi} \right)}{B_{gi}} + 1359 C_{gi} \rho_c \left(1 - f_a - f_m \right) \right]$$

G_i Gas in place at initial reservoir conditions, scf
A Area of accumulation, acres
h Thickness, ft
ϕ_f Interconnected fracture (effective) porosity, fraction
S_{wfi} Interconnected fracture water saturation, fraction
C_{gi} Initial sorbed gas concentration, scf/ton
ρ_c Coal density, g/cm^3
f_a Average weight fraction of ash, fraction
f_m Average weight fraction of moisture, fraction

Shale Gas Reserves Estimation

$$G_i = 1359 A h_s \rho C_{gi}$$

G_i Gas in place at initial reservoir conditions, scf
A Area of accumulation, acres
h_s Shale thickness, ft
C_{gi} Initial sorbed gas concentration, scf/ton

1.8 Reservoir Simulation

Molar Conservation Equation for Component k

Dispersion

$$\nabla \cdot \left[\sum_{\ell=1}^{n_p} \phi S_\ell \, \underline{D}_{k\ell} \rho_\ell \cdot \nabla x_{k\ell} \right]$$

Convection

$$-\nabla \cdot \left[\sum_{\ell=1}^{n_p} x_{k\ell} \rho_\ell V_\ell \right]$$

Source/Sink

$$+Q_k$$

Accumulation

$$= \frac{\partial}{\partial t} \left[\phi \sum_{\ell=1}^{n_p} x_{k\ell} \rho_\ell S_\ell \right]$$

Darcy's Law

$$V_\ell = -\underline{K} \frac{k_{r\ell}}{\mu_\ell} \cdot \left(\nabla P_\ell - \gamma_\ell \nabla z \right)$$

$\underline{D}_{kl}$ Dispersion tensor of component k in phase l
$\underline{K}$ Permeability tensor
k_{rl} Relative permeability of phase l
n_c Number of component
n_p Number of phases

P_l Pressure of phase l
S_l Saturation of phase l
V_l Darcy's velocity for phase l
x_{kl} Mole fraction of component k in phase l
γ_l Pressure gradient of phase l
μ_l Viscosity of phase l
ρ_l Density of phase l
ϕ Porosity

Finite Difference Approximation

Fluid Flow Equation

$$\frac{\partial}{\partial x}\left[\frac{Kk_r}{\mu B}\left(\frac{\partial P}{\partial x}\right)\right] + q_s \delta(x - x_0) = \frac{\partial}{\partial t}\left(\frac{\phi S}{B}\right)$$

Discretizing Region Into Gridblock Δx

$$\frac{\partial P}{\partial x} \approx \frac{P_{i+1} - P_i}{x_{i+1} - x_i} = \frac{\Delta P}{\Delta x}$$

Discretizing Time Into Timesteps Δt

$$\frac{\partial S}{\partial x} \approx \frac{S^{n+1} - S^n}{t^{n+1} - t^n} = \frac{\Delta S}{\Delta x}$$

Conservation Equation for Block i

$$\text{M}_{iI}^{n+1} - \text{M}_{iI}^n = \Delta t\left(\sum_{j=1}^{j=N} q_{ijI} - q_{iI}\right) \qquad I = 1, 2, \ldots n$$

M_{iI} Mass of component I in gridblock i
q_{ijI} Interblock flow rate of component I from neighbor block j to block i, volume/time
q_{iI} Interblock flow rate of component I from neighbor block j to block i, volume/time

Interblock Flow Term (Implicit and Explicit)

$$q_{ijI} = T_{ij} \sum_{J=1}^{J=3} \lambda_j \rho_J x_{iJ}\left(\Delta p_J - \gamma_J \Delta Z\right)$$

q_{ijI} Interblock flow rate of component I from neighbor block j to block I, volume/time
T_{ij} Transmissibility connecting locks i and j, md-ft/cp
λ_j Phase mobility of block j, md/cp
ρ_J Density of component J, mass/volume
x_{iJ} Mole fraction of component I in phase J
Δp_J Pressure difference in phase J
γ_J Phase density of J, psi/ft
ΔZ Depth difference to gridblock center, ft

Mass Conservation Equations for a Timestep From T to $T + \Delta T$

$$V_{pa}^{T+\Delta T} \cdot m_{ca}^{T+\Delta T} - V_{pa}^T \cdot m_{ca}^T = \Delta T \cdot \left(Q_{ca} + \sum_b \sum_p F_{cpab}\right)$$

V_{pa} Pore volume of cell a
m_{ca} Density of conserved component c in cell a
Q_{ca} Injection or production rate of component c because of wells
F_{cpab} Flow rate of component c in phase p from cell a to its neighbor b

Total Runtime of Any Streamline Simulation

$$T \propto \sum_{1}^{n_{ts}} \left(t^{\text{solver}} + \sum_{1}^{n_{sl}} t_j^{sl} \right)$$

n_{ts} Number of timesteps (number of streamline updates)

t^{solver} Time required to solve for the global pressure field $Ax = b$ at each timestep

n_{sl} Number of streamlines at each timesteps

t_j^{sl} Time to solve transport equation for each streamline

Governing Implicit Pressure Explicit Saturation (IMPES) Equations for Streamline Method

$$\nabla \cdot \sum_{j=1}^{n_p} \frac{\bar{k} k_{rj}}{\mu_j} \left(\nabla \cdot P + \rho_j \vec{g} D \right) = 0$$

$$\phi \frac{\partial S_j}{\partial t} + \vec{u_t} \cdot \nabla f_j + \nabla \cdot \vec{G_j} = 0$$

$$f_j = \frac{k_{rj}}{\mu_j} \frac{1}{\sum_{j=1}^{n_p} k_{rj} \Big/ \mu_j}$$

$$\vec{G_j} = \bar{k} \cdot g f_j \nabla D \sum_{j=1}^{n_p} k_{ri} \left(\rho_i - \rho_j \right) / \mu_j$$

k Permeability

k_{rj} Relative permeability of phase j

k_{ri} Relative permeability of phase i

μ_i Viscosity

ρ_i Phase density of phase i

ρ_j Phase density of phase j

g Gravitational acceleration

u_t Total velocity

S_j Saturation of phase j

G_j Phase velocity of phase j

f_j Fractional flow of phase j

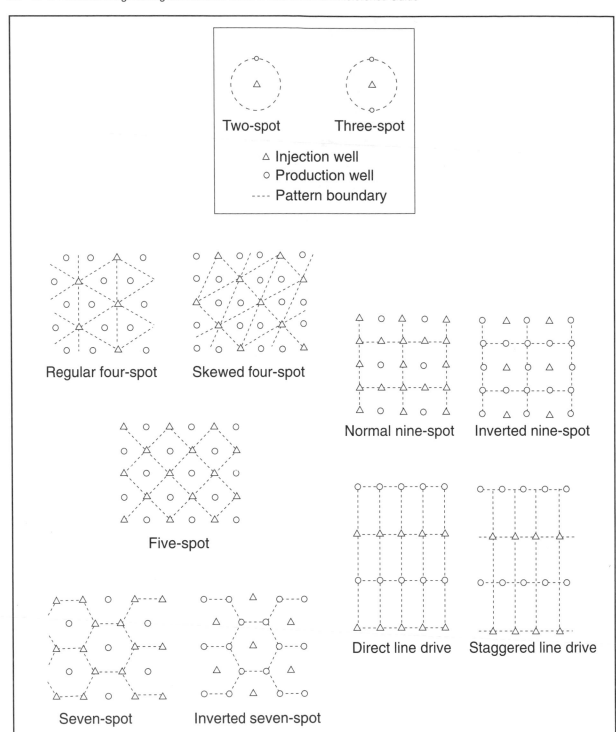

Fig. 1.1—Waterflooding well patterns (Willhite 1986).

Bounded reservoirs	ln C_A	C_A	for $\dfrac{kt}{\varphi\mu cA} >$		ln C_A	C_A	for $\dfrac{kt}{\varphi\mu cA} >$
		Stabilized conditions				**Stabilized conditions**	
⬤ circle	3.45	31.6	0.1	rect dot top	2.38	10.8	0.3
⬛ square	3.43	30.9	0.1	rect dot right	1.58	4.86	1.0
⬡ hexagon	3.45	31.6	0.1	rect dot left-center	0.73	2.07	0.8
△ triangle	3.32	27.6	0.2	rect	1.00	2.72	0.8
▱ parallelogram	3.30	27.1	0.2	rect	−1.46	0.232	2.5
right triangle 1/3 / 1	3.12	21.9	0.4	rect	−2.16	0.115	3.0
rect 1/2	3.12	22.6	0.2	square grid	1.22	3.39	0.6
rect 1/4	1.68	5.38	0.7	rect grid	1.14	3.13	0.3
rect 1/5	0.86	2.36	0.7	rect grid	−0.50	0.607	1.0
square grid	2.56	12.9	0.6	rect grid	−2.20	0.111	1.2
square grid	1.52	4.57	0.5	triangle 3 / 4	−2.32	0.098	0.9

In water-drive reservoirs

	ln C_A	C_A	for $\dfrac{kt}{\varphi\mu cA} >$
⊙	2.95	19.1	0.1

In reservoirs of unknown production character

	ln C_A	C_A	for $\dfrac{kt}{\varphi\mu cA} >$
⊙	3.22	25	0.1

Fig. 1.2—Dietz shape factor for various geometries (Dake 1978).

Chapter 2

Drilling Engineering

This chapter contains equations to the solutions of various drilling problems. Included are equations estimating formation pressure, fracture gradient pressure, geomechanics, and methods to estimate stresses. Furthermore, the chapter includes nearly all the major equations to design drilling and completion fluids such as those to calculate weight, rheological properties, solids content of mud, and trip calculations. One can also find the equations for various hydraulics calculations, such as those for pump design, cutting transport calculations, and well control equations. The chapter also holds many equations for the design of drilling rig equipment and auxiliary units such as pumps, motors, and turbines. The section on tubular mechanics includes the relationships for tubing and drillstring design, casing design, cementing, and jar calculations. The section on well planning also includes equations for predicting well trajectory and path, and directional well calculations. Finally, the chapter includes many equations for such drilling problems as stuck pipe calculations, lost circulation, and hole cleaning.

2.1 Geomechanics

Formation Pressure

Hubbert and Willis Method

$$\sigma_z = \sigma_{ob} - p_p$$

$$p_{ff\min} = \frac{1}{3}\left(\sigma_{ob} + 2p_p\right)$$

$$p_{ff\max} = \frac{1}{2}\left(\sigma_{ob} + p_p\right)$$

σ_z Matrix stress, psi
σ_{ob} Overburden pressure, psi
p_p Pore pressure, psi
p_{ff} Fracture pressure, psi

Matthews and Kelly Correlation

$$p_{ff} = F_\sigma \sigma_z + p_p$$

p_{ff} Fracture pressure, psi
σ_z Matrix stress, psi
p_p Pore pressure, psi
F_σ Matrix coefficient

Eaton Method

$$p_{ff} = \left(\frac{\mu}{1-\mu}\right)\left(\sigma_{ob} - p_p\right) + p_p$$

p_{ff} Fracture pressure, psi

σ_{ob} Overburden pressure, psi

P_p Pore pressure, psi
μ Poisson's ratio

Christman Method

$$p_{ff} = \left(\rho_w D_w - \rho_b D_f \right)$$

p_{ff} Fracture pressure, psi
ρ_w Water density, g/cm³
ρ_b Bulk density, g/cm³
D_w Water depth, ft
D_f Formation depth, ft

Leakoff Pressure

$$p_{ff} = \frac{p_s}{0.052 \times D_v} + \rho_{test}$$

p_{ff} Equivalent mud weight to fracture the formation, ppg
p_s Surface leakoff pressure during the test, psi
D_v True vertical depth of the formation tested, ft
ρ_{test} Mud weight during the test, ppg

Horizontal Stress and Pore Pressure

$$\Delta S_{Hmax} = \Delta S_{Hmin} = \alpha \left(1 - 2v \right) / \left(1 - v \right) \Delta P_p$$

ΔS_{Hmax} Change in greatest horizontal stress, psi
ΔS_{Hmin} Change in least horizontal stress, psi
α Biot poroelastic coefficient $= 1 - K_{dry}/K_{grain}$
v Poisson's ratio
K_{dry} Bulk modulus of the dry frame of a porous rock, GPa
K_{grain} Bulk modulus of the grains that make up the rock, GPa

Effective Stress and Pore Pressure

$$\sigma_{ij} = S_{ij} - \delta_{ij} P_p$$

σ_{ij} Effective stress acting in the i direction on a plane perpendicular to the j direction, psi
S_{ij} Component of stress tensor acting in the x_j direction on a plane perpendicular to x_i, psi
δ_{ij} Kronecker delta ($\delta_{ij} = 1$, if $i = j$; $\delta_{ij} = 0$ otherwise)
P_p Pore pressure, psi

Rock Elasticity

$$\sigma_{ij} = M_{ijkl} \varepsilon_{kl} \qquad \text{where} \qquad \varepsilon_{kl} = \Delta l_k / l_l$$

σ_{ij} Effective stress acting in the i direction on a plane perpendicular to the j direction, psi
M_{ijkl} Component of the modulus tensor that relates the ij component of the stress tensor to the kl component of the strain tensor, psi
ε_{kl} Component of strain acting in the l direction per unit length in the k direction

Effective Hoop Stress

$$\sigma_{\theta\theta} = S_{Hmin} + S_{Hmax} - 2 \left(S_{Hmax} - S_{Hmin} \right) \cos 2\theta - 2P_p - \Delta P - \sigma^{\Delta T}$$

θ Angle around the wellbore measured from the S_{Hmax} direction, degree
$\sigma_{\theta\theta}$ Effective hoop stress, psi
ΔP Difference between the wellbore pressure (mud weight) and the pore pressure
P_p Pore pressure, psi

S_{Hmax} Maximum horizontal stress, psi

S_{Hmin} Minimum horizontal stress, psi

$\sigma^{\Delta T}$ Thermal stress induce by cooling of the wellbore by ΔT, psi

ΔT Temperature difference between the fluid in a well and the adjacent rock

Thermal Effect of the Wellbore Wall

$$\sigma_{\theta\theta}^{\Delta T} = \left(\alpha E \Delta T\right)/\left(1-v\right)$$

α Biot poroelastic coefficient

E Young's modulus, GPa

ΔT Temperature difference between the fluid in a well and the adjacent rock

v Poisson's ratio

Overburden Pressure

$$S_v\left(Z_o\right) = \int_0^{Z_o} \rho_b G dz$$

G Gravitational coefficient

S_v Vertical stress, psi

ρ_b Bulk density

Z_o Depth, ft

Pore Pressure

Equivalent Depth Method

$$P_z = P_a + \left(S_z - S_a\right)$$

P_z Pore pressure at depth z, psi

P_a Pore pressure at depth a, psi

S_z Stress at depth z, psi

S_a Stress at depth a, psi

Ratio Methods

$$P_p = P_{hyd}\Delta T_{log}/\Delta T_n$$

$$P_p = P_{hyd}\rho_n/\rho_{log}$$

$$P_p = P_{hyd}R_n/R_{log}$$

P_p Pore pressure, psi

P_{hyd} Hydrostatic pressure, psi

ΔT_{log} Measured value of sonic transit time at a given depth, μs/ft

ΔT_n Normal value of sonic transit time at a given depth, μs/ft

R_{log} Measured value of resistivity, ohm-m

R_{log} Normal value of resistivity, ohm-m

Eaton Methods

$$P_p = S - \left(S - P_{hyd}\right)\left(R_{log}/R_n\right)^{1.2}$$

$$P_p = S - \left(S - P_{hyd}\right)\left(\Delta T_n/\Delta T_{log}\right)^{3.0}$$

P_p Pore pressure, psi

P_{hyd} Hydrostatic pressure, psi

S Total stress, psi

ΔT_{log} Measured value of sonic transit time at a given depth, μs/ft

ΔT_n Normal value of sonic transit time at a given depth, μs/ft
R_{log} Measured value of resistivity, ohm-m
R_{log} Normal value of resistivity, ohm-m

Effective Stress Methods

$$P_p = S_v - \left[1/\beta \ln\left(\phi_o / \phi \right) \right] \quad \text{where} \quad \phi = 1 - \left(\Delta t_{ma} / \Delta t \right)^{1/f}$$

P_p Pore pressure, psi
S_v Vertical stress, psi
ϕ Porosity
Δt Transit time, μs/ft
Δt_{ma} Matrix transit time, μs/ft

Mud-Rock Interactions

$$\Delta P = E_m \left(RT / V \right) \ln \left(A_p / A_m \right)$$

ΔP Difference between the wellbore pressure (mud weight) and the pore pressure
E_m Membrane efficiency, ratio
R Gas constant, J/mol/°K
T Absolute temperature, °K
V Molar volume of water, L/mol
A_p Pore fluid activity, ratio
A_m Mud activity, ratio

2.2 Drilling Fluids

Equivalent Mud Weight

$$EMW = \frac{P}{0.052 \times L_{tvd}}$$

EMW Equivalent mud weight, ppg
P Wellbore or formation pressure, psi
L_{tvd} True vertical depth, ft, $= D_h \cos \alpha$ for deviated wells

Mud Weighting

Required Weighting Material

$$W_{wm} = \frac{42 \left(\rho_f - \rho_o \right)}{1 - \left(\rho_f / \rho_{wm} \right)}$$

W_{wm} Required amount of weighting materials, lbm/bbl
ρ_f Final mud density, ppg
ρ_o Original mud density, ppg
ρ_{wm} Density of weighting material, ppg

Average Weight Density

$$\rho_{av} = \frac{\rho_i \rho_j}{f_w f_i + \left(1 + f_w \right) \rho_j}$$

ρ_{av} Average weight density, ppg
ρ_i Weight of material i, ppg
ρ_j Weight of material j, ppg
f_w Weight fraction of material j with respect to added weights of materials i and j
f_i Weight fraction of material i with respect to added weights of materials i and j

Required Liquid Volume

$$V_l = V_f \left(\frac{1-\left(\rho_f / \rho_a\right)}{1-\left(\rho_l / \rho_a\right)_j} \right)$$

V_l Amount of liquid volume required to make a mud, bbl
V_f Total mud volume, bbl
ρ_f Total mud weight, ppg
ρ_a Weight density of added material, ppg
ρ_l Weight density of liquid, ppg

Required Amount of Solids

$$w_i = \frac{\left(1-f_w\right)\left(\rho_f - \rho_o\right)}{\left[1-f_w\left(\rho_o / \rho_i\right)-\left(1-f_w\right)\left(\rho_o / \rho_i\right)\right]}$$

w_i Solid materials i of final mud, lbm/bbl
f_w Weight fraction of material j with respect to added weights of materials i and j
ρ_f Final mud density, ppg
ρ_o Original mud density, ppg
ρ_i Weight of material i, ppg

Final Mud Density

$$\rho_f = \frac{\rho_o + \alpha \rho_l}{1+\alpha}$$

ρ_f Final mud density, ppg
ρ_l Density of liquid, ppg
α $= V_l / V_o$
V_l Liquid volume, bbl
V_o Original volume, bbl

Mud Dilution

$$\rho_f = \rho_o + \left(\frac{V_a}{V_o}\right)\left(\rho_o - \rho_a\right)$$

ρ_f Density of the diluted mud, ppg
ρ_o Original mud weight, ppg
ρ_a Density of the material added, ppg
V_a Original volume, bbl
V_o Final volume, bbl

Base Fluid Water/Oil Ratio

$$\frac{P_b}{P_w} = \frac{VR_b}{VR_w}$$

P_b Percentage of base fluid
P_w Percentage of base water
VR_b Volume percentage of base fluid
VR_w Volume percentage of water

Fluid Loss

$$V_f = A\left[\frac{2k\left(f_{vc}/f_{vm}-1\right)\Delta pt}{\mu}\right]^{\frac{1}{2}} + V_s$$

V_f Filter volume
A Filtration area
k Cake permeability
Δp Differential pressure
t Filtration time
μ Filtrate viscosity
V_s Volume of solids deposited in mudcake
f_{vc} Volume of fraction of solids in cake
f_{vm} Volume of fraction of solids in mud

Acidity-Alkalinity

$$pH = -\log\left(\left[H^+\right]\right)$$

$$pH = -\log\left(\left[OH^-\right]\right)$$

$\left[H^+\right]$ Hydrogen ion concentration, mol/L
$\left[OH^-\right]$ Hydroxide ion concentration, mol/L

Mud Rheology

Newtonian Fluid

$$\tau = \mu\gamma$$

Bingham Plastic Model

$$\tau = \tau_y + \mu_p\gamma$$

$$\mu_p = \frac{300}{N_2 - N_1}\left(\theta_{N_2} - \theta_{N_1}\right)$$

$$\tau_y = \theta_{N_1} - \mu_p \frac{N_1}{300}$$

Power-Law Model

$$\tau = K\gamma^n$$

$$n = \frac{\log\left(\theta_{N_2}/\theta_{N_1}\right)}{\log\left(N_2/N_1\right)} \qquad K = \frac{510\,\theta_N}{\left(1.703 \times N\right)^n}$$

τ Share stress, dynes/cm^2, lbm/100 ft^2
γ Shear rate, sec^{-1}
μ Newtonian viscosity, poise, cp
τ_y Yield stress, dynes/cm^2, lbm/100 ft^2
μ_p Bingham plastic viscosity, poise, cp
K Consistency index, lb-sec^n/ft^2
n Flow behavior index, lb-sec^n/ft^2
N Fann, rev/min
θ_N Fann dial reading at N rev/min

Solids Calculation

Low-Gravity Solids

$$V_{LG} = \frac{100\rho_f}{\left(\rho_B - \rho_{LG}\right)} + \frac{\left(\rho_B - \rho_f\right)}{\left(\rho_B - \rho_{LG}\right)}V_s - \frac{12}{\left(\rho_B - \rho_{LG}\right)}MW - \frac{\left(\rho_f - \rho_o\right)}{\left(\rho_B - \rho_{LG}\right)}V_o$$

ρ_f Density of filtrate, g/cm^3
ρ_B Density of barite, g/cm^3

ρ_{LG} Density of low-gravity solids, g/cm³
ρ_o Density of oil, g/cm³
V_S Volume percentage of suspended solids
V_o Volume percentage of oil
MW Mud weight, ppg

Density of the Filtrate

$$\rho_f = 1.0 + 6.45 \times 10^{-7}[NaCl] + 1.67 \times 10^{-3}[KCl] + 7.6 \times 10^{-7}[CaCl_2] + 7.5 \times 10^{-7}[MgCl_2]$$

$[NaCl]$ Concentration of NaCl in filtrate, mg/L
$[KCl]$ Concentration of KCl in filtrate, ppb
$[CaCl_2]$ Concentration of CaCl₂ in filtrate, mg/L
$[MgCl_2]$ Concentration of MgCl₂ in filtrate, mg/L

Total Suspended Solids

$$V_S = 100 - V_o - \frac{V_W}{\left(\rho_f - 10^{-6}\left\{[NaCl] + [CaCl_2] + [MgCl_2] - 0.00286[KCl]\right\}\right)}$$

V_W Volume percentage of water
V_o Volume percentage of oil

Low-Gravity Solids in Water-based Drilling Fluid

$$\% \text{ vol Low-Gravity Solids} = \frac{(\% \text{ vol solids})(\text{Barite SG-ASG})}{(\text{Barite SG} - \text{Low-Gravity SG})}$$

$$ASG = \frac{12 MW - (\% \text{ vol water})(\rho_w) - (\% \text{ vol oil})(\rho_o)}{\% \text{ vol solids}} \qquad \text{ASG: Average Specific Gravity}$$

Drilling Wastes

$$S = \varepsilon \times HV / F_s$$

S Volume of wet drilled solids, bbl
ε Efficiency of solids control, fraction
HV Hole volume, bbl
F_s Fraction of solids in the discard stream

$$L = HV \times (1 - \varepsilon) / T \qquad \text{or} \qquad L = DS_L / T$$

L Liquid discard, bbl
HV Hole volume, bbl
ε Efficiency of solids control, fraction
T Tolerance of the fluid system to solids contamination, fraction
DS_L Solids buildup in the drilling fluid

Pressure Gradient Using Mud Weight

$$\text{Pressure Gradient (psi / ft)} = \text{Mud Weight (ppg)} \times 0.052$$

Hydrostatic Pressure (HP) Using Mud Weight

$$HP = \text{Mud Weight (ppg)} \times 0.052 \times \text{True Vertical Depth (ft)}$$

Specific Gravity (SG) Using Mud Weight

$$SG = \text{Mud Weight}\,(\text{ppg}) \div 8.33$$

Equivalent Circulating Density (ECD)

$$\text{ECD (ppg)} = \frac{\text{annular pressure loss (psi)}}{0.052 \times \text{True Vertical Depth (ft)}} + \text{Mud Weight in Use (ppg)}$$

Maximum Allowable Mud Weight From Leakoff Test Data

$$\text{Maximum allowable mud weight (ppg)} = \frac{\text{leakoff pressure (psi)}}{0.052 \times \text{Casing Shoe TVD (ft)}} + \text{Mud Weight (ppg)}$$

Total Solids Generated

$$W_{cg} = 350Ch \times L\,(1-P)\,SG$$

W_{cg} Solids generated, lbm
Ch Capacity of hole, bbl/ft
L Footage drilled, ft
SG Specific gravity of cuttings
P Porosity, %

Maximum Drilling Rate (MDR) Using Mud Weight

$$\text{MDR (ft/hr)} = \frac{67 \times \left(\dfrac{\text{mud wt}}{\text{out, ppg}} - \dfrac{\text{mud wt}}{\text{in, ppg}}\right) \times \left(\dfrac{\text{circulation}}{\text{rate, gpm}}\right)}{Dh^2}$$

Buoyancy Factor (BF) Using Mud Weight

$$BF = \frac{65.5 - \text{mud weight, ppg}}{65.5}$$

Hydrostatic Pressure (HP) Decrease When Pulling Pipe Out of the Hole

When Pulling DRY Pipe

$$\text{HP decrease, psi} = \frac{\text{barrels displaced}}{\left(\begin{array}{c}\text{casing}\\\text{capacity,}\\\text{bbl/ft}\end{array}\right) - \left(\begin{array}{c}\text{pipe}\\\text{displacement,}\\\text{bbl/ft}\end{array}\right)} \times 0.052 \times \text{mud weight, ppg}$$

$$\text{barrels displaced} = \begin{array}{c}\text{number}\\\text{of stands}\\\text{pulled}\end{array} \times \begin{array}{c}\text{average}\\\text{length per}\\\text{stand, ft}\end{array} \times \begin{array}{c}\text{pipe}\\\text{displacement,}\\\text{bbl/ft}\end{array}$$

When Pulling WET Pipe

$$\text{HP decrease, psi} = \frac{\text{barrels displaced}}{\left(\begin{array}{c}\text{casing}\\\text{capacity,}\\\text{bbl/ft}\end{array}\right) - \left(\begin{array}{c}\text{pipe disp., bbl/ft}\\+\\\text{pipe cap., bbl/ft}\end{array}\right)} \times 0.052 \times \text{mud weight, ppg}$$

$$\text{barrels displaced} = \begin{array}{c}\text{number}\\\text{of stands}\\\text{pulled}\end{array} \times \begin{array}{c}\text{average}\\\text{length per}\\\text{stand, ft}\end{array} \times \left(\begin{array}{c}\text{pipe disp., bbl/ft}\\+\\\text{pipe cap., bbl/ft}\end{array}\right)$$

Loss of Overbalance Due to Falling Mud Level

Feet of Pipe Pulled DRY to Lost Overbalance

$$= \frac{\text{overbalance, psi (casing cap.} - \text{pipe disp., bbl/ft)}}{0.052 \times \text{mud weight, ppg} \times \text{pipe disp., bbl/ft}}$$

Feet of Pipe Pulled WET to Lost Overbalance

$$= \frac{\text{overbalance, psi (casing cap.} - \text{pipe cap.} - \text{pipe disp., bbl/ft)}}{0.052 \times \text{mud weight, ppg} \times \left(\text{pipe disp.} + \text{pipe cap., bbl/ft}\right)}$$

Formation Temperature

$$\text{FT, °F} = \begin{pmatrix} \text{ambient} \\ \text{surface} \\ \text{temperature, °F} \end{pmatrix} + \begin{pmatrix} \text{temperature} \\ \text{increase °F per ft of depth} \times \text{TVD, ft} \end{pmatrix}$$

Increase Mud Density

Mud Weight Increase With Barite

$$\text{Barite, sack/100 bbl} = \frac{1470\left(W_2 - W_1\right)}{35 - W_2}$$

Mud Weight Increase With Calcium Carbonate

$$\text{Sacks/100 bbl} = \frac{945\left(W_2 - W_1\right)}{22.5 - W_2}$$

Mud Weight Increase With Hematite

$$\text{Sacks/100 bbl} = \frac{1680\left(W_2 - W_1\right)}{40 - W_2}$$

W_2 Kill fluid weight, ppg
W_1 Original fluid weight, ppg

Dilution

Mud Weight Reduction With Water or Diesel Oil

$$\text{Water, bbl} = \frac{V_1\left(W_1 - W_2\right)}{W_2 - D_w}$$

D_w Water weight, ppg
V_1 First mud volume, bbl
W_2 Second mud weight, ppg
W_1 First mud weight, ppg

Mixing Fluids of Different Densities

$$\left(V_1 D_1\right) + \left(V_2 D_2\right) = V_F D_F$$

V_1 Volume of fluid 1 (bbl, gal, etc)
D_1 Density of fluid 1 (bbl, gal, etc)
V_2 Volume of fluid 2 (bbl, gal, etc)
D_2 Density of fluid 1 (bbl, gal, etc)

V_F Volume of final fluid mix
D_F Density of final fluid mix

Oil-based Mud Calculation

Density of Oil/Water Mixture Being Used

$$\left(V_1\right)\left(D_1\right)+\left(V_2\right)\left(D_2\right)=\left(V_1+V_2\right)D_F$$

V_1 Volume of fluid 1 (bbl, gal, etc)
D_1 Density of fluid 1 (bbl, gal, etc)
V_2 Volume of fluid 2 (bbl, gal, etc)
D_2 Density of fluid 1 (bbl, gal, etc)
D_F Density of final fluid mix

Starting Volume of Liquid (Oil Plus Water) Required To Prepare a Desired Volume of Mud

$$SV = \frac{35-W_2}{35-W_1}\times DV$$

SV Starting volume, bbl
SV Initial density of oil/water mixture, ppg
SV Desired density, ppg
SV Desired volume, bbl

Solids Fractions

Maximum Recommended Solids Fractions (SF)

$$SF = \left(2.917\times MW\right)-14.17$$

Maximum Recommended Low-Gravity Solids (LGS)

$$LGS = \left\{\frac{SF}{100}-\left[0.3125\times\left(\frac{MW}{8.33}-1\right)\right]\right\}\times 200$$

SF   Maximum recommended solids fractions, % by vol
MW   Mud weight, ppg
LGS   Maximum recommended low-gravity solids, % by vol

Dilution of Mud System

$$V_{wm}=\frac{V_m\left(F_{ct}-F_{cop}\right)}{F_{cop}-F_{ca}}$$

V_{wm} Barrels of dilution water or mud required
V_m Barrels of mud in circulating system
F_{ct} Percent low-gravity solids in system
F_{cop} Percent total optimum low-gravity solids desired
F_{cop} Prcent low-gravity solids (bentonite and/or chemicals added)

Evaluation of Hydrocyclone

Volume Fraction of Solids

$$SF = \frac{MW-8.22}{13.37}$$

Mass Rate of Solids (MS)

$$MS = 19530 \times SF \times \frac{V}{T}$$

Volume Rate of Solids (WR)

$$WR = 900\,(1 - SF)\frac{V}{T}$$

SF   Barrels of dilution water or mud required
MW   Average density of discarded mud, ppg
MS   Mass rate of solids removed by one cone of a hydrocyclone, lbm/hr
V   Volume of slurry sample collected, quarts
T   Time to collect slurry sample, seconds
WR   Volume of water ejected by one cone of hydrocyclone, gal/hr

Trip Calculations

$$\text{Trip Margin}_{\text{pcf}} = \frac{0.6394 \times YP_{\text{mud}}}{\text{Hole Diameter}_{\text{inches}} - \text{Pipe}\,OD_{\text{inches}}}$$

$$\text{Trip Margin}_{\text{pcf}} = \frac{\text{Annular Pressure Loss}_{\text{psi}}}{0.007 \times TVD_{\text{ft}}}$$

$$\text{Slug Weight}_{\text{pcf}} = MW_{\text{pcf}} + \frac{MW_{\text{pcf}} \times \text{Length Dry Pipe}_{\text{ft}} \times DP\,Cap_{\text{bbl/ft}}}{\text{Volume of Slug}_{\text{bbl}}}$$

$$\text{Slug Volume}_{\text{bbl}} = \frac{MW_{\text{pcf}} \times \text{Length Dry Pipe}_{\text{ft}} \times DP\,Cap_{\text{bbl/ft}}}{\text{Slug Weight}_{\text{pcf}} - MW_{\text{pcf}}}$$

$$\text{Pit Gain}_{\text{bbl}} = \text{Slug Volume}_{\text{bbl}} \times \frac{\text{Slug Weight}_{\text{pcf}} - MW_{\text{pcf}}}{MW_{\text{pcf}}}$$

$$\text{Depth Slug Falls}_{\text{ft}} = \frac{\text{Pit Gain From Slug}_{\text{bbl}}}{DP\,Cap_{\text{bbl/ft}}}$$

$$\Delta P_{\text{psi/ft}} = \frac{0.007 \times MW_{\text{pcf}} \times DP\,Disp_{\text{bbl/ft}}}{\text{Annulus Cap}_{\text{bbl/ft}} + DP\,Cap_{\text{bbl/ft}}}$$

$$\Delta P_{\text{psi/ft}} = 0.007 \times MW_{\text{pcf}} \frac{DP\,Cap_{\text{bbl/ft}} + DP\,Disp_{\text{bbl/ft}}}{\text{Annulus Cap}_{\text{bbl/ft}}}$$

$$\text{Length}_{\text{ft}} = \frac{\Delta P_{\text{psi}} \times \left(\text{Annulus Cap}_{\text{bbl/ft}} + DP\,Cap_{\text{bbl/ft}}\right)}{0.007 \times MW_{\text{pcf}} \times DP\,Disp_{\text{bbl/ft}}}$$

$$\text{Length}_{\text{ft}} = \frac{\Delta P_{\text{psi}} \times \text{Annulus Cap}_{\text{bbl/ft}}}{0.007 \times MW_{\text{pcf}} \times \left(DP\,Disp_{\text{bbl/ft}} + DP\,Cap_{\text{bbl/ft}}\right)}$$

YP   Yield point
OD   Outer diameter
TVD   True vertical depth
MW   Mud weight
DP Cap Drillpipe capacity
DP Disp Drillpipe displacement

2.3 Fluid Mechanics

Critical Velocity

$$V_c = \frac{1.08\mu_p + 1.08\sqrt{\mu_p^2 + 12.34\rho_m D_i^2 \tau_y}}{\rho_m D_i}$$

V_c Critical velocity from laminar to turbulent for Bingham plastic model, ft/sec
μ_p Plastic viscosity, cp
τ_y Yield point, lbm/100 ft^2
ρ_m Mud density, ppg
D_i Inside diameter of the pipe, in.

Pump Calculations

$$P_p = \Delta p_b + P_d$$

P_p Pump pressure, psi
Δp_b Bit pressure drop, psi
P_d Frictional pressure losses, psi

$$HHP = \frac{Q \times \Delta p_b}{1714}$$

HHP Hydraulic horsepower of the bit, hp
Q Flow rate, gpm
Δp_b Bit pressure drop, psi

Bit Hydraulics

$$A_n = \frac{\pi S_n^2}{64}$$

$$\Delta P_b = \frac{\rho_m Q^2}{10858 \times A_n^2}$$

$$F_{imp} = \frac{Q \times \sqrt{\rho_m \times \Delta P_b}}{57.66}$$

A_n Nozzle flow area, in.^{2}
S_n Nozzle diameter, in.
ΔP_b Pressure drop across the bit, psi
F_{imp} Hydraulic (jet) impact force (IF), lbf
ρ_m Mud density, ppg
Q Flow rate, gpm
A_n Nozzle flow area, in.^{2}

Optimization Calculations

$$\Delta P_{b_{opt}} = \frac{m}{m+2} \Delta P_{P_{max}}$$

$$Q_{opt} = Q_a a \log\left[\frac{1}{m}\log\left(\frac{\Delta P_{d_{opt}}}{\Delta P_{d_{Q_a}}}\right)\right]$$

$$m = \frac{\log(p_{d2}/p_{d1})}{\log(Q_2/Q_1)}$$

$\Delta P_{b_{opt}}$ Optimum bit pressure drop, psi
Q_{opt} Optimum flow rate, gpm

$\Delta P_{p_{max}}$	Maximum pump operating pressure difference, psi
Q_a	Flow rate, gpm
ΔP_{dQ_a}	Frictional pressure loss for Q_a, psi
$\Delta P_{d_{opt}}$	Optimum frictional pressure loss, psi
m	Flow index
P_{d1}, P_{d2}	Frictional pressure 1 and 2, psi
Q_1, Q_2	Flow rates 1 and 2, gpm

Bingham Plastic Model

Reynolds Number of a Pipe

$$N_{Rep} = \frac{928\rho_m v_p D_i}{\mu_{ep}}$$

Pressure Gradient for the Laminar Flow in a Pipe

$$\left(\frac{dp_f}{dL}\right) = \frac{\mu_p v_p}{1500 D_i^2} + \frac{\tau_y}{225 D_i} \qquad \text{psi/ft}$$

ρ_m	Mud weight, ppg
v_p	Velocity of the fluid, ft/sec, $= Q/(2.448 D_i^2)$
D_i	Inside diameter of the pipe, in.
Q	Flow rate, gpm
μ_{ep}	Equivalent viscosity of the fluid, cp, $= \mu_p + \left[(20 D_i \tau_y)/(3 v_p)\right]$
τ_y	Yield point, lbf/100 ft^2
μ_p	Plastic viscosity, cp

Reynolds Number of the Annulus

$$N_{Rea} = \frac{757\rho_m v_a (D_2 - D_p)}{\mu_{ep}}$$

Pressure Gradient for the Laminar Flow in the Pipe

$$\left(\frac{dp_f}{dL}\right) = \frac{\mu_p v_a}{1000(D_2 - D_p)^2} + \frac{\tau_y}{200(D_2 - D_p)} \qquad \text{psi/ft}$$

ρ_m	Mud weight, ppg
v_a	Velocity of the fluid, ft/sec, $= Q/(2.448(D_2^2 - D_p^2))$
D_p	Outside diameter of the pipe, in.
D_2	Annulus diameter, in.
Q	Flow rate, gpm
μ_{ep}	Equivalent viscosity of the fluid, cp, $= \mu_p + \left[(5(D_2 - D_p)\tau_y)/(v_a)\right]$
τ_y	Yield point, lbf/100 ft^2
μ_p	Plastic viscosity, cp

Reynolds Number of a Pipe

$$N_{Rep} = \frac{928\rho_m v_p D_i}{\mu_{ep}}$$

$$\mu_{ep} = 100 K_p \left(\frac{96 v_p}{D}\right)^{n_p - 1} \left(\frac{3 n_p + 1}{4 n_p}\right)^{n_p}$$

$$K_p = \frac{510 \theta_{300}}{511^{n_p}} \qquad\qquad n_p = 3.32 \log\left(\frac{\theta_{600}}{\theta_{300}}\right)$$

Friction Pressure Loss Gradient in a Pipe

$$\left(\frac{dP}{dL}\right)_{dp} = \frac{f_p v_p^2 \rho_m}{25.81 D_i} \qquad \text{psi/ft}$$

$$f_p = \frac{16}{N_{Re\,p}} \qquad \text{For } N_{Re\,p} < 2100$$

$$f_p = \frac{a}{N_{Re}^b} \qquad a = \frac{\log n_p + 3.93}{50}, \quad b = \frac{1.75 - \log n_p}{7} \qquad \text{For } N_{Re\,p} > 2100$$

ρ_m Mud weight, ppg
v_p Velocity of the fluid, ft/sec
D_i Inside diameter of the pipe, in.
μ_{ep} Equivalent viscosity of the fluid, cp
K_p Fluid consistency index of the pipe, lb-sec^n/ft^2
n_p Power-law constant of the pipe
f_p Friction factor of the pipe

Reynolds Number of the Annulus

$$N_{Re_a} = \frac{757 \rho_m v_a (D_2 - D_p)}{\mu_{ea}}$$

$$\mu_{ea} = 100 K_a \left(\frac{144 v_a}{D_2 - D_p}\right)^{n_a - 1} \left(\frac{2n_p + 1}{3n_a}\right)^{n_a}$$

$$K_a = \frac{510 \theta_{100}}{511^{n_a}} \qquad\qquad n_a = 0.657 \log\left(\frac{\theta_{100}}{\theta_3}\right)$$

Friction Pressure Loss Gradient in the Annulus

$$\left(\frac{dP}{dL}\right)_{dp} = \frac{f_a v_a^2 \rho_m}{25.81(D_2 - D_p)} \qquad \text{psi / ft}$$

$$f_a = \frac{16}{N_{Re\,a}} \qquad \text{For } N_{Re\,a} < 2100$$

$$f_a = \frac{a}{N_{Re}^b} \qquad a = \frac{\log n_a + 3.93}{50} , \quad b = \frac{1.75 - \log n_a}{7} \qquad \text{For } N_{Re\,a} > 2100$$

ρ_m Mud weight, ppg
v_a Velocity of the fluid, ft/sec
D_p Outside diameter of the pipe, in.
D_2 Annulus diameter, in.
μ_{ea} Equivalent viscosity of the fluid, cp
K_a Fluid consistency index of the annulus, lb-sec^n/ft^2
n_a Power-law constant of the annulus
f_a Friction factor of the annulus

Gel Breaking Pressure

For Pipe

$$P = \frac{\tau_g L}{300 D_i}$$

P Gel breaking pressure, psi
τ_g Gel strength, lbf/100 ft^2

L Length of the pipe, ft
D_i Inside diameter of the pipe, in.

For Annulus

$$P = \frac{\tau_g L}{300\left(D_h - D_p\right)}$$

P Gel breaking pressure, psi
τ_g Gel strength, lbf/100 ft^2
L Length of the pipe, ft
D_h Diameter of the hole, in.
D_p Outside diameter of the pipe, in.

Hole Cleaning–Cutting Transport

Cutting Concentration for 45° With One Tool

$$C_c = 3.22\left(1 + N_{Ta}\right)^{-0472} + 5703.6\, N_{Re}^{-0.776} + 69.3\, N_{Re}^{-0.051} - 63.3$$

Cutting Concentration for 90° With One Tool

$$C_c = -5.22 \times 10^{-5}\, N_{Ta}^{1.36} + 605.714\, N_{Re}^{-0.0124} + 8.86\, e^{230.43}\, N_{ROP}^{-77.58} - 529.4$$

Cutting Concentration for 45° With No Tools

$$C_c = 1.8\left(1 + N_{Ta}\right)^{-8.13} + 21.25\, e^{177.57}\, N_{Re}^{-24.63} + 15.7\, e^{3.54}\, N_{ROP}^{-0.03} - 487.67$$

Cutting Concentration for 90° With No Tools

$$C_c = -14.04\, e^{-316}\left(1 + N_{Ta}\right)^{36.33} + 284.96\, N_{Re}^{-0.073} + 58.2\, e^{30.9}\, N_{ROP}^{-12.46} - 140.88$$

$$1450 < N_{Re} < 3700 \qquad 0 < N_{Ta} < 5800 \qquad 19.7 < N_{ROP} < 23$$

$$N_{Ta} = \frac{\omega \rho_m D_h^2}{\mu_{eff}}$$

$$N_{Re} = \frac{\rho_m V^{2-n} D_h^n}{K 8^{n-1}}$$

$$N_{ROP} = \frac{\rho_m D_h \times ROP}{\mu_{eff}}$$

N_{Ta} Taylor's number
N_{Re} Reynolds number
N_{ROP} ROP number
ω Angular velocity of the tool, rad/sec
ρ_m Mud density, ppg
D_h Diameter of the hole, in.
V Fluid velocity, ft/sec
n Power-law index
K Consistency index, lbm-sec^n/ft^2
μ_{eff} Effective viscosity, cp
ROP Rate of penetration, ft/sec

Transport Velocity

$$\bar{V}_{ca} = \bar{V}_{cr} + \bar{V}_{cs}$$

$\bar{V}_{ca}$ Critical transport average annular fluid velocity
$\bar{V}_{cr}$ Cutting average rise velocity
$\bar{V}_{cs}$ Cutting average slip velocity

$$\bar{V}_{cr} = \frac{1}{\left\{1 - \left[\left(D_h - D_p\right)/D_h^2\right]\left[0.64 + 18.16/ROP\right]\right\}}$$

$$\bar{V}_{cs} = V_{cs} C_{ang} C_{size} C_{mwt}$$

$$V_{cs} = 0.00516\mu_a + 3.006 \qquad \mu_a \le 53\,\text{cp}$$

$$V_{cs} = 0.02554\mu_a + 3.280 \qquad \mu_a > 53\,\text{cp}$$

$$\mu_a = PV + 1.12\gamma P\left(D_h - D_p\right) \qquad PV < 20\,\text{cp} \qquad \gamma P < 20\,\text{lbm}/100\,\text{ft}^2$$

$$\mu_a = PV + 0.9\gamma P\left(D_h - D_p\right) \qquad PV > 20\,\text{cp} \qquad \gamma P > 20\,\text{lbm}/100\,\text{ft}^2$$

$$C_{ang} = 0.0342\alpha - 0.000233\alpha^2 - 0.213$$

$$C_{size} = -1.04D_{50} + 1.286$$

$$C_{mwt} = 1 - 0.0333\left(\rho_m - 8.7\right)$$

D_h Hole diameter, in.
D_p Pipe outside diameter, in.
ROP Rate of penetration, ft/sec
μ_a Mud viscosity in the annulus, cp
ρ_m Mud density, ppg
α Hole inclination from vertical, degree
D_{50} Cutting average size, in.
C_{ang} Correction factor for change in hole angle
C_{size} Correction factor for change in cutting size
C_{mwt} Correction factor for change in mud weight

Nonmoving Cuttings Concentration in the Annulus for Subcritical Flow

$$C_{corr} = C_{cal} C_{bed}$$

$$C_{cal} = \left[1 - \frac{Q_{opr}}{Q_{crit}}\right](1 - \phi)100$$

$$C_{bed} = 0.97 - 0.00231\mu_a$$

C_{corr} Corrected concentration, percent
C_{cal} Calculated concentration, percent
C_{bed} Bed correction factor
Q_{opr} Operating flow rate, gpm
Q_{crit} Critical flow rate, gpm
ϕ Bed porosity, fraction
μ_a Mud viscosity in the annulus, cp

Stokes' law

$$V_s = \frac{2.15 \times 10^{-7} D_E^2 g (\rho_s - \rho_L)}{\mu}$$

V_s Settling or terminal velocity, ft/sec
g Acceleration (gravity or apparatus), ft/sec^2
D_E Particle equivalent diameter, microns
ρ_s Specific gravity of solids (cutting, barite, etc.)
ρ_L Specific gravity of liquid phase
μ Viscosity of media, cp

Lost Returns, Loss of Overbalance

Equivalent mud weight at Total Depth, ppg = mud weight, ppg − (BHP decrease, psi ÷ 0.052 ÷ TVD, ft)

BHP decrease, psi = $\left(\begin{array}{c}\text{mud} \\ \text{weight, ppg}\end{array} \times \begin{array}{c}\text{weight of} \\ \text{water, ppg}\end{array}\right) \times 0.052 \times \left(\begin{array}{c}\text{feet of} \\ \text{water added}\end{array}\right)$

feet of water in annulus = water added, bbl ÷ annular capacity, bbl/ft

Pump Calculations

Hydraulic Horsepower

$$HHP = \frac{P \times Q}{1714}$$

HHP Hydraulic horsepower
P Circulating pressure, psi
Q Circulating rate, gpm

Triplex Pump Output (PO)

Formula 1

PO (bbl/stroke) = $0.000243 \times \left[\text{Liner Diameter (in.)}\right]^2 \times \left[\text{Stroke Length, (in.)}\right]$

Formula 2

PO (gpm) = $\left[3 \left(D^2 \times 0.7854\right) S\right] 0.00411 \times SPM$

D Liner diameter, in.
S Stroke length, in.
SPM Strokes per minute

Duplex Pump Output

Formula 1

PO (bbl/stroke) @ 100% eff. =
$\left[\text{Stroke Length, (in.)}\right] \times \left\{0.000324 \times \left[\text{Liner Diameter (in.)}\right]^2 - 0.000162 \times \left[\text{Rod Diameter (in.)}\right]^2\right\}$

Formula 2

PO (bbl/stroke) = $0.000162 \times S \left[2 \left(D\right)^2 - d^2\right]$

D Liner diameter, in.
S Stroke length, in.
d Rod diameter, in.

Annular Velocity (AV) Using Pump Output

$$AV\ (ft\,/\,min) = \frac{24.5 \times Q}{Dh^2 - Dp^2}$$

Q Circulation rate, gpm
Dh Inside diameter of casing or hole size, in.
Dp Outsize diameter of pipe, tubing or collars, in.

Pump Pressure/Pump Stroke Relationship

$$\text{New circulating pressure, psi} = \text{present circulating pressure, psi} \times \left(\frac{\text{new pump rate, spm}}{\text{old pump rate, spm}}\right)^2$$

Depth of a Washout

Method 1

$$\begin{array}{c}\text{Depth of}\\\text{washout, ft}\end{array} = \begin{array}{c}\text{strokes}\\\text{required}\end{array} \times \begin{array}{c}\text{pump}\\\text{output, bbl/stroke}\end{array} \div \begin{array}{c}\text{drillpipe}\\\text{capacity, bbl/ft}\end{array}$$

Method 2

$$\begin{array}{c}\text{Depth of}\\\text{washout, ft}\end{array} = \begin{array}{c}\text{strokes}\\\text{required}\end{array} \times \begin{array}{c}\text{pump}\\\text{output, bbl/stroke}\end{array} \div \left(\begin{array}{c}\text{drillpipe}\\\text{capacity, bbl/ft}\end{array} + \text{annular capacity, bbl/ft}\right)$$

Centrifugal pump

$$H_i = \left(u_2 \times c_{u2}\right) / g$$

H_i Theoretical head developed by the centrifugal pump, ft
u_2 Rotational velocity of the impeller at the outer diameter, ft/sec
c_{u2} Rotational velocity of the fluid as it leaves the impeller, ft/sec
g Gravitational constant, ft/sec^2

Evaluation of Centrifuge

Underflow mud volume

$$QU = \frac{\left[QM \times \left(MW - PO\right)\right] - \left[QW \times \left(PO - PW\right)\right]}{PU - PO}$$

Fraction of old mud in underflow

$$FU = \frac{35 - PU}{35 - MW + \left(\dfrac{QW}{QM}\right) \times \left(35 - PW\right)}$$

Mass rate of clay

$$QC = \frac{CC \times \left[QM - \left(QU \times FU\right)\right]}{42}$$

Mass rate of additives

$$QC = \frac{CD \times \left[QM - \left(QU \times FU\right)\right]}{42}$$

Water flow rate into mixing pit

$$QP = \frac{\left[QM \times (35 - MW)\right] - \left[QU \times (35 - PU)\right] - (0.6129 \times QC) - (0.6129 \times QD)}{35 - PW}$$

Mass rate for API barite

$$QB = QM - QU - QP - \frac{QC}{21.7} - \frac{QD}{21.7} \times 35$$

MW   Mud density into centrifuge, ppg
QM   Mud volume into centrifuge, gpm
PW   Dilution water density, ppg
QW   Dilution water volume, gpm
PU   Underflow mud density, ppg
PO   Overflow mud density, ppgx
CC   Clay content in mud, lbm/bbl
CD   Additive content in mud, lbm/bbl
QU   Underflow mud volume, gpm
FU   Fraction of old mud in underflow
QC   Mass rate of clay, lbm/min
QD   Mass rate of additives, lbm/min
QP   Water flow rate into mixing pit, gpm
QB   Mass rate of API barite, lbm/min

2.4 Well Control

Pressure (P)

Pressure, psi = Force, lbf / Area, in.^{2}

Pressure Gradient (G)

Mud Gradient, psi/ft = Mud Weight, ppg × 0.052

Hydrostatic Pressure (hp)

Hydrostatic Pressure, hp = Mud Weight, ppg × 0.052 × TVD, ft

Bottomhole Pressure (bhp)

Under Static Condition

Bottomhole Pressure (bhp) = Hydrostatic Pressure (hp) + Surface Pressure (sp)

Under Dynamic Condition

bhp = Hydrostatic Pressure (hp) + Surface Pressure (sp) + Frictional Pressure (FrP)

Formation Pressure (fp)

fp = Hydrostatic Pressure (hp) + Shut-in Drillpipe Pressure (SIDPP)

Equivalent Circulating Density (ecd)

ecd, ppg = (annular pressure loss, psi) ÷ 0.052 ÷ TVD, ft + current mud weight, ppg

Leakoff Test Equivalent Mud Weight (lot)

lot, ppg = (lot pressure, psi) ÷ 0.052 ÷ (Casing Shoe TVD, ft) + (Mud Weight used for lot, ppg)

Maximum Initial Shut-In Casing Pressure (misicp)
This calculation is based on shoe fracture, which is equal to leakoff test pressure

misicp (psi) = [lot, ppg − Current Mud Weight, ppg] × 0.052 × Shoe TVD, ft

Kill Mud Weight to Balance Formation (kmw)

kmw, ppg = {Shut-In Drillpipe Pressure (SIDP), psi ÷ [0.052 × True Vertical Depth (TVD) of the well, ft]}
            + Original Mud Weight, ppg

Slow Circulation Rate (SCR)

SCR, psi = Initial Circulating Pressure, psi − Shut-In Drillpipe Pressure, psi

Annulus Capacity Factor (ACF)

$$\text{ACF, bbl/ft} = \frac{\left(\text{Casing or Openhole ID, in.}\right)^2 - \left(\text{Work String OD, in.}\right)^2}{1029.4}$$

Final Circulating Pressure (FCP)

$$\text{FCP, psi} = \text{SCR Pressure, psi} \times \frac{\text{kmw, ppg}}{\text{Original MW, ppg}}$$

Surface to Bit Strokes

$$\text{Surface to Bit Strokes, strokes} = \frac{\text{Drillstring Capacity, bbl}}{\text{Pump Output, bbl/stroke}}$$

Circulating Time

$$\text{Circulating Time, minutes} = \frac{\text{Volume, bbl}}{\text{Pump Output, bbl/stroke} \times \text{SPM}}$$

Capacity Factor (CF)

$$\text{CF, bbl/ft} = \frac{\left(\text{Diameter, in.}\right)^2}{1029.4}$$

Open-Ended Pipe Displacement

$$\text{Open-Ended Pipe Displacement, bbl/ft} = \frac{\left(\text{Pipe OD, in.}\right)^2 - \left(\text{Pipe ID, in.}\right)^2}{1029.4}$$

Close-Ended Pipe Displacement

$$\text{Close-Ended Pipe Displacement, bbl/ft} = \frac{\left(\text{Pipe OD, in.}\right)^2}{1029.4}$$

Height of Influx

$$\text{Height of Influx, ft} = \frac{\text{Influx Volume, bbl}}{\text{Annular Capacity Factor, bbl/ft}}$$

Approximate Gas Migration Rate

$$\text{Approximate gas migration rate, ft/hr} = \frac{\text{Change in Shut-In Casing Pressure, psi}}{\text{Mud Weight, ppg} \times 0.052 \times \text{Time for change, hr}}$$

Sacks of Barite Required for Weight Up

$$\text{Barite, sacks} = \text{Volume to weight up, bbl} \times \frac{15 \times \text{Increase in MW, ppg}}{35.0 - \text{kwm, ppg}}$$

Volume Gain From Slug

$$\text{Gain, bbl} = \text{Volume of slug, bbl} \; \frac{\text{Slug weight, ppg} - \text{Current MW, ppg}}{\text{Current MW, ppg}}$$

Triplex Pump Output Volume

$$\text{Output, bbl/strokes} = \text{Efficiency \%} \times 0.000243 \times (\text{Liner ID, in.})^2 \times \text{Stroke Length, in.}$$

Pump Output

$$\text{Output, bbl/min} = \text{Output Volume, bbl/strokes} \times \text{Pump Speed, spm}$$

New Pump Pressure With New Pump Strokes

$$\text{New Pressure, psi} = \text{Original Pressure, psi} \times \left(\frac{\text{New Rate, spm}}{\text{Old Rate, spm}} \right)^2$$

Boyle's Law—Gas Pressure and Volume Relationship

$$V_2 = \frac{P_1 V_1}{P_2} \qquad P_2 = \frac{P_1 V_1}{V_2}$$

Mud Increment for Volumetric Method (MI)

$$\text{MI, bbl} = \frac{\text{Pressure Increment, psi} \times \text{Annular Capacity Factor, bbl/ft}}{0.052 \times \text{MW, ppg}}$$

Lube Increment for Lubricate and Bleed Method (LI)

$$\text{LI, bbl} = \frac{\text{Pressure Increment, psi} \times \text{Annular Capacity Factor, bbl/ft}}{0.052 \times \text{MW, ppg}}$$

Bottle Capacity Required

$$\text{Bottle Volume, gal} = \frac{\text{Volume Fluid Required, gals}}{\left(\dfrac{\text{Precharge Pressure, psi}}{\text{Minimum Operating Pressure, psi}} \right) - \left(\dfrac{\text{Precharge Pressure, psi}}{\text{Maximum Operating Pressure, psi}} \right)}$$

Volume of Usable Fluid

Volume of usable fluid, gal

$$= \text{Bottle volume, gal} \times$$

$$\left(\frac{\text{Precharge Pressure, psi}}{\text{Minimum Operating Pressure, psi}} \right) - \left(\frac{\text{Precharge Pressure, psi}}{\text{Maximum Operating Pressure, psi}} \right)$$

Snubbing Force for Snubbing Operation

Snubbing force (SF) =

Force at Wellhead (Fp) + Frictional Force − Buoyed Weight of String (Wb)

Force at Wellhead (Fp)

$$Fp = \frac{\pi \times (OD, in.)^2}{4} \times \text{Wellhead pressure, psi} \qquad \text{or}$$

$$Fp = (\text{Pipe OD, in.})^2 \times 0.7854 \times \text{Wellhead pressure, psi}$$

Buoyed Weight of Open-Ended Tubular (Wb)

$$Wb, \text{lbm/ft} = W_{air}, \text{lbm/ft} \times \frac{65.4 - MW, ppg}{65.4}$$

Buoyed Weight of Close-Ended Tubular Without Fluid in the Pipe (Wb)

$$Wb, \text{lbm/ft} = W_{air}, \text{lbm/ft} - \frac{(\text{Pipe OD, in.})^2}{24.5} \times MW, ppg$$

Buoyed Weight of Close-Ended Tubular After Filling the Pipe (Wb)

$$Wb, \text{lbm/ft} = W_{air}, \text{lbm/ft} - \frac{(OD, in.)^2 \times \text{Fluid Weight, ppg}}{24.5} - \frac{(ID, in.)^2 \times \text{Fluid Weight, ppg}}{24.5}$$

The Balance Point for Close-Ended and Unfilled Pipe

This is where the weight of pipe in the fluid equates to force created by wellhead pressure.

$$L, \text{ft} = \frac{Fp, lb}{W_{air}, \text{lbm/ft} - \left[(OD, in.)^2 \times \text{Fluid Weight}_{well}, ppg / 24.5\right]}$$

The Balance Point for Close-Ended and Filled Pipe

This is where the weight of pipe in the fluid equates to force created by wellhead pressure.

$$L, \text{ft} =$$

$$\frac{Fp, lb}{W_{air}, \text{lb/ft} - \left[(OD, in.)^2 \times \text{Fluid Weight}_{well}, ppg / 24.5 - (ID, in.)^2 \times \text{Fluid Weight}_{pipe}, ppg / 24.5\right]}$$

The Maximum Down Force on Jacks

Maximum Down Force, lbf = $0.7 \times$ Critical Buckling Load, lbf from pipe data

Effective Area of Snubbing Jacks

Effective area, sq in = Number of Jacks $\times 0.7854 \times \left[(\text{ID Cylinder, in.})^2 - (\text{OD Rod, in.})^2\right]$

Hydraulic Pressure to Snub

$$\text{Hydraulic Pressure to Snub, psi} = \frac{\text{Maximum Down Force, lbf}}{\text{Effective Area, in.}}$$

Kill Sheet Calculations

$$KWM_{pcf} = \frac{SIDPP_{psi}}{\left(0.007 \times TVD_{ft}\right)} + OMW_{pcf}$$

$$ICP_{psi} = SIDPP_{psi} + SPRP_{psi}$$

$$FCP_{psi} = \frac{SPRP_{psi} \times KWM_{pcf}}{OMW_{pcf}}$$

$$STB = \frac{\text{Drillstring Volume}_{bbl}}{\text{Output}_{bbl/stroke}}$$

$$\text{Strokes to Shoe} = \frac{\text{Openhole Annular Volume}_{bbl}}{\text{Output}_{bbl/stroke}} + STB$$

$$\text{Strokes to Surface} = \frac{\text{Total Annular Volume}_{bbl}}{\text{Output}_{bbl/stroke}} + STB$$

$$\text{Time to Bit}_{min} = \frac{STB}{SPM}$$

$$\text{Time to Shoe}_{min} = \frac{\text{Strokes to Shoe}}{SPM}$$

$$\text{Time to surface}_{min} = \frac{\text{Strokes to Surface}}{SPM}$$

KWM	Kill weight mud
OMW	Original mud weight
SIDPP	Shut-in drillpipe pressure
TVD	True vertical depth
ICP	Initial circulating pressure
FCP	Final circulating pressure
SPRP	Slow pump rate pressure
STB	Strokes to bit
SPM	Strokes per minute

Kick Related Formulas

Length of Influx

$$\text{Influx Length}_{ft} = \frac{\text{Influx Size}_{bbl}\left(\text{or Pit Gain}\right)}{\text{Lower Annular Cap}_{bbl/ft}}$$

Expected Pit Gain With a Gas Kick in Water-Based Mud System

$$MPG_{bbl} = \sqrt{\frac{FP_{psi} \times \text{Original Gain}_{bbl} \times \text{Annular Cap}_{bbl/ft}}{0.007 \times KWM_{pcf}}}$$

MPG	Expected pit gain
KWM	Kill weight mud

Expected Surface Pressure From a Gas Kick in Water-Based Mud System

$$MSP_{psi} = \sqrt{\frac{0.007 \times KWM_{pcf} \times FP_{psi} \times \text{Original Gain}_{bbl}}{\text{Surface Annular Cap}_{bbl/ft}}}$$

MSP	Expected surface pressure
KWM	Kill weight mud

Maximum Allowable Mud Weight

$$MAMW_{pcf} = \frac{\text{Surface Applied}_{psi}\left(\text{from Integrity to Leakoff test}\right)}{0.007 \times \text{Casing Shoe } TVD_{ft}} + \text{Test } MW_{pcf}$$

Maximum Allowable Shut-In Casing Pressure

$$MAASP_{psi} = 0.007 \times \left(MAMW_{pcf} - MW_{pcf}\right) \times \text{Casing Shoe } TVD_{ft}$$

MAMW   Maximum allowable mud weight
MW   Mud weight
TVD   Total vertical depth

Kick Tolerance With Influx

$$KT_{pcf} = \left[\left(MAMW_{pcf} - MW_{pcf}\right) \times \frac{\text{Casing Shoe } TVD_{ft}}{TVD_{ft}}\right] - \left[\left(MW_{pcf} - MWI_{pcf}\right) \times \frac{\text{Influx Height } TVD_{ft}}{TVD_{ft}}\right]$$

Estimated Kick Density

$$\text{Kick Density}_{pcf} = MW_{pcf} - \frac{SICP_{psi} - SIDPP_{psi}}{0.007 \times \text{Kick length } TVD_{ft}}$$

SICP   Shut-in casing pressure
SIDPP   Shut-in drillpipe pressure

Kick Gradient

$$\text{Kick Gradient}_{psi/ft} = \left(MW_{pcf} \times 0.007\right) - \frac{SICP_{psi} - SIDPP_{psi}}{\text{Kick length } TVD_{ft}}$$

Gas Migration Distance

$$\text{Distant } TVD_{ft} = \frac{\text{Rise in } SICP_{psi}}{MW_{pcf} \times 0.007}$$

Rate of Gas Migration

$$\text{Migration Rate } TVD_{ft/min} = \frac{\text{Distance of Rise } TVD_{ft}}{\text{Time for Rise}_{min}}$$

Bottom Hole Pressure While Circulating on the Choke

$$BHP_{psi} = \text{Hydrostatic Pressure}_{psi}\text{Mud in Drillstring} + SIDPP$$

Equivalent Mud Weight at Bottom Hole while Circulating out a Kick

$$EMW_{pcf} = \frac{BHP_{psi}}{0.007 \times TVD_{ft}}$$

Shut-In Casing Pressure

$$SICP_{psi} = SIDPP_{psi} + 0.007 \times \left(MW_{pcf} - \text{Kick Density}_{ppg}\right) \times \text{Length of Influx}_{VDft}$$

Formation Pressure

$$FP_{psi} = SIDPP_{psi} + 0.007 \times OMW_{pcf} \times TVD_{ft}$$

$$FP_{psi} = SICP + 0.007 \times \left[\left(\text{Kick Length}_{VDft} \times \text{Kick Density}_{pcf} \right) + \left(\text{Mud Column}_{ft} \times OMW_{pcf} \right) \right]$$

SIDPP   Shut-in drillpipe pressure
OMW   Original mud weight
TVD   Total vertical depth

%Reduction in Hydrostatic Pressure Due to Gas-Cut Mud

$$\%\Delta P_{\text{gas-cut mud}} = \frac{100 \times \left(OMW_{pcf} - GCMW_{pcf} \right)}{GCMW_{pcf}}$$

OMW   Original Mud Weight
GCMW   Gas-Cut Mud Weight

Leakoff Test Pressure and Equivalent Mud Weight at Shoe

$$LOT \left(\text{at bottom} \right)_{psi} = 0.007 \times \text{Test MW}_{pcf} \times \text{Casing Shoe } TVD_{ft} + \text{Surface Applied Pressure to Leakoff}_{psi}$$

$$LOT\ EMW_{pcf} = \frac{LOT_{psi}}{0.007 \times \text{Casing Shoe } TVD_{ft}}$$

Formation Integrity Test Pressure and Equivalent Mud Weight at Shoe

$$FIT \left(\text{at bottom} \right)_{psi} = 0.007 \times \text{Test MW}_{pcf} \times \text{Casing Shoe } TVD_{ft} + \text{Surface Applied Pressure}_{psi}$$

$$FIT\ EMW_{pcf} = \frac{LOT_{psi}}{0.007 \times \text{Casing Shoe } TVD_{ft}}$$

Maximum Formation Pressure That Can Be controlled With a Well Shut-In

$$Max\ FP_{psi} = 0.007 \times \left(KT_{pcf} + MW_{pcf} \right) \times TVD_{ft}$$

Maximum Kick Height Possible not to Exceed MAASP

$$\text{Kick Height}_{VDft} = \frac{MAASP}{\text{Mud Gradient}_{psi/ft} - \text{Kick Gradient}_{psi/ft}}$$

MAASP   Maximum allowable annular surface pressure

Maximum Kick Volume Possible not to Exceed MAASP

$$\text{Kick Volume}_{VDft} = \text{Kick Height}_{ft} \times \text{Annulus Cap}_{bbl/ft}$$

Bullheading Calculations

$$KWM_{pcf} = \frac{\text{Formation Pressure}_{psi}}{0.007 \times \text{Perfs } TVD_{ft}}$$

$$FIT_{psi} = 0.007 \times \left(FIT\ EMW_{pcf} \text{at perf} \right) \times \text{Perfs } TVD_{ft}$$

$$HP_{psi} = FP_{psi} - SIDPP_{psi}$$

$$IMDPP_{psi} = FIT_{psi} - HP_{psi}$$

$$KMHP_{psi} = 0.007 \times KWM_{pcf} \times Perfs\ TVD_{ft}$$

$$FMDPP_{psi} = FIT_{psi} - KMHP_{psi}$$

Lubricated and Bleed Calculations

Cycle Hydrostatic Pressure Gain per Barrel

$$\Delta HP_{psi/bbl} = \frac{Gradient\ Lube\ Mud_{psi/ft}}{Annulus\ Cap_{bbl/ft}\ at\ top\ of\ hole}$$

Cycle Hydrostatic Pressure Increase or Lubricated Volume To Be Bled Off

$$\Delta HPI_{psi} = \Delta HP_{psi} \times Lubricated\ Vol_{bbl}$$

Stripping Calculations

$$P_{strip\ psi} = \frac{Weight\ DC_{ppf} \times Length\ DC\ Stand_{ft}}{0.785 \times OD_{DC}{}^2}$$

$$\Delta Height_{ft} = \frac{Pipe\ Length_{strip} \times \left(DP\ Cap_{bpf} + DP\ Disp_{bpf}\right)}{Annulus\ Cap_{bpf}}$$

$$\Delta SICP_{psi} = \Delta Height_{ft} \times \left(Gradient_{mud} - Gradient_{influx}\right)$$

$$Bleed\ Mud_{bbl} = \frac{Csg\ Pressure\ Increment_{psi} \times Annulus\ Cap_{bbl/ft}}{Mud\ Gradient_{psi/ft}}$$

Estimating Temperature Drop Across a Choke or Orifice

$$T_{drop} = \frac{\left(P_h - P_L\right)\ psi}{15\ psi} \times 1°F$$

T_{drop} Temperature drop, degree
P_h Gas pressure before the chokes, psi
P_L Gas pressure after the choke, psi

Estimating Gas Well Flow Rates

$$Q = \frac{24 \times \left(P_L + 15\right) \times D_{ch}{}^2}{1000}$$

Q Flow rate, MMscf/D
P_L Pressure upstream of choke, psi
D_{ch} Choke size, in.

2.5 Drilling Mechanics

Rig Equipment

Overall Efficiency of Engines

$$\eta_o = 100 \frac{P_o}{P_i}$$

$$P_o = \frac{2\pi NT}{33000}$$

$$P_i = \frac{Q_f H}{2545}$$

$$Q_f = 48.46 \frac{NT}{\eta_o H}$$

η_o Overall efficiency of power generating systems
P_o Output power, hp
P_i Input power, hp
N Engine rotary speed, rev/min
T Torque, ft-lbf
Q_f Rate of fuel consumption, lbm/hr
H Fuel heating value in BTU/lb

Blocks and Drilling Line

$$\eta = \frac{F_h}{nF_f}$$

η Efficiency of block and tackle system
F_h Load hoisted, lb, (buoyed weight of the string + traveling block, compensator, etc.)
F_f Load in fast line, lb
n Number of lines strung between the crown block and traveling block

Derrick Load

$$F_s = \frac{n+2}{n} F_h$$

$$F_d = \left(\frac{1+E+En}{En} \right) \times F_h \qquad\qquad F_{de} = \left(\frac{n+4}{n} \right) \times F_h$$

$$E_d = \frac{F_d}{F_{de}} = \frac{E(n+1)+1}{E(n+4)}$$

$$E = \frac{\mu^n - 1}{\mu^s n(\mu - 1)}$$

F_s Static derrick load, lbm
F_h Load hoisted, lbm
F_d Dynamic derrick load, lbm
F_{de} Maximum equivalent derrick load, lbm
E_d Derrick efficiency factor
E Overall block efficiency factor
μ Friction factor, ~1.04
n Number of rolling sheaves, (usually $s = n$)

Crown Block Capacity

$$R_c = \frac{(H_L + S)(n+2)}{n}$$

R_c Required crown block rating, lbm
H_L Net static hook load capacity, lbm
S Effective weight of suspended equipment, lbm
n Number of lines strung to the traveling block

Rotary Power

$$H_{rp} = \frac{2\pi NT}{33000}$$

H_{rp} Rotary horsepower, hp
N Rotary table speed, rev/min
T Torque, ft-lbf

Riser Angle

$$\theta \cong \sqrt{\theta_x^2 + \theta_y^2}$$

θ Resultant riser angle, degree
θ_x Riser angle in x-direction, degree
θ_y Riser angle in y-direction, degree

Mud Pumps

For single-acting pump

$$V_t = \left(\frac{\pi}{4} D_L^2 L_s\right) N_c$$

For double-acting pump

$$V_t = \frac{\pi}{4} N_c L_s \left(2D_L^2 - D_r^2\right)$$

Pump Factor

Duplex pump

$$PF_d = \frac{\pi}{2} L_s \left(2D_L^2 - D_r^2\right)$$

Triplex pump

$$PF_t = \frac{3\pi}{4} D_L^2 L_s$$

V_t Theoretical volume of fluid displaced, gal/stroke
D_L Liner or piston diameter, in.
D_r Rod diameter, in.
L_s Stroke length, in.
N_c Number of cylinders, 2 for duplex, 3 for triplex
PF_d Duplex pump factor, gal/stroke
PF_t Triplex pump factor, gal/stroke

Environmental Forces in Offshore Vessels

Wind Force

$$F_w = 0.00338 V_w^2 C_h C_s A$$

F_w Wind force, lbf
V_w Wind velocity, knots
C_s Shape coefficient
C_h Height coefficient
A Projected area of all exposed surfaces, ft^2

Current Force

$$F_c = g_c V_c^2 C_s A$$

F_c Current drag force, lbf
V_c Current velocity, ft/sec
C_s Drag coefficient same as wind coefficient
A Projected area of all exposed surfaces, ft^2
g_c Gravitational force, ft/sec^2

Wave Force

$$F_{bow} = \frac{0.273 H^2 B^2 L}{A^4} \qquad\qquad \text{If } A > 0.332\sqrt{L}$$

$$F_{bow} = \frac{0.273 H^2 B^2 L}{\left(0.664\sqrt{L} - A\right)^4} \qquad \text{If } A < 0.332\sqrt{L}$$

$$F_{beam} = \frac{2.10 H^2 B^2 L}{A^4} \qquad\qquad \text{If } A > 0.642\sqrt{B+2D}$$

$$F_{beam} = \frac{2.10 H^2 B^2 L}{\left(1.28\sqrt{B+2D} - A\right)^4} \qquad \text{If } A < 0.642\sqrt{B+2D}$$

F_{bow} Bow force, lbf
F_{beam} Beam force, lbf
A Wave period, sec
L Vessel length, ft
H Significant wave height, ft
B Vessel beam length, ft
D Vessel draft, ft

Ton-Mile (TM) Calculations

$$T_f = \frac{L_h\left(L_s + L_h\right)W_{dp} + 4L_h\left(W_b + \frac{1}{2}W_1 + \frac{1}{2}W_2 + \frac{1}{2}W_3\right)}{10560000}$$

T_f Round-trip ton-miles, ton-miles
L_h Measured depth of the hole or trip depth, ft
L_s Length of the stand, ft
W_{dp} Buoyed weight of the drillpipe per foot, ppf
W_b Weight of block, hook, etc., lbm
W_1 Excess weight of drill collar in mud, lbm
W_2 Excess weight of heavy weight pipe in mud, lbm
W_3 Excess weight of miscellaneous drilling tools in mud, lbm

Drilling or Ton-Miles Calculations

When a Hole Is Drilled Only Once Without Any Reaming

$$T_d = 2\left(T_{i+1} - T_i\right)$$

When a Hole Is Drilled With One Time Reaming

$$T_d = 3\left(T_{i+1} - T_i\right)$$

When a Hole Is Drilled With Two Times Reaming

$$T_d = 4\left(T_{i+1} - T_i\right)$$

T_d Drilling ton-miles, ton-miles
T_i Round-trip ton-miles calculated

Casing Ton-Miles Calculations

$$T_f = \frac{1}{2}\left(\frac{L_h\left(L_s + L_h\right)W_c + 4L_hW_b}{10,560,000}\right)$$

T_c Casing ton-miles, ton-miles
L_h Measured depth of the hole or trip depth, ft
L_s Length of the stand, ft
W_c Buoyed weight of the casing per foot, ppf
W_b Weight of block, hook, etc., lbm

Drilling Tools

Stretch Calculations

$$L = \frac{E \times e \times W}{144 \times \Delta T \times \rho_s}$$

L Approximate depth of stuck point, ft
E Young's modulus, psi
e Measured elongation corresponding to the differential tension (pull), in.
W Air weight of the pipe, lbm/ft
ΔT Differential pull or hook load, in.
ρ_s Density of steel, lbm/in.^{3}

Back-Off Calculations

Force at back-off depth = Axial force down to well depth − axial force down to back-off depth

Surface axial force when the workstring is at a measured depth (MD) =
        ΣMD × (Weight Gradient + Drag Force Gradient)

Rotary table torque at surface = Torque at back-off depth + Back-off depth torque

Overpull/Slackoff Calculations

$$F_{sp} = F_{td} - F_{sd}$$

F_{sp} Force at stuck point depth, lbm
F_{td} Axial force down to well depth, lbm
F_{sd} Axial force down to stuck depth, lbm

Motor Calculations

Type I Motor

$$\delta = \frac{200}{L_{12} + L_{23}} \times a_{em}$$

$$a_{em} = a_{bh} - a_1 + a_2$$

$$a_1 = \frac{360 r_{c1}}{24\pi}\left(\frac{1}{L_{12}} + \frac{1}{L_{23}}\right)$$

$$a_2 = \frac{360\, r_{c2}}{24\,\pi}\left(\frac{1}{L_{23}}\right)$$

δ Build rate angle, degree

a_{em} Equivalent motor angle, degree

a_{bh} Bent housing angle, degree

a_1 Angle adjustment for the first under gauge stabilizer, degree

a_2 Angle adjustment for the second under gauge stabilizer, degree

L_{12} Distance from the bit to the bent housing, ft

L_{23} Distance from the bent housing to the second stabilizer, ft

r_{c1}, r_{c2} Radial clearance between the wellbore and the respective stabilizer blade diameter, in.

Type II Motor

$$a_{em} = \left(\frac{L_{34}}{L_{23}+L_{34}}\right)a_{bh} - a_1 + a_2$$

$$a_1 = \frac{360\, r_{c1}}{24\,\pi}\left(\frac{1}{L_{12}}+\frac{1}{L_{23}+L_{34}}\right)$$

$$a_2 = \frac{360\, r_{c2}}{24\,\pi}\left(\frac{1}{L_{23}+L_{34}}\right)$$

L_{12} Distance from the bit to the first stabilizer, ft

L_{23} Distance from the first stabilizer to the bent housing, ft

L_{34} Distance from the bent housing to the second stabilizer, ft

Type III Motor

$$a_{em} = a_{bh} + \left(\frac{L_{45}}{L_{34}+L_{45}}\right)\left(\frac{L_{34}+L_{45}}{L_{23}+L_{34}+L_{45}}\right)a_{bs} - a_1 + a_2$$

$$a_1 = \frac{360\, r_{c1}}{24\,\pi}\left(\frac{1}{L_{12}}+\frac{1}{L_{23}+L_{34}+L_{45}}\right)$$

$$a_2 = \frac{360\, r_{c2}}{24\,\pi}\left(\frac{1}{L_{23}+L_{34}+L_{45}}\right)$$

a_{bs} Bent sub angle, degree

Type IV Motor

$$a_{em} = \left[a_{bh} + \left(\frac{L_{45}}{L_{34}+L_{45}}\right)a_{bs}\right]\left(\frac{L_{34}+L_{45}}{L_{23}+L_{34}+L_{45}}\right) + \left(\frac{L_{12}}{L_{12}+L_{23}}\right)a_{tdb} - a_1 + a_2$$

$$a_1 = \frac{360\, r_{c1}}{24\,\pi}\left(\frac{1}{L_{12}+L_{23}}+\frac{1}{L_{23}+L_{34}+L_{45}}\right)$$

$$a_2 = \frac{360\, r_{c2}}{24\,\pi}\left(\frac{1}{L_{23}+L_{34}+L_{45}}\right)$$

a_{tdb} Tilted bushing angle, degree

Stabilizer Jamming Angle

$$a_{sj} = \frac{360 \times r_{chs}}{\pi L_{sb}}$$

a_{sj} Stabilizer jamming angle, degree
r_{chs} Radial clearance between the stabilizer blade diameter and the wellbore, in.
L_{sb} Length of the stabilizer blade, in.

Percussion Hammer

$$\text{Work done, } HP = \frac{\Delta p_m \times A_p \times \ell \times n_b}{396000}$$

Δp_m Pressure drop across the piston chamber, psi
A_p Cross-sectional area of the piston, in.²
ℓ Stroke length, in.
n_b Number of blows of the piston per minute

Positive-Displacement Motor (PDM)

$$Q = 0.79 \frac{i(i+1)}{(2-i)^2} p_h D_h^2 N$$

$$T = 0.01 \Delta p_m \frac{i(i+1)}{(2-i)^2} p_h D_h^2 \eta$$

Q Flow rate required to rotate the shaft at N rev/min for a multilobe motor, gpm
p_h Pitch of the motor, in.
D_h Diameter of the motor, in.
N Rotational speed, rev/min
T Torque, ft-lbf
Δp_m Pressure drop across the motor, psi
η Overall efficiency of the motor, = useful power at the bit/HHP
i Winding ratio of the motor

Rotor Nozzle Sizing

$$A_{nr}^2 = \frac{8.311 \times 10^{-5} \times Q_{rn}^2 \times \rho_m}{C_d^2 \times \Delta p_m}$$

A_{nr} Area of the rotor nozzle, in.²
Q_{nr} Bypass flow rate through the rotor nozzle, gpm
ρ_m Mud density of the circulation fluid, ppg
C_d Discharge coefficient
Δp_m Pressure drop across the motor, psi

Downhole Turbine

$$MHP = \frac{N_r \left(T - T^2 / T_s\right)}{550} \left(\frac{2\pi}{60}\right)$$

$$N_r = 18.38 \frac{\tan \beta_e Q \eta_v}{\pi h \bar{r}^2}$$

$$T = 2\pi Q \rho_m \bar{r}^2 n_s N \eta$$

$$T_s = 8.6595 \times 10^{-5} \frac{\tan \beta_e n_s \rho_m Q^2 \eta_m}{2\pi h}$$

MHP	Mechanical horsepower, hp
T	Torque, ft-lbf
T_s	Stall torque of a turbine, ft-lbf
N_r	Runaway speed, rpm
Q	Flow rate, gpm
ρ_m	Mud weight, ppg
$\overline{r}^2$	Square of the mean blade radius, in.^{2}
n_s	Number of turbine stages
N	Rotation speed of the turbine, rev/min
η	Overall efficiency
η_m	Mechanical efficiency
η_v	Volumetric efficiency
β_e	Exit angle, degree
h	Height of the vane, in.

Jar Calculations

Force Calculations for Up Jars

$$F_{es} = -\left(F_s + F_{pof}\right)$$

$$F_{et} = F_{ts} - F_{pof}$$

$$F_{emw} = F_{ti} - F_s - F_{pof}$$

$$F_{tmw} = F_{to} + F_t - F_{pof}$$

Force Calculations for Down Jars

$$F_{es} = -\left(F_s - F_{pof}\right)$$

$$F_{et} = -\left(F_{ts} + F_{pof}\right)$$

$$F_{emw} = F_{to} + F_s - F_{pof}$$

$$F_{tmw} = F_{ti} - F_t - F_{pof}$$

F_{es}	Effective jar set (cock) force
F_s	Set force
F_{pof}	Pump open force
F_{et}	Effective jar trip force
F_t	Trip force
F_{emw}	Set measured weight
F_{ti}	Trip in axial force
F_{tmw}	Trip measured weight
F_{to}	Trip out axial force

Specific Energy

$$E_s = \frac{W_{eff}}{A} + \frac{120\pi NT}{R \times A} + \frac{Q\Delta P_b}{R \times A}$$

$$W_{eff} = W - \frac{Q}{58}\sqrt{\rho_m \Delta P_b}$$

$$\Delta P_b = \frac{8.311 \times 10^{-5} \rho_m Q^2}{C_d^2 A_n^2}$$

$$\eta_d = \frac{E_{Smin}}{E_s}$$

E_s Generalized specific energy, psi

E_{smin} Minimum specific energy, roughly equal to the compressive strength of the formation drilled, psi

W Weight on the bit, kips

W_{eff} Effective weight on the bit, kips

A Cross-sectional area of the hole drilled, in.^{2}

R Rate of penetration, ft/hr

N Bit speed, rev/min

T Torque, ft-lbf

Q Flow rate, gpm

ΔP_b Bit pressure drop, psi

ρ_m Mud weight, ppg

C_d Nozzle discharge coefficient

A_n Total nozzle area, in.^{2}

η_d Drilling efficiency

Drillstring Design

Length of Bottomhole Assembly Necessary for a Desired Weight on Bit (WOB)

$$\text{Length, ft} = \frac{WOB \times f}{Wdc \times BF}$$

WOB   Desired weight to be used while drilling, lbm

f   Safety factor to place neutral point in drill collars

Wdc   Drill collar weight, lbm/ft

BF   Buoyancy factor

Feet of Drillpipe That Can Be Used With a Specific Bottomhole Assembly (BHA)

$$\text{Length}_{max}, \text{ft} = \frac{\left[(T \times f) - MOP - Wbha\right] \times BF}{Wdp}$$

T   Tensile strength, lbm for new pipe

f   Safety factor to correct new pipe to No. 2 pipe

MOP   Margin of overpull

Wbha   BHA weight in air, lbm/ft

Wdp   Drillpipe weight in air, lbm/ft, including tool joint

BF   Buoyancy factor

Stuck Pipe Calculations

Method 1

$$\text{free pipe, ft} = \frac{\text{stretch, in.} \times \text{free point constant}}{\text{pull force in thousands of pounds}}$$

$$\text{free point constant} = A_S \times 2500$$

A_S Pipe wall cross-sectional area, in.^{2}

Method 2

$$\text{free pipe, ft} = \frac{735294 \times e \times Wdp}{\text{differential pull, lbm}}$$

e   Pipe stretch, in.

Wdp   Drillpipe weight, lbm/ft (plain end)

Drillpipe/Drill Collar Calculations

$$\text{Capacity, bbl/ft} = \frac{\text{ID, in.}^2}{1029.4}$$

$$\text{Displacement, bbl/ft} = \frac{\text{OD, in.}^2 - \text{ID, in.}^2}{1029.4}$$

$$\text{Weight, lbm/ft} = \text{Displacement, bbl/ft} \times 2747 \text{ lb/bbl}$$

Drilling Time

$$\frac{dD}{dt} = Ke^{-2.303aD}$$

$$t_d = \frac{1}{2.303aK}\left(e^{2.203aD} - 1\right)$$

t_d Drilling time, hr
D Drilling depth, ft
K Constant
a Constant, $= \text{logcycle}/\Delta D$

2.6 Tubular Mechanics

Drill Collar Size

$$D_{dc} = 2D_{csg} - D_b$$

D_{dc} Diameter of the drill collar, in.
D_{csg} Diameter of the casing coupling, in.
D_b Diameter of the bit, in.

Drill Collar Length

$$L_{dc} = \frac{WOB \times DF}{\omega_{dc} \times BF \times \cos\alpha}$$

L_{dc} Length of the drill collar, ft
WOB Weight on bit, lbm
DF Design factor
ω_{dc} Unit weight of the collar in lbf/ft
BF Buoyancy factor
α Wellbore inclination, degree

Bending Stress Ratio (BSR)

$$BSR = \frac{\left(D^4 - b^4\right)/D}{\left(R_t^4 - d^4\right)/R_t}$$

D Connection or toll outside diameter, in.
b Thread root diameter of box threads at the end of the pin, in.
R_t Thread root diameter of pin threads ¾ in. from the shoulder of the pin, in.
d Pin inside diameter, in.

Pipe Wall Thickness

$$D_{cp} = c \times D_p + D_i\left(1 - c\right)$$

D_{cp} Corrected pipe diameter, in.
D_p Original pipe diameter, in.

D_i Inside pipe diameter, in.
c Class multiplier
N New, $c = 1.000$ P Premium, $c = 0.800$ C Critical, $c = 0.875$
       2 Class 2, $c = 0.700$ 3 Class 3, $c = 0.650$

Tension

$$F_e = \sum \left[W_s \cos\alpha + F_D + \Delta F_{area} \right] - F_{bottom} - WOB + F_{bs}$$

F_e Effective tension, lbm
W_s Air weight of the segment, $= L\omega_{air}$
L Length of drillstring hanging below point, ft
ω_{air} Weight per foot of drillstring in air, lbm/ft
F_D Drag force, lbm
ΔF_{area} Change in force due to the change in area, lbm
F_{bottom} Bottom pressure force, lbf
WOB Weight on bit, lbm
F_{bs} Buckling stability force, lbm
α Well inclination, degree

Drag Force

$$F_D = F_s \times \mu_v \times \frac{|V_{ts}|}{|V_{rs}|}$$

F_D Drag force, lbm
F_s Side or normal force, lbm
V_{ts} Trip speed, in./sec
V_{rs} Resultant speed, $= \sqrt{V_{ts}^2 + \omega^2}$
ω Angular speed, ft/min, $= \text{Diameter} \times \pi \times RPM / 60$
μ_v Variable friction coefficient
μ_s Static friction coefficient, $= \mu_s \times e^{-k|V_{ts}|}$
k Speed constant

Side Force Calculations

$$F_s = \sqrt{\left(F_e \Delta\phi \sin\alpha_{avg} \right)^2 + \left(F_e \Delta\alpha + W_b \sin\alpha_{avg} \right)^2}$$

F_s Axial force at the bottom of the section, lbm
F_e Effective tension, lbm
$\Delta\phi$ Change in azimuth over the section length, degree
α_{avg} Average inclination over the section, degree
$\Delta\alpha$ Change in inclination over the section length, degree
W_b Buoyed weight of the section, lb, $= \omega_b S_L$
ω_b Buoyed weight per unit length of the section
S_L Section length, ft

Torque

$$T = \frac{\mu_v}{\sqrt{1 + \mu_v^2}} \times F_s \times r \times \frac{|\omega|}{|V_{rs}|}$$

$$\psi = \tan^{-1}\left(\frac{F_e \Delta\phi \sin\alpha_{avg}}{F_e \Delta\alpha + W_b \sin\alpha_{avg}} \right) + \tan^{-1}(\mu)$$

T Torque when the pipe is rotated and reciprocated, ft-lbf
μ_v Variable friction coefficient

F_s Side or normal force, lbm

F_e Effective tension, lbm

r Radius of the component

V_{rs} Resultant speed, ft/min

ω Angular speed, ft/min

ψ Angle due to pipe rotation with perfect contact

$\Delta\phi$ Change in azimuth over the section length, degree

$\Delta\alpha$ Change in inclination over the section length, degree

α_{avg} Average inclination over the section, degree

$\Delta\alpha$ Change in inclination over the section length, degree

W_b Buoyed weight of the section, lbm

μ Friction coefficient

Buckling

$$F_b = -F_a + P_i A_i - P_o P_o$$

F_b Buckling force

F_a Axial force

P_i Internal pressure

A_i Cross-sectional area, $= \pi r_i^2$

P_o External pressure

A_o Cross-sectional area, $= \pi r_o^2$

$$F_p = \sqrt{\frac{4EI\omega\sin\alpha}{r}}$$

F_p Paslay buckling force

ω Distributed buoyed weight of the casing

EI Pipe bending stiffness

α Wellbore angle with the vertical

r Radial annular clearance

Maximum Permissible Dogleg

$$c = \frac{432000\sigma_b}{\pi E D_p} \frac{\tanh(KL)}{KL}$$

c Maximum permissible dogleg, degree/100 ft

σ_b Maximum permissible bending stress, psi

For a drillpipe of grade E when the tensile stress is less than or equal to 67000:

$$\sigma_b = 19500 - \frac{10}{67}\sigma_t - \frac{0.6}{670^2}(\sigma_t - 33500)^2$$

For a drillpipe of grade S when the tensile stress is less than or equal to 133400:

$$\sigma_b = 20000\left(1 - \frac{\sigma_t}{145000}\right)$$

σ_t Axial stress, psi

$$\sigma_t = \frac{F_{dls}}{A}$$

F_{dls} Buoyed weight supported below the dogleg, lbm

A Cross-sectional area of the drillpipe body, in.^{2}

K Factor:

$$= \sqrt{\frac{T}{EI}}$$

T Torque, ft-lbf
E Young's modulus, psi
$\quad = 30 \times 10^6$ for steel
$\quad = 10.5 \times 10^6$ for aluminum
I Drillpipe moment of inertia with respect to its diameter, in.^{4}, $= \dfrac{\pi}{64}\left(D^4 - ID^4\right)$
D_p Drillpipe OD, in.
L Half distance between the tool joints, in., = 180 for Range 2 drillpipe

Expected Value of Lateral Force or the Force at the Tool Joint

$$F_s = \frac{\pi \times c \times L \times T}{10800}, \text{ lb}$$

Radial Stress

$$\sigma_r(r) = \frac{P_i r_i^2 - P_o r_o^2}{r_o^2 - r_i^2} + \left(\frac{r_i^2 r_o^2}{r^2}\right)\frac{(P_o - P_i)}{(r_o^2 - r_i^2)} \qquad r_i \le r \le r_o$$

Hoop Stress (Tangential or Circumferential)

$$\sigma_h(r) = \frac{P_i r_i^2 - P_o r_o^2}{r_o^2 - r_i^2} - \left(\frac{r_i^2 r_o^2}{r^2}\right)\frac{(P_o - P_i)}{(r_o^2 - r_i^2)} \qquad r_i \le r \le r_o$$

r Radius of the pipe, in.
r_i Inside radius of the pipe, in.
r_o Outside radius of the pipe, in.
P_i Internal pressure of the pipe, psi
P_o External pressure of the pipe, psi

Bending Stress

$$\sigma_b = \frac{rE\kappa M}{68754.9}$$

r Radius of the pipe, in.
E Modulus of elasticity, psi
κ Wellbore curvature as dogleg severity, degree/100 ft
M Bending stress magnification factor

$$\kappa_p = \kappa(KL)\frac{\sinh(KL) - KL - \left(\frac{1}{2} + \frac{r}{L_c^2}\right)KL\left[\cosh(KL) - 1\right]}{2\left[\cosh(KL) - 1\right] - KL\sinh\sinh(KL)}$$

κ_p Pipe curvature at the tool joint, rad/in.
K $= \sqrt{F/EI}$
F Tensile force applied to the pipe, lb
E Modulus of elasticity, psi
I Drillpipe moment of inertia, in.^{4}
L Half distance between the tool joints, in.
κ Wellbore curvature on the distance between tool joints, degree/100 ft
r $= \left(D_{otj} - D_p\right)/2$
D_{otj} Tool joint outside diameter, in.
D_p Drillpipe diameter, in.

Torsional or Twisting Shear Stress

$$\tau_{tor} = \frac{12rT}{J}$$

τ_{tor} Torsional shear stress, psi
J Polar moment of inertia, in.^{4}
T Torque, ft-lbf
r Radius of the pipe, in.

Transverse Shear Stress

$$\tau_s = \frac{2\sqrt{F_1^2 + F_2^2}}{A}$$

F_1 Radial force in the vertical plane, lb
F_2 Radial force in the horizontal plane, lb
A Cross-sectional area of the component, in.^{2}

von Mises Stress

$$\sigma_{vm} = \frac{1}{\sqrt{2}} \sqrt{\left(\sigma_r - \sigma_h\right)^2 + \left(\sigma_h - \sigma_a\right)^2 + \left(\sigma_a - \sigma_r\right)^2}$$

σ_{vm} von Mises failure criteria known as the maximum energy of distortion theory, psi
σ_r Radial stress, psi
σ_h Hoop stress, psi
σ_a Axial stress, psi

Stress Ratio

$$X = \frac{\sigma_y \times \%\text{Yield}}{\sigma_{vm}}$$

X Stress ratio, when $X \leq 1$, there is a concern of failure
σ_y Yield stress of the pipe, psi
%Yield   A percentage used to reduce the yield strength of the pipe as a factor of additional safety
σ_{vm} von Mises stress, psi

Fatigue Ratio

$$FR_F = \frac{\left|\sigma_b\right| + \left|\sigma_{buck}\right|}{\sigma_{fl}}$$

σ_b Bending stress, psi
σ_{buck} Buckling stress, psi
σ_{fl} Fatigue limit, psi:
       For tension:

$$\sigma_{fl} = \sigma_{el}\left(1 - \frac{F_e}{F_y}\right)$$

       For compression:

$$\sigma_{fl} = \sigma_{el}$$

σ_{el} Fatigue endurance limit of the pipe, psi:
F_e Effective tension, lbf
F_y Yield tension, lbf

Bending Stress Magnification Factor (BSMF) Calculations for Tensile Force

$$BSMF = -\frac{\left\{\left(\frac{\xi^2}{2} + a^2 \Delta D \frac{R}{2}\right)(\cosh \xi - 1) - \xi(\sinh \xi - \xi)\right\}}{\gamma} \qquad \text{if } \Delta D \le \Delta D_2$$

$$BSMF = \frac{\left\{-\eta\left(\frac{\eta}{2} + a\Delta D \frac{R}{L}\right)(\cosh \eta - 1) + \eta(\sinh \eta - \eta)\right\}}{\Delta} \qquad \text{if } \Delta D \le \Delta D_1$$

$$BSMF = \frac{\eta \cosh \eta}{\sinh \eta} \qquad \text{if neither of considtions were true}$$

$$a^2 \Delta D \frac{R}{2} = 2 + \frac{\left[-2\xi \sinh \xi + \xi^2 \frac{(\cosh \xi + 1)}{2}\right]}{\cosh \xi - 1} \qquad \text{to compute } \xi$$

$$\gamma = 2(\cosh \xi - 1) - \xi \sinh \xi$$

$$\Delta D_1 = \frac{\left(\frac{\eta}{2} + \frac{1 - \cosh \eta}{\sinh \eta}\right)L}{aR}$$

$$\Delta D_2 = \frac{\left(\frac{2}{\eta} + \frac{(1 + \eta \cosh \eta) - 2\sinh \eta}{\cosh \eta - 1}\right)L}{aR}$$

$$\Delta D = D_{tj} - D_p$$

$$\eta = \frac{aL}{2} \qquad a = \sqrt{\frac{F_a}{EI}}$$

D_{tj} Tool joint outside diameter, in.
D_p Pipe body outside diameter, in.
F_a Axial force, lbf
E Modulus of elasticity, psi
I Drillpipe moment of inertia, in.^{4}
L Distance between joints, ft
R Radius of curvature of the wellbore, in.

Slip Crushing

$$F_{max} = \frac{F_y}{\sqrt{1 + \frac{2D_p^2 fA_p}{(D_p^2 - D_i^2)A_s} + \left[\frac{2D_p^2 fA_p}{(D_p^2 - D_i^2)A_s}\right]^2}}$$

F_{max} Maximum allowable static axial load, lbf
F_y Tensile strength of the pipe, lbf
A_s Contact area between slip and pipe, in.^{2}, $= \pi D_p L_s$
A_p Cross-sectional area of the pipe, in.^{2}
D_p Outside diameter of the pipe, in.
D_i Inside diameter of the pipe, in.
L_s Length of the slips, in.
f Lateral load factor of slips, $= (1 - \mu \tan a)/(\mu + \tan a)$
μ Coefficient of friction between slips and bushings
a Slip taper angle, degree

Cumulative Fatigue Calculations

$$FC = \frac{n}{N_f} \qquad n = \frac{N \times \Delta D}{ROP}$$

N_f: from $\log S = -m \log N_f + c$ curves for each pipe grade

FC	Cumulative fatigue, fraction
n	Number of revolutions of drillpipe along the drilled interval
N	Drillstring revolutions, rev/min
N_f	Number of revolutions to fail, cycles
ΔD	Depth drilled, ft
ROP	Rate of penetration, ft/hr
S	Cyclic stress corrected by Soderberg factor, psi, $= (FC_s)(\sigma_{x,c})$
FC_s	Soderberg correction factor, $= \Upsilon_p / (\Upsilon_p - \sigma_{x,m})$
Υ_p	Yield strength of the pipe, psi
$\sigma_{x,m}$	Medium stress of the pipe, psi, $= T/A_c$ $\qquad A_c = \pi(D_o^2 - D_i^2)/4$
$\sigma_{x,c}$	Cyclic (bending) stress, psi, $= Ec_o D_o / 2$ $\qquad c_o = c(KL)/\tanh(KL)$
c	Maximum permissible dogleg, degree/100 ft
K	$= \sqrt{T/EI}$
T	Tension below the dogleg, lb
E	Modulus of elasticity, psi
I	Drillpipe moment of inertia, in.⁴
L	Half distance between the tool joints, in.
D_o	Outside diameter of the pipe, in.
D_i	Inside diameter of the pipe, in.

2.7 Casing Design

Tension

Axial Force

$$F_a = \sigma_y A_s$$

F_a	Axial force, lbf
σ_y	Minimum yield strength, psi
A_s	Pipe cross-sectional area, in.², $= \frac{\pi}{4}(d_o^2 - d_i^2)$
d_o	Outside diameter, in.
d_i	Internal diameter, in.

Tensional Force for Fracture

$$F_{aj} = 0.95 \sigma_{up} A_{jp}$$

Tensional Force for Joint Pullout

$$F_{aj} = 0.95 A_{jp} L_{et} \left[\frac{0.74 d_o^{-0.59} \sigma_{up}}{0.5 L_{et} + 0.14 d_o} + \frac{\sigma_y}{L_{et} + 0.14 d_o} \right]$$

F_{aj}	Tensional force for joint failure, lbf
σ_{up}	Minimum ultimate yield strength of the pipe, psi
L_{et}	Length of engaged thread, in.
A_{jp}	Pipe cross-sectional area, in.², $= \frac{\pi}{4}\left[(d_o - 0.1425)^2 - d_i^2 \right]$
d_o	Outside diameter, in.
d_i	Internal diameter, in.

Tensional Force for Coupling Thread Failure

$$F_{aj} = 0.95 \sigma_u A_{sc}$$

Tensional Force for Pipe Thread Failure

$$F_{aj} = 0.95\sigma_u A_{sp}\left[1.008 - 0.0396\left(1.083 - \frac{\sigma_y}{\sigma_u}\right)d_o\right]$$

F_{aj} Tensional force for joint failure, lbf
σ_u Minimum ultimate yield strength of the material, psi
σ_y Minimum yield strength, psi
A_{sp} Area of steel in pipe body, in.$^2 = A_s = \dfrac{\pi}{4}(d_o^2 - d_i^2)$

A_{sc} Area of steel in coupling, in.$^2 = \dfrac{\pi}{4}(d_{co}^2 - d_{root}^2)$
d_o Outside diameter, in.
d_i Internal diameter, in.
d_{co} Outside diameter of coupling, in.
d_{root} Diameter at the root of the coupling thread of the pipe in the power-tight position rounded to the nearest 0.001 in. for API buttress thread casing, in.

Tensional Force for Pipe Failure

$$F_{aj} = \frac{\pi\sigma_u}{4}(d_o^2 - d_i^2)$$

Tensional Force for Box Failure

$$F_{aj} = \frac{\pi\sigma_u}{4}(d_{jo}^2 - d_{box}^2)$$

Tensional Force for Pin Failure

$$F_{aj} = \frac{\pi\sigma_u}{4}(d_{pin}^2 - d_{ji}^2)$$

F_{aj} Tensional force for joint failure, lbf
σ_u Minimum ultimate yield strength of the material, psi
d_o Outside diameter, in.
d_i Internal diameter, in.
d_{jo} External diameter of the joint, in.
d_{box} Internal diameter of the box under the last perfect thread, in.
d_{pin} External diameter of the pin under the last perfect thread, in.
d_{ji} Internal diameter of the joint, in.

Suspended Weight

$$F_a = F_{air} - F_{bu} = F_{air}BF$$

F_a Resultant axial force, lbf
F_{air} Weight of the string in the air, lbf
F_{bu} Buoyancy force, lbf
BF Buoyancy factor, $= 1 - \gamma_m / \gamma_s$
γ_m Specific weight of drilling fluid, ppg
γ_s Specific weight of steel, 65.4 ppg

Bending Force

Full Fracture Strength

$$F_{au} = 0.95\sigma_{up}A_{jp}$$

Jump-Out and Recorded Fracture Strength

$$F_{aj} = 0.95 A_{jp} L_{et} \left[\frac{0.74 d_o^{-0.59} \sigma_{up}}{0.5 L_{et} + 0.14 d_o} + \frac{(1+0.5z)\sigma_y}{L_{et} + 0.14 d_o} \right]$$

Bending Load Failure Strength

$$F_{ab} = 0.95 A_{jp} \left[\sigma_{up} - \left(\frac{140.5 \theta d_o}{\left(\sigma_{up} - \sigma_y \right)^{0.8}} \right)^5 \right] \qquad \text{when} \qquad F_{ab} / A_{jp} \geq \sigma_{up}$$

$$F_{ab} = 0.95 A_{jp} \left[\frac{\sigma_{up} - \sigma_y}{0.644} + \sigma_y - 218.15 \theta d_o \right] \quad \text{when} \quad F_{ab} / A_{jp} < \sigma_{up}$$

F_{ab} Total tensile failure load with bending θ, lbf
F_{au} Total tensile load at fracture, lbf
F_{aj} Minimum joint strength, lbf
σ_{up} Minimum ultimate yield strength of the pipe, psi
σ_y Minimum yield strength, psi
A_{jp} Cross-sectional area of pipe wall under the last perfect thread, in.²,

$$= \frac{\pi}{4} \left[\left(d_o - 0.1425 \right)^2 - \left(d_o - 2t \right)^2 \right]$$

L_{et} Length of engaged thread, in.
d_o Outside diameter, in.
t Wall thickness, in.
z Ratio of internal pressure stress to yield strength, $= \dfrac{p_i d_o}{2\sigma_y t}$
p_i Internal pressure, psi

Shock Load

$$F_s = \frac{2\gamma_s V_p V_s A_s}{g}$$

$$F_s = 3200 W_n \qquad \text{field units}$$

F_s Shock load, lbf
γ_s Specific weight of steel, 489.5 lbm/ft³
V_p Velocity at which pipe is running into hole, ft/sec, = 3.04 for 40 ft of casing (field units)
V_s Velocity of induced stress wave in casing, ft/sec, = 17028 (field units)
A_s Pipe cross-sectional area, in.², = W_n/3.46 (field units)
g Gravity force, ft/sec², = 32.174 (field units)
W_n Nominal weight per unit length, lbm/ft

Drag Force

$$F_d = -f_b |F_n|$$

$$f_b = \frac{F_h - F_{bu_v} \pm F_{vd}}{\int_0^\ell W_d \left(l, f_b \right) dl}$$

F_d Drag force, lbf
f_b Borehole friction factor
$|F_n|$ Absolute value of the normal force
F_h Hook load, lbf
F_{bu_v} Vertically projected component of buoyant weight, lbf

F_{vd} Hydrodynamic viscous drag force, lbf

$W_d\left(l, f_b\right)$ Unit drag or rate of change of drag, lb/ft

l Length of casing, ft

ℓ Measured depth, ft

Burst Pressure

$$P_{br} = 0.875 \frac{2\sigma_y}{\left(d_o / t\right)}$$

P_{br} Burst pressure rating as defined by the API, psi

d_o Outside diameter of the cylinder, in.

t Cylinder wall thickness, in.

σ_y Yield strength of the pipe material, psi

Collapse Pressure

Elastic Collapse

$$p_e = \frac{46.95 \times 10^6}{d_o / t \left(d_o / t - 1\right)^2}$$

Transition Collapse

$$p_t = Y_{pa}\left(\frac{F_4}{d_o / t} - F_5\right)$$

Plastic Collapse

$$p_p = Y_{pa}\left(\frac{F_1}{d_o / t} - F_2\right) - F_3$$

Yield Collapse

$$p_y = 2Y_{pa}\left[\frac{d_o / t - 1}{\left(d_o / t\right)^2}\right]$$

p_e Elastic collapse pressure, psi

p_t Transition collapse pressure, psi

p_p Plastic collapse pressure, psi

p_y Yield collapse pressure, psi

Y_{pa} Yield strength of axial stress equivalent grade, psi $= \sigma_y\left\{\left[1 - 0.75\left(\frac{\sigma_a}{\sigma_y}\right)^2\right]^{0.5} - 0.5\left(\frac{\sigma_a}{\sigma_y}\right)\right\}$

σ_y Minimum yield strength, psi

σ_a Axial stress, psi

$F_1 \ldots F_5$ Empirical coefficient from tables using Grade and d_o / t

Casing Setting Depths

Maximum Kick-Imposed Pressure

$$p_k = \left(G_{p_f} + SM\right)D_i - G_{p_f}\left(D_i - D_s\right)$$

p_k Kick-imposed pressure at depth D_s, psi

G_{p_f} Formation fluid gradient at depth D_i, psi/ft

SM Safety margin
D_i Setting depth for intermediate casing, ft
D_s Setting depth for surface casing, ft

Special Design Consideration

Changing Internal Pressure

$$\Delta F_a = +0.471 d_i^2 \Delta p_i$$

ΔF_a Change in axial force, lbf
d_i Inside diameter of the pipe, in.
Δp Change in internal pressure, psi

Changing External Pressure

$$\Delta F_a = -0.471 d_o^2 \Delta p_i$$

ΔF_a Change in axial force, lbf
d_o Outside diameter of the pipe, in.
Δp_e Change in external pressure, psi

Subsidence Effects

$$\sigma_z = \frac{E_f \Delta p \left(1 - 2\mu_f\right)\left(1 + \mu_f\right)}{E_f \left(1 - \mu_f\right)}$$

σ_z Axial stress resulting from subsidence, psi
E_f Young's modulus of elasticity for the formation
Δp Change in formation pressure, psi
μ_f Poisson's ration for the formation

2.8 Cementing

Cement Slurry Requirements

$$N_c = \frac{V_{sl}}{\Upsilon}$$

N_c Number of sacks of cement, sacks
V_{sl} Slurry volume, ft^3
Υ The yield of cement, ft^3/sack

Yield of Cement

$$\Upsilon = \frac{V_{sl}}{7.48}$$

Υ The yield of cement, ft^3/sack
V_{sl} Slurry volume, gal, $= V_c + V_w + V_a$
V_c Cement volume, gal
V_w Water volume, gal
V_a Additive volume, gal

$$V_{mw} = V_{ms_i} \times N_c$$

V_{mw} Mix water requirement, ft^3
V_{ms_i} Mix water per sack, ft^3
N_c Number of sacks of cement, sacks

$$N_a = N_c \times A_\%$$

N_a Number of sacks of additive, sacks
N_c Number of sacks of cement, sacks
$A_\%$ Percentage of additive

$$W_a = N_a \times 94$$

W_a Weight of additive, lbm
N_a Number of sacks of cement

Slurry Density

$$\rho_{sl} = \frac{W_c + W_w + W_a}{V_c + V_w + V_a}$$

ρ_{sl} Slurry density, ppg
W_c Weight of cement, lbm
W_w Weight of water, lbm
W_a Weight of additive, lbm
V_c Cement volume, gal
V_w Water volume, gal
V_a Additive volume, gal

Hydrostatic Pressure Reduction

$$\Delta p = 0.292 \left(\rho_m - \rho_s \right) C_{an} \times V_s$$

Δp Hydrostatic pressure reduction due to the spacer, psi
ρ_m Density of the mud, ppg
ρ_s Density of the spacer, ppg
C_{an} Annular capacity, ft³/ft
V_s Spacer volume, bbl

Contact Time

$$V_t = t_c \times q \times 5.616$$

V_t Volume of cement needed for removal of mudcake by turbulent flow, ft³
t_c Contact time, minutes
q Displacement rate, bbl/min

Gas Migration Potential (GMP)

$$P_r = 1.67 \times \frac{L}{D_h - D_p} \qquad GMP = \frac{P_{rmax}}{P_{ob}}$$

P_r Pressure reduction for the cement column, psi
L Length of the pipe column exposed to the cement from the reservoir zone, ft
D_h Diameter of the hole, in.
D_p Outside diameter of the casing pipe, in.
P_{ob} Reservoir pressure, psi
GMP Gas migration potential, 0–3 low, 3–8 moderate, >8 high

Cement Plug

$$N_c = \frac{L_p \times V_h}{\Upsilon}$$

N_c Number of sacks of cement required for placing a cement plug, sacks
L_p Length of plug, ft

Υ The yield of cement, ft³/sack
V_h Capacity of the hole, ft³/ft

$$V_{sa} = \frac{V_{sb} \times C_{an}}{V_{dp}}$$

V_{sa} Volume of spacer ahead of the slurry, bbl
V_{sb} Volume of spacer behind the slurry, bbl
C_{an} Annular volume, ft³
V_{dp} Pipe volume, ft³

$$V_m = \left(L_{dp} - L_p\right)V_{dp} - V_{sb}$$

V_m Volume of mud required to displace the pipe, bbl
L_{dp} Length of drillpipe, ft
L_p Length of plug, ft
V_{dp} Volume capacity of the pipe, bbl/ft
V_{sb} Volume of spacer behind the slurry, bbl

Cementing Calculations

Cement Additives

Weight of additives per sack of cement, lbm = percent of additive × 94 lbm/sack

$$\text{Total water requirement gal/sack, of cement} = \frac{\text{Cement water}}{\text{requirement, gal/sack}} + \frac{\text{Additive water}}{\text{requirement, gal/sack}}$$

$$\frac{\text{Volume of}}{\text{slurry, gal/sack}} = \frac{94\ \text{lbm}}{\text{SG of cement} \times 8.33\ \text{ppg}} + \frac{\text{weight od additive, lbm}}{\text{SG of additive} \times 8.33\ \text{ppg}} + \text{water volume, gal}$$

$$\text{Slurry yield, ft}^3/\text{sack} = \frac{\text{vol of slurry, gal/sack}}{7.48\ \text{gal/ft}^3}$$

$$\text{Slurry density, ppg} = \frac{94 + \text{wt of additive} + (8.33 \times \text{vol of water/sack})}{\text{vol of slurry, gal/sack}}$$

Water Requirements

Weight of materials, lbm/sack = $94 + (8.33 \times \text{vol of water, gal}) + (\% \text{of additive} \times 94)$

$$\text{Volume of slurry, gal/sack} = \frac{94\ \text{lb/sack}}{\text{SG} \times 8.33} + \frac{\text{wt of additive, lb/sack}}{\text{SG} \times 8.33} + \text{water vol, gal}$$

Weighted Cement Calculations

$$x = \frac{\left(\dfrac{\text{wt} \times 11.207983}{\text{SGc}}\right) + \left(\text{wt} \times \text{CW}\right) - 94 - \left(8.33 \times \text{CW}\right)}{\left(1 + \dfrac{\text{AW}}{100}\right) - \left(\dfrac{\text{wt}}{\text{SGa} \times 8.33}\right) - \left(\text{wt} + \dfrac{\text{AW}}{100}\right)}$$

x Additive required, pounds per sack of cement
Wt Required slurry density, ppg
SG_c Specific gravity of cement
CW Water requirement of cement
AW Water requirement of additive
SG_a Specific gravity of additive

Bottomhole Pressure Using Geothermal Gradient

$$BHT = \left(\frac{D}{100} \times G\right) + T_A$$

BHT Bottomhole temperature, °F
D Depth of interest, ft
G Geothermal gradient, °F/100 ft
T_A Average ambient temperature, °F

Dimensionless Time Values

$$T_D = \frac{T_{AC}}{T_C + T_{AC}}$$

T_D Dimensionless time
T_{AC} Time after circulation, hr
T_C Circulation time, hr

2.9 Well Planning

Well Path Design

Average Curvature–Average Dogleg Severity (DLS)

$$\bar{\kappa} = \sqrt{\left(\frac{\Delta\alpha}{\Delta L}\right)^2 + \left(\frac{\Delta\phi}{\Delta L}\right)^2 \sin^2 \bar{\alpha}} \qquad \text{and} \qquad \bar{\kappa} = \frac{\beta}{\Delta L}$$

$\bar{\kappa}$ Average borehole curvature, degree
α Inclination, degree
ϕ Azimuth or direction, degree
$\bar{\alpha}$ Average inclination angle, degree
β Bending angle, degree

Borehole Curvature

$$\kappa = \sqrt{\kappa_V^2 + \kappa_H^2 \sin^4 \alpha}$$

$$\kappa_V = \frac{d\alpha}{dL}$$

$$\kappa_H = \frac{d\phi}{dS} = \frac{d\phi}{dL \sin \alpha}$$

κ Curvature of the wellbore trajectory, degree/100 ft
κ_V Curvature of the wellbore trajectory in a vertical position plot, degree/100 ft
κ_H Curvature of the wellbore trajectory in a horizontal projection plot, degree/100 ft
ϕ Azimuth or direction, degree
L Curved section length, ft
S Arc length in the azimuthal direction, ft

Borehole Radius of Curvature

$$R = \frac{180 C_\kappa}{\pi \kappa}$$

R Borehole radius of curvature, degree/100 ft
C_κ Constant related to the unit of borehole curvature, =100
κ Curvature of the wellbore trajectory, degree/100 ft

Bending Angle

$$\cos\beta = \cos\alpha_1 \cos\alpha_2 + \sin\alpha_1 \sin\alpha_2 \cos\Delta\phi$$

β Bending angle, degree
$\Delta\phi$ Section increment of azimuth angle, degree
α_1 Inclination angle at survey point 1, degree
α_2 Inclination angle at survey point 2, degree

Tool Face Angle

$$\gamma = arc\cos\left(\frac{\cos\alpha_1 \cos\beta - \cos\alpha_2}{\sin\alpha_2 \sin\beta}\right)$$

γ Tool face rotation angle, degree
β Bending angle, degree
α_1 Inclination angle at survey point 1, degree
α_2 Inclination angle at survey point 2, degree

Borehole Torsion

$$\tau = \frac{\kappa_a \dot{\kappa}_\phi - \kappa_\phi \dot{\kappa}_a}{\kappa^2}\sin\alpha + \kappa_\phi\left(1 + \frac{\kappa_a^2}{\kappa^2}\right)\cos\alpha$$

Cylindrical Helical Method

$$\tau = \kappa_H\left(1 + \frac{2\kappa_V^2}{\kappa^2}\right)\sin\alpha \cos\alpha$$

τ Torsion of wellbore trajectory, degree/100 ft
κ Curvature of the wellbore trajectory, degree/100 ft
κ_a Vertical curvature, degree/100 ft, $= \kappa_V$
$\dot{\kappa}_a$ The first derivative of inclination change rate, that is, the second derivative of inclination angle
κ_ϕ Directional curvature, degree/100 ft, $= \kappa_H \sin\alpha$
$\dot{\kappa}_\phi$ The first derivative of azimuth change rate, that is, the second derivative of azimuth angle
κ_V Curvature of the wellbore trajectory in a vertical position plot, degree/100 ft
κ_H Curvature of the wellbore trajectory in a horizontal projection plot, degree/100 ft
α Inclination, degree

Well Path Length Calculations

Circular Arc

$$L_c = \frac{\alpha_2 - \alpha_1}{BRA}$$

Vertical Distance

$$V = R_b\left(\sin\alpha_2 - \sin\alpha_1\right) = L_t \cos\alpha$$

Horizontal Distance

$$H = R_b\left(\cos\alpha_1 - \cos\alpha_2\right) = L_t \sin\alpha$$

α_1 Inclination angle at survey point 1, degree
α_2 Inclination angle at survey point 2, degree
BRA Built rate angle, degree/100 ft
R_b Built rate radius, ft

L_s Length of arc, ft
L_t Length of tangent, ft

Well Path Trajectory Calculations From Survey Data

Minimum Curvature Method

$$\Delta N_i = \lambda_i \left(\sin\alpha_{i-1} \cos\phi_{i-1} + \sin\alpha_i \cos\phi_i \right)$$

$$\Delta E_i = \lambda_i \left(\sin\alpha_{i-1} \sin\phi_{i-1} + \sin\alpha_i \sin\phi_i \right)$$

$$\Delta H_i = \lambda_i \left(\cos\alpha_{i-1} + \cos\alpha_i \right)$$

$$\lambda_i = \frac{180}{\pi} \frac{\Delta L_i}{\varepsilon_i} \tan\frac{\beta_i}{2}$$

$$\cos\varepsilon_i = \cos\alpha_{i-1} \cos\alpha_i + \sin\alpha_{i-1} \sin\alpha_i \cos\Delta\phi_i$$

ΔN_i South to north coordinate
ΔE_i West to east coordinate
ΔH_i Vertical depth coordinate
β_i Angle change between stations i and $i-1$

Radius of Curvature Method

$$\Delta N_i = r_i \left(\sin\phi_i - \sin\phi_{i-1} \right)$$

$$\Delta E_i = r_i \left(\cos\phi_{i-1} - \cos\phi_i \right)$$

$$\Delta H_i = R_i \left(\sin\alpha_i - \sin\alpha_{i-1} \right)$$

$$R_i = \frac{180}{\pi} \frac{\Delta L_i}{\Delta\alpha_i} \qquad\qquad r_i = \frac{180}{\pi} \frac{R_i}{\Delta\phi_i} \left(\cos\alpha_{i-1} - \cos\alpha_i \right) \qquad\qquad \Delta\alpha_i = \alpha_i - \alpha_{i-1}$$

$$\cos\varepsilon_i = \cos\alpha_{i-1} \cos\alpha_i + \sin\alpha_{i-1} \sin\alpha_i \cos\Delta\phi_i$$

ΔN_i South to north coordinate
ΔE_i West to east coordinate
ΔH_i Vertical depth coordinate
β_i Angle change between stations i and $i-1$
R Radius of curvature in the vertical plane, degree/100 ft
r Radius of curvature on the horizontal projection, degree/100 ft

Natural Curve Method

$$\Delta N_i = \frac{1}{2}\left[F_C\left(A_{P,i}, \kappa_{P,i}, \Delta L_i\right) + F_C\left(A_{Q,i}, \kappa_{Q,i}, \Delta L_i\right) \right]$$

$$\Delta E_i = \frac{1}{2}\left[F_S\left(A_{P,i}, \kappa_{P,i}, \Delta L_i\right) + F_S\left(A_{Q,i}, \kappa_{Q,i}, \Delta L_i\right) \right]$$

$$\Delta H_i = F_S\left(\alpha_{i-1}, \kappa_{\alpha,i}, \Delta L_i\right)$$

$$\begin{cases} \kappa_{a,i} = \dfrac{\Delta\alpha_i}{\Delta L_i} \\[2mm] \kappa_{\phi,i} = \dfrac{\Delta\phi_i}{\Delta L_i} \end{cases} \qquad \begin{cases} A_{P,i} = \alpha_{i-1} - \phi_{i-1} \\[2mm] A_{Q,i} = \alpha_{i-1} + \phi_{i-1} \end{cases} \qquad \begin{cases} \kappa_{P,i} = \kappa_{\alpha,i} - \kappa_{\phi,i} \\[2mm] \kappa_{Q,i} = \kappa_{\alpha,i} + \kappa_{\phi,i} \end{cases}$$

$$F_C(\theta,\kappa,\lambda) = \begin{cases} \lambda\sin\theta, & \kappa = 0 \\ \dfrac{180}{\pi\kappa}\big[\cos\theta - \cos(\theta+\kappa\lambda)\big], & \kappa \neq 0 \end{cases}$$

$$F_S(\theta,\kappa,\lambda) = \begin{cases} \lambda\cos\theta, & \kappa = 0 \\ \dfrac{180}{\pi\kappa}\big[\sin(\theta+\kappa\lambda) - \sin\theta\big], & \kappa \neq 0 \end{cases}$$

Constant Tool Face Angle Method

$$\Delta N_i = \begin{cases} R_i\big(\cos\alpha_{i-1} - \cos\alpha_i\big)\cos\phi_i, & when\,\alpha_{i-1} = 0\ or\,\alpha_i = 0 \\ r_i\sin\alpha_i\big(\sin\phi_i - \sin\phi_{i-1}\big), & when\,\Delta\alpha_i = 0 \\ \displaystyle\int_{L_1}^{L_2}\sin\alpha(L)\cos\phi(L)dL, & for\,rest\,of\,the\,conditions \end{cases}$$

$$\Delta E_i = \begin{cases} R_i\big(\cos\alpha_{i-1} - \cos\alpha_i\big)\sin\phi_i, & when\,\alpha_{i-1} = 0\ or\,\alpha_i = 0 \\ r_i\sin\alpha_i\big(\cos\phi_{i-1} - \cos\phi_i\big), & when\,\Delta\alpha_i = 0 \\ \displaystyle\int_{L_1}^{L_2}\sin\alpha(L)\sin\phi(L)dL, & for\,rest\,of\,the\,conditions \end{cases}$$

$$\Delta H_i = \begin{cases} \Delta L_i\cos\alpha_i, & \Delta\alpha_i = 0 \\ R_i\big(\sin\alpha_i - \sin\alpha_{i-1}\big), & \Delta\alpha_i \neq 0 \end{cases}$$

$$R_i = \frac{180}{\pi}\frac{\Delta L_i}{\Delta\alpha_i} \qquad\qquad r_i = \frac{180}{\pi}\frac{\Delta L_i}{\Delta\phi_i}$$

$$\tan\omega_i = \frac{\pi}{180}\frac{\Delta\phi_i}{\ln\dfrac{\tan\dfrac{\alpha_i}{2}}{\tan\dfrac{\alpha_{i-1}}{2}}}$$

$$\alpha(L) = \alpha_{i-1} + \frac{\Delta\alpha_i}{\Delta L_i}(L - L_{i-1}) \qquad\qquad \phi(L) = \phi_{i-1} + \frac{180}{\pi}\tan\omega_i\cdot\ln\frac{\tan\dfrac{\alpha(L)}{2}}{\tan\dfrac{\alpha_{i-1}}{2}}$$

Tool Face Angle Change

$$\gamma = arc\cos\left(\frac{\cos\alpha\cos\beta - \cos\alpha_n}{\sin\alpha\sin\beta}\right) \qquad or \qquad \gamma = arc\sin\left(\frac{\sin\alpha_n\sin\Delta\phi}{\sin\beta}\right)$$

$$\alpha_n = arc\cos\big(\cos\alpha\cos\beta - \sin\alpha\sin\beta\cos\gamma\big)$$

$$\Delta\phi = arc\tan\left(\frac{\tan\beta\sin\gamma}{\sin\alpha + \tan\beta\cos\alpha\cos\gamma}\right)$$

Horizontal Displacement

$$H_t = \sqrt{\big(N_t - N_o\big)^2 + \big(E_t - E_o\big)^2}$$

$$\varphi_t = \tan^{-1}\left(\frac{E_t - E_o}{N_t - N_o}\right)$$

H_t Displacement of the target point on the horizontal plane, ft
N_t Northing of target, ft
N_o Northing of slot, ft
E_t Easting of target, ft
E_o Easting of slot, ft
φ_t Target bearing, degree

Tortuosity

Absolute and Relative Tortuosity

$$\Gamma_{(abs)n} = \frac{\sum_{i=1}^{i=n} \alpha_{adj}}{D_n + \Delta D_n}$$

$$\alpha_{adj} = \alpha_i + \Delta D_i \times \beta_i$$

α_{adj} Dogleg adjusted, summed total inclination angle

$$\Gamma_{(rel)n} = \Gamma_{(abs)_n}^{tor} - \Gamma_{(abs)_n}^{notor} \qquad \text{degree}/100\,\text{ft}$$

Sine Wave Method

$$\Delta\alpha = \sin\left(\frac{D}{P} \times 2\pi\right) \times M$$

If $\Delta\alpha < 0$ and $\phi_n = \phi + \Delta\alpha$ is negative, then $\phi_n = \phi + \Delta\alpha$:

$$\alpha_n = \alpha + \Delta\alpha$$

$$\phi_n = \phi + \Delta\alpha + \psi_{cvc}$$

If $\alpha_n < 0$ then $\psi_{cvc} = 180$ $\alpha_n = |\alpha_n|$

If $\alpha_n \geq 0$ then $\psi_{cvc} = 0$

D Measured depth, ft
P Period
M Magnitude
ψ_{cvc} Cross-vertical correction

Helical Method

$$f(u) = a\cos(u) + b\sin(u) + bu$$

$$\begin{cases} x(u) = M\cos(u) \\ y(u) = M\sin(u) \\ z(u) = \frac{P}{2\pi}u \end{cases}$$

Random Inclination Azimuth Method

$$\alpha_n = \alpha + \Delta\alpha$$

$$\phi_n = \phi + \Delta\alpha + \psi_{cvc}$$

ψ_{cvc} Cross-vertical correction

Random Inclination Dependent Azimuth Method

$$\Delta \alpha = \zeta \times \delta$$

$$\delta = \frac{\Delta MD}{P} M$$

$$\alpha_n = \alpha + \Delta \alpha$$

$$\phi_n = \phi + \frac{\Delta \alpha}{2 \sin \alpha_n} + \psi_{cvc}$$

ζ Random number

Well Profile Energy

$$E_{(abs)n} = \frac{\sum_{i=1}^{i=n} \left(\kappa_i^2 + \tau_i^2 \right) \Delta D_i}{D_n + \Delta D_n}$$

$$E_{s(rel)n} = E_{s(abs)_n}^{tor} - E_{s(abs)_n}^{notor}$$

τ Torsion of wellbore trajectory, degree/100 ft
κ Curvature of the wellbore trajectory, degree/100 ft

Magnetic References and Interference

Magnetic Declination − Grid Convergence = Total Correction

Magnetic Azimuth + Total Correction = Corrected Azimuth

Wellbore Trajectory Uncertainty

$$S_{or} = \sqrt{\left(x_n - x_r \right)^2 + \left(y_n - y_r \right)^2 + \left(z_o - z_r \right)^2}$$

x_o, y_o, z_o Coordinates of the object point
x_r, y_r, z_r Coordinates of the reference point
S_{or} Nominal distance between object point and reference point

$$\phi = arc \sin \frac{\sqrt{U_r^2 + V_r^2}}{S_{or}}$$

$$\theta = arc \tan \frac{V_r}{U_r}$$

ϕ Azimuth angle, degree
θ Dip angle, degree
U_r First component of the reference matrix
V_r Second component of the reference matrix

$$k_p = \frac{S_{or}}{\sqrt{\sigma_1^2 \cos^2 \theta \sin^2 \phi + \sigma_2^2 \sin^2 \theta \sin^2 \phi + \sigma_3^2 \cos^2 \phi}}$$

k_p Amplifying factor corresponding to the ellipsoid on which the signal point lies

$$P_p = 1 - \frac{4}{\sqrt{\pi}} \int_0^{\frac{k_p}{\sqrt{2}}} \exp\left[-r^2 \right] r^2 dr$$

P_p Minimum probability of intersection

Well Cost

Drilling Cost

Cost Per Foot

$$C_{di} = \frac{C_{bi} + C_r \left(T_{di} + T_{ti} + T_{ci} \right)}{\Delta D_i}$$

i	Drill-bit number
C_{di}	Drilling cost, dollar/ft
C_{bi}	Bit cost, dollar
C_r	Rig cost, dollar/hr
T_{di}	Drilling time, hr
T_{ti}	Trip time, hr
T_{ci}	Connection time, hr
ΔD_i	Formation interval drilled, ft

$$T_{ti} = 2 \left(\frac{t_s}{L_s} \right) D_i$$

T_{ti}	Trip time required to change a bit and resume drilling operations, hr
t_s	Average time required to handle one stand of drillstring, hr
L_s	Average length of one stand of drillstring, ft
D_i	Depth where the trip was made, ft

$$T_{di} = \frac{1}{ka} \left[e^{aD_{i+1}} - e^{aD_i} \right]$$

$$D_{i+1} = \frac{1}{a} \ln \left(ak\overline{T}_b + e^{aD_i} \right)$$

T_{di}	Drilling time, hr
$\overline{T}_b$	Average bit life for given bit group in a given hole interval, hr
D_i	Depth where the trip was made, ft
D_{i+1}	Depth of the next trip, ft
a,k	Constants determined from past field data

Coring Costs

$$C_c = \left(\frac{C_b + C_r \left(t_t + t_r + t_{cc} + t_{rc} + t_c \right)}{\Delta D} \right) \frac{1}{R_c}$$

C_c	Coring cost, dollar/ft
C_b	Core bit cost, dollar
C_r	Rig daily rental cost, dollar
t_t	Trip time, hr
t_r	Rotating time, hr
t_{cc}	Connection time, hr
t_{rc}	Core recovery, laying down core barrel, hr
t_c	Coring time, hr
ΔD	Formation cored that is a function of rate of penetration, ft
R_c	Core recovery percentage

Future Value

$$FV = PV \left(1 + \frac{r}{n} \right)^{n \times m}$$

For Continuous Compounding

$$FV = PVe^{r \times n}$$

FV   Future value
PV   Present value
r   Periodic interest rate or growth rate in fraction
n   Number of payments per year
m   Number of years

Expected Value

$$EV = \sum_i p_i C_i$$

p_i Probability of the ith event
C_i Cost of the ith event

Price Elasticity

$$E = \frac{(R_2 - R_1)/[(R_1 + R_2)/2]}{(P_2 - P_1)/[(P_1 + P_2)/2]}$$

R   Number of drilling wells
P   Crude oil price
E   Drilling price elasticity

   $E < 1$: Inelastic
   The number of drilling rigs does not respond strongly to the oil price change

   $E > 1$: Elastic
   The number of drilling rigs responds strongly to the oil price change

   $E = 0$: Perfectly Inelastic
   The number of drilling rigs does not respond to the oil price change

   $E = \infty$: Perfectly Elastic
   The number of drilling rigs responds infinitely to the oil price change

   $E = 1$: Unit Elastic
   The number of drilling rigs responds by the same percentage to the oil price change

Dogleg Calculation Technique Based on the Tangential Method

$$DL = \frac{100}{L\left[(\sin I_1 \sin I_2)(\sin A_1 \sin A_2 + \cos A_1 \cos A_2 + \cos I_1 \cos I_2)\right]}$$

DL   Dogleg, *degree* / 100 ft
L   Course length, ft
I_1, I_2 Inclination at upper and lower surveys, degree
A_1, A_2 Direction at upper and lower surveys, degree

2.10. Drilling Problems

Stuck Point Calculations

$$\Delta L_t = \frac{12 E L_p}{A_p \times F}$$

ΔL_t Total axial stretch or contraction, or the distance between two reference points, in.
F Tension or compression force applied, or difference in hook load

L_p Length of the pipe, ft
E Modulus of elasticity, psi, $= 30 \times 10^6$ for steel
A_p Cross-section metal area of the pipe, in.^{2}

Differential Sticking Force

$$F_{pull} = \mu \Delta P A_c$$

F_{pull} Differential sticking point due to fluid filtration, lbm
μ Coefficient of friction
ΔP Differential pressure, psi, $= P_m - P_f$
P_m Pressure due to drilling fluid, psi, $= 0.052 \times \rho_m \times D_v$
P_f Formation pressure or pore pressure, psi
ρ_m Mud weight, ppg
D_v Vertical depth of the calculation or stuck depth, ft
A_c Contact surface area, in.^{2}

Method 1

$$A_c = 2 \times 12 \times L_p \left\{ \left(\frac{D_h}{2} - t_{mc} \right)^2 - \left[\frac{D_h}{2} - t_{mc} \frac{D_h - t_{mc}}{D_h - D_p} \right]^2 \right\}^{\frac{1}{2}}$$

D_h Hole diameter, in.
D_p Outer pipe diameter, in.
t_{mc} Mudcake thickness, in.
L_p Embedded pipe length, ft

Method 2

$$A_c = L_p \left(\frac{D_p D_h}{D_h - D_p} \right)^{\frac{1}{2}} \left\{ \left(\frac{1-x}{x} \right) \left(\frac{Q_f t_{mc}}{A_f} \right) \left(\frac{\Delta p}{\Delta p_f} \right) \left(\frac{\mu_f}{\mu_{df}} \right) \left(\frac{t}{t_f} \right) \right\}^{\frac{1}{4}}$$

Q_f Measured filtrate volume, gpm
A_f Filtration area, in.^{2}
Δp_f Filtration test differential pressure, psi
μ_f Filtrate viscosity at test conditions, cp
μ_{df} Filtrate viscosity at downhole conditions, cp
x Contact ratio
t Total test time, min
t_f Total stuck time, min

Method 3

$$A_c = \left(\frac{\alpha}{2} \right) D_p \times L_p$$

$$\sin \alpha = \frac{\left[\varepsilon (X + \varepsilon)(X + D_p + \varepsilon)(D_p - \varepsilon) \right]^{\frac{1}{2}}}{\left(\frac{1}{2} X + \varepsilon \right) D_p}$$

X $= D_h - D_p - 2t_{mc}$
α Angle of contact between the BHA section and the mudcake, rad
ε Deformation of the mudcake at the midpoint of contact, in.

Spotting Fluid Requirements

$$L_s = \frac{\Delta p}{0.052\left(\rho_m - \rho_s\right)}$$

L_s Height of the spotting fluid in the annulus, ft
Δp Differential pressure due to spotting fluid, psi
ρ_m Mud weight, ppg
ρ_s Spotting fluid density, ppg

Loss Circulation

$$L_l = \frac{V_l}{C_{an/dp}} \qquad\qquad V_l < V_{an/dp}$$

$$L_l = L_{dc} + \frac{V_l - V_{an/dc}}{C_{an/dc}} \qquad\qquad V_l > V_{an/dc}$$

L_l Length of the low-density fluid required to balance the formation pressure, ft
L_{dc} Length of the drill collar, ft
V_l Volume of the low-density fluid pumped to balance the formation pressure, ft
$V_{an/dc}$ Annulus volume against the drill collar, bbl
$V_{an/dp}$ Annulus volume against the drillpipe, bbl
$C_{an/dc}$ Annulus capacity behind the drill collar, bbl/ft
$C_{an/dp}$ Annulus capacity behind the drillpipe, bbl/ft

$$p_{ff} = 0.052 \times D_w \times \rho_w + 0.052 \times \left(D_v - D_w\right) \times \rho_m$$

p_{ff} Formation pressure, psi
D_v Vertical depth of the well where loss occurred, ft
D_w Water depth, ft
ρ_w Seawater density, ppg
ρ_m Mud density, ppg

Increased ECD Due to Cuttings

$$\rho_{eff} = \frac{\rho_m Q + 141.4296 \times 10^{-4} \times ROP \times d_b^2}{Q + 6.7995 \times 10^{-4} \times ROP \times d_b^2}$$

$$\rho_{eff} - \rho_f = \rho_c = \frac{ROP \times d_b^2 \times 10^{-4}\left(141.4296 - 6.7995 \times \rho_f\right)}{Q + 6.7995 \times 10^{-4} \times ROP \times d_b^2}$$

$$ECD = \rho_f + \rho_a + \rho_c$$

ρ_{eff} Effective mud density in the hole due to cuttings generation, ppg
ρ_m Mud density without cuttings, ppg
Q Mud flow rate, gpm
ROP Rate of penetration, ft/hr
d_b Diameter of the bit or diameter of the hole drilled, in.
ECD Equivalent circulating density due to cuttings, ppg
ρ_f Mud density with cuttings, ppg
$\Delta\rho_a$ Equivalent mud weight increase due to annular frictional pressure losses, ppg
$\Delta\rho_c$ Equivalent mud weight increase due to cuttings, ppg

Mud Weight Increase Due to Cuttings

$$V_c = \frac{(1-\phi)D_b^2 \times ROP}{1469.4}$$

V_c Volume of the cuttings entering the mud system, gpm
ϕ Average formation porosity, fraction
D_b Diameter of the bit, in.
ROP Rate of penetration, ft/hr

$$\rho_m = \frac{\rho_{ps}Q + 0.85D_h^2 ROP}{Q + 0.0408D_h^2 ROP}$$

ρ_m Average annular mud weight, ppg
ρ_{ps} Measured mud weight at the pump suction, ppg
Q Flow rate, gpm
D_h Diameter of the hole, in.
ROP Penetration rate based on the time the pump is on before, during, and after the joint is drilled down, ft/hr

Hole Cleaning—Slip Velocity Calculations

The Chien Correlation

$$v_s = 0.458\beta \left[\sqrt{\left(\frac{36800d_s}{\beta}\right)\left(\frac{\rho_s - \rho_m}{\rho_m}\right) + 1} - 1 \right] \qquad\qquad \beta > 10$$

$$v_s = 86.4d_s\sqrt{\frac{\rho_s - \rho_m}{\rho_m}} \qquad\qquad \beta < 10$$

$$\beta = \frac{\mu_a}{\rho_m d_s} \qquad \mu_a = \mu_p + \frac{300\tau_y d_s}{V_a} \qquad V_a = \frac{60Q}{2.448\left(D_h^2 - D^2\right)}$$

v_s Slip velocity, ft/min
ρ_m Mud density, ppg
ρ_s Cuttings density, ppg
d_s Equivalent spherical diameter of cutting, in.
μ_a Mud apparent viscosity, cp
μ_p Mud plastic viscosity, cp
τ_y Mud yield value, lbm/100 ft^2
V_a Average annular fluid velocity, ft/min
Q Flow rate, gpm
D_h Inside diameter of casing or diameter of the hole, in.
D Outside diameter of the pipe, in.

The Moore Correlation

$$v_s = 9.24\sqrt{\frac{\rho_s - \rho_m}{\rho_m}} \qquad\qquad N_R > 2000$$

$$v_s = 4972\left(\rho_s - \rho_m\right)\frac{d_s^2}{\mu_a} \qquad\qquad N_R \leq 1$$

$$v_s = \frac{174d_s\left(\rho_s - \rho_m\right)^{0.667}}{\left(\rho_m\mu_a\right)^{0.333}} \qquad\qquad 1 < N_R < 2000$$

$$\mu_a = \frac{K}{144}\left(\frac{D_h - D_{op}}{V_a / 60}\right)^{1-n}\left(\frac{2+1/n}{0.0208}\right)^n$$

v_s Slip velocity, ft/min
ρ_m Mud density, ppg
ρ_s Cuttings density, ppg
d_s Equivalent spherical diameter of cutting, in.
μ_a Mud apparent viscosity, cp
N_R Reynolds number of particles
K Mud consistency index, eq. cp, $= 510\theta_{300}/511^n$
n Mud power-law index, $= 3.32\log\left(\theta_{600}/\theta_{300}\right)$
D_h Hole diameter, in.
D_{op} Outer pipe diameter, in.
V_a Average annular fluid velocity, ft/min

Walker Mays Correlation

$$v_s = 131.4\sqrt{h_s\left(\frac{\rho_s - \rho_m}{\rho_m}\right)} \qquad N_R > 100$$

$$v_s = 1.22\tau\sqrt{\frac{d_s\gamma}{\sqrt{\rho_m}}} \qquad N_R < 100$$

$$\mu_a = 511\tau/\gamma \qquad \tau = 7.9\sqrt{h_s\left(\rho_s - \rho_m\right)}$$

v_s Slip velocity, ft/min
ρ_m Mud density, ppg
ρ_s Cuttings density, ppg
d_s Equivalent spherical diameter of cutting, in.
N_R Reynolds number of particles
μ_a Mud apparent viscosity, cp
τ Shear stress, lbm/100 ft^2
γ Shear rate corresponding to shear stress τ, sec^{-1}
h_s Cutting thickness, in.

Transport Velocity and Ratio

$$V_t = v_s - V_a \qquad\qquad R_t = 1 - \frac{v_s}{V_a} \qquad\qquad \eta_t = \left(1 - \frac{v_s}{V_a}\right)\times 100$$

V_t Cutting thickness, in.
v_s Slip velocity, ft/min
V_a Average annular fluid velocity, ft/min
R_t Transport ratio
η_t Transport efficiency

Keyseating

Side Force to Create a Keyseat

$$F_L = T\sin\beta \qquad\qquad F_L = 2T\sin\frac{\beta}{2} \qquad\qquad F_L = T\beta L$$

F_L Lateral force, lbf
T Tension in the drillstring just above the keyseat area, lbf
L Length of the dogleg, ft
β Dogleg angle, degree/100 ft

Depth of the Formation Cut Due to Keyseating

$$d_{key} = C_{sc} \sqrt{\frac{T \kappa L_{dl}}{OD_{tj}}} \left(\frac{L_{tj}}{ROP} \right) N$$

d_{key}	Depth of the keyseat, ft
C_{sc}	Side cutting coefficient of the tool joint
T	Drillstring tension at the keyseat, lbm
κ	Dogleg curvature, degree
L_{dl}	Length of the dogleg, in.
OD_{tj}	Outside diameter of the tool joint, in.
L_{tj}	Length of the tool joint, in.
ROP	Rate of penetration, ft/hr
N	rev/min

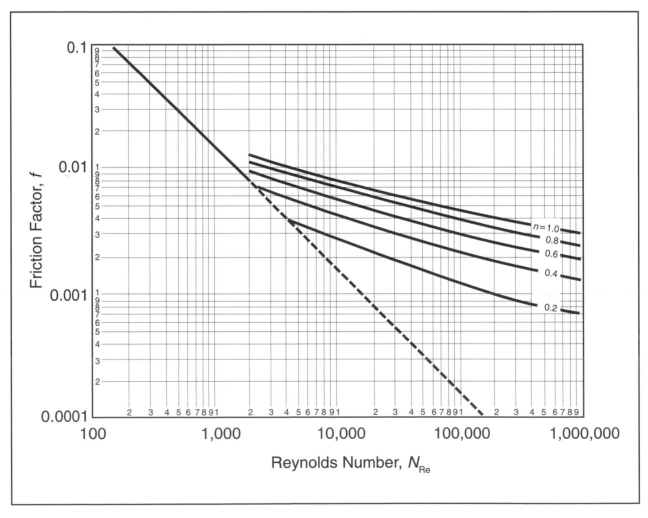

Fig. 2.1—Friction factors for power-law fluid model (Bourgoyne 1986).

TABLE 2.1—DRILLPIPE RANGE II (WILD WELL CONTROL 2014)

Pipe Size (in.)	Nom. Wt. (lb/ft)	Wall Thick. (in.)	Pipe ID (in.)	Plain End Wt. (lb/ft)	Upset Wt. (lb)	Pipe End Dia. ID	Pipe End Dia. OC	API Designation	OD (in.)	Tool Joint OD (in.)	Tool Joint Length (ft)	Tool Joint Weight (ft)	With Tool Joint Capacity (bbl/ft)	With Tool Joint Displ (bbl/ft)	Without Tool Joint Capacity (bbl/ft)	Without Tool Joint Displ. (bbl/ft)
								External Upset—Grade E								
2⅞	10.40	0.362	2.151	9.72	2.40	2.151	3.219	OH	3.875	2.156	1.29	34.99	0.00451	0.00389	0.00449	0.00353
3½	13.30	0.368	2.764	12.31	4.00	2.602	3.824	NC 38 (IF)	4.750	2.688	1.54	61.10	0.00741	0.00515	0.00742	0.00448
3½	15.50	0.449	2.602	14.63	2.80	2.602	3.824	NC 38 (IF)	5.000	2.563	1.59	74.82	0.00658	0.00606	0.00658	0.00532
								Internal External Upset—Grade X								
5	19.50	0.362	4.276	17.93	16.80	3.653	5.188	NC 50 (EH)	6.375	3.500	1.65	120.23	0.01745	0.00784	0.01776	0.00652
								External Upset—Grade G								
4	14.00	0.330	3.340	12.93	14.40	3.063	4.625	NC 46 (IF)	6.000	3.250	1.70	108.76	0.01082	0.00587	0.01084	0.00471
4½	16.60	0.337	3.826	14.98	17.20	3.563	5.188	NC 50 (IF)	6.375	3.750	1.67	113.10	0.01421	0.00663	0.01422	0.00545
								Internal External Upset—Grade G								
4½	20.00	0.430	3.640	18.69	17.60	2.813	4.250	NC 46 (EH)	6.250	2.500	1.71	142.46	0.01252	0.00830	0.01287	0.00680
5	19.50	0.362	4.276	17.93	16.80	3.563	5.188	NC 50 (IF)	6.625	2.750	1.70	157.97	0.01719	0.00827	0.01776	0.00652
5	25.60	0.500	4.000	24.03	15.40	3.313	5.188	5½ FH	7.250	3.250	1.82	188.17	0.01523	0.01075	0.01554	0.00874
5	25.60	0.500	4.000	24.03	15.40	3.313	5.188	5½ FH	7.250	3.500	1.82	179.97	0.01535	0.01066	0.01554	0.00874
5½	21.90	0.361	4.778	19.81	21.00	3.813	5.563	5½ FH	7.250	3.500	1.79	184.41	0.02162	0.00925	0.02218	0.00721
								Internal External Upset—Grade S								
5½	21.90	0.361	4.778	19.81	21.00	3.813	5.563	HT 55	7.000	4.000	2.33	199.19	0.02172	0.00925	0.02218	0.00721
5½	24.70	0.415	4.670	22.54	18.40	3.813	5.563	HT 55	7.000	3.750	2.31	210.15	0.02067	0.01042	0.02119	0.00820
6⅝	25.20	0.330	5.965	22.19	25.87	5.315	6.929	HT 65	8.000	5.000	2.35	240.81	0.03385	0.01078	0.03456	0.00807
6⅝	27.70	0.362	5.901	24.21	24.00	5.315	6.929	HT 65	8.000	4.750	2.39	284.15	0.03297	0.01194	0.03383	0.00881

TABLE 2.2—HEAVYWEIGHT DRILLPIPE (WILD WELL CONTROL 2014)

Nominal Size (in.)	Nominal Tube Dimensions		Tool Joint			Approx. Weight Tube & Joints (lb/ft)	Make-up Torque (ft-lb)	Capacity (bbl/ft)	Displacement (bbl/ft)
	Inside Dia. (in.)	Wall Thickness (in.)	Connection Size (in.)	Outside Dia. (in.)	Inside Dia. (in.)				
3½	2¹/₁₆	0.719	NC 38 (3½ IF)	4¾	2³/₁₆	25.3	9,900	0.0042	0.0092
3½	2¼	0.625	NC 38 (3½ IF)	4¾	2⅜	23.2	9,900	0.0050	0.0084
4	2⁹/₁₆	0.719	NC 40 (4 FH)	5¼	2¹¹/₁₆	27.2	13,250	0.0073	0.0100
4½	2¾	0.875	NC 46 (4 IF)	6¼	2⅞	41.0	21,800	0.0074	0.0149
5	3	1.000	NC 50 (4½ IF)	6⅝	3¹/₁₆	49.3	29,400	0.0088	0.0179
5½	3⅜	1.063	5½ FH	7	3½	57.0	33,200	0.0111	0.0207
6⅝	4½	1.063	6⅝ FH	8	4½	70.8	46,900	0.0196	0.0257

TABLE 2.3—DRILLPIPE CAPACITY AND DISPLACEMENT (WILD WELL CONTROL 2014)					
DP OD (in.)	Weight (ppf)	ID Tube (in.)	DP Capacity (bbl/ft)	Displacement (bbl/ft)	Closed-End (bbl/ft)
2⅜	4.85	1.995	0.00387	0.0016	0.0055
	6.65	1.815	0.00320	0.0025	0.0055
2⅞	6.45	2.469	0.00592	0.0021	0.0080
	6.85	2.441	0.00579	0.0022	0.0080
	8.35	2.323	0.00524	0.0028	0.0080
	10.40	2.151	0.00449	0.0040	0.0080
3½	8.50	3.063	0.00911	0.0028	0.0119
	9.50	2.992	0.00870	0.0035	0.0119
	11.20	2.900	0.00817	0.0037	0.0119
	13.30	2.764	0.00742	0.0048	0.0119
	15.50	2.602	0.00658	0.0056	0.0119
4	11.85	3.476	0.01174	0.0038	0.0155
	14.00	3.340	0.01084	0.0051	0.0155
	15.70	3.240	0.01020	0.0053	0.0155
4½	12.75	4.000	0.01554	0.0046	0.0197
	13.75	3.958	0.01522	0.0050	0.0197
	16.60	3.826	0.01422	0.0064	0.0197
	20.00	3.640	0.01287	0.0073	0.0197
5	16.25	4.408	0.01888	0.0054	0.0243
	19.50	4.276	0.01776	0.0065	0.0243
	20.50	4.214	0.01725	0.0071	0.0243
5½	21.90	4.778	0.02218	0.0080	0.0294
	24.70	4.670	0.02119	0.0082	0.0294
6⅝	22.20	6.065	0.03573	0.0069	0.0426
	25.20	5.965	0.03457	0.0081	0.0426
	31.90	5.761	0.03224	0.0104	0.0426
7⅝	29.25	6.969	0.04718	0.0093	0.0565

TABLE 2.4—DRILL COLLARS (WILD WELL CONTROL 2014)

OD	ID Capacity	1½ in. 0.0022	1¾ in. 0.0030	2 in. 0.0039	2¼ in. 0.0049	2½ in. 0.0061	2¾ in. 0.0073	3 in. 0.0087	3¼ in. 0.0103	3½ in. 0.0119	3¾ in. 0.0137
4-in.	Wt lb/ft	36.7	34.5	32.0	29.2	—	—	—	—	—	—
	Disp bbl/ft	0.0133	0.0125	0.0116	0.0106	—	—	—	—	—	—
4¼-in.	Wt lb/ft	42.2	40.0	37.5	34.7	—	—				
	Disp bbl/ft	0.0153	0.0145	0.0136	0.0126	—	—				
4½-in.	Wt lb/ft	48.1	45.9	43.4	40.6	—	—				
	Disp bbl/ft	0.0175	0.0167	0.0158	0.0148	—	—				
4¾-in.	Wt lb/ft	54.3	52.1	49.6	46.8	43.6	—				
	Disp bbl/ft	0.0197	0.0189	0.0181	0.0170	0.0159	—				
5-in.	Wt lb/ft	60.8	58.6	56.1	53.3	50.1	—	—	—	—	—
	Disp bbl/ft	0.0221	0.0213	0.0204	0.0194	0.0182	—	—	—	—	—
5¼-in.	Wt lb/ft	67.6	65.4	62.9	60.1	56.9	53.4	—	—	—	—
	Disp bbl/ft	0.0246	0.0238	0.0229	0.0219	0.0207	0.0194	—	—	—	—
5½-in.	Wt lb/ft	74.8	72.6	70.1	67.3	64.1	60.6	56.8	—	—	—
	Disp bbl/ft	0.0272	0.0264	0.0255	0.0245	0.0233	0.0221	0.0207	—	—	—
5¾-in.	Wt lb/ft	82.3	80.1	77.6	74.8	71.6	68.1	64.3	—	—	—
	Disp bbl/ft	0.0299	0.0291	0.0282	0.0272	0.0261	0.0248	0.0234	—	—	—
6-in.	Wt lb/ft	90.1	87.9	85.4	82.6	79.4	75.9	72.1	67.9	63.4	—
	Disp bbl/ft	0.0328	0.0320	0.0311	0.0301	0.0289	0.0276	0.0262	0.0247	0.0231	—
6¼-in.	Wt lb/ft	98.0	95.8	93.3	90.5	87.3	83.8	80.0	75.8	71.3	—
	Disp bbl/ft	0.0356	0.0349	0.0339	0.0329	0.0318	0.0305	0.0291	0.0276	0.0259	—
6½-in.	Wt lb/ft	107.0	104.8	102.3	99.5	96.3	92.8	89.0	84.8	80.3	—
	Disp bbl/ft	0.0389	0.0381	0.0372	0.0362	0.0350	0.0338	0.0324	0.0308	0.0292	—
6¾-in.	Wt lb/ft	116.0	113.8	111.3	108.5	105.3	101.8	98.0	93.8	89.3	—
	Disp bbl/ft	0.0422	0.0414	0.0405	0.0395	0.0383	0.0370	0.0356	0.0341	0.0325	—
7-in.	Wt lb/ft	125.0	122.8	120.3	117.5	114.3	110.8	107.0	102.8	98.3	93.4
	Disp bbl/ft	0.0455	0.0447	0.0438	0.0427	0.0416	0.0403	0.0389	0.0374	0.0358	0.0340
7¼-in.	Wt lb/ft	134.0	131.8	129.3	126.5	123.3	119.8	116.0	111.8	107.3	102.4
	Disp bbl/ft	0.0487	0.0479	0.0470	0.0460	0.0449	0.0436	0.0422	0.0407	0.0390	0.0372
7½-in.	Wt lb/ft	144.0	141.8	139.3	136.5	133.3	129.8	126.0	121.8	117.3	112.4
	Disp bbl/ft	0.0524	0.0516	0.0507	0.0497	0.0485	0.0472	0.0458	0.0443	0.0427	0.0409
7¾-in.	Wt lb/ft	154.0	151.8	149.3	146.5	143.3	139.8	136.0	131.8	127.3	122.4
	Disp bbl/ft	0.0560	0.0552	0.0543	0.0533	0.0521	0.0509	0.0495	0.0479	0.0463	0.0445
8-in.	Wt lb/ft	165.0	162.8	160.3	157.5	154.3	150.8	147.0	142.8	138.3	133.4
	Disp bbl/ft	0.0600	0.0592	0.0583	0.0573	0.0561	0.0549	0.0535	0.0520	0.0503	0.0485
8¼-in.	Wt lb/ft	176.0	173.8	171.3	168.5	165.3	161.8	158.0	153.8	149.3	144.4
	Disp bbl/ft	0.0640	0.0632	0.0623	0.0613	0.0601	0.0589	0.0575	0.0560	0.0543	0.0525
8½-in.	Wt lb/ft	187.0	184.8	182.3	179.5	173.3	172.8	169.0	164.8	160.3	155.4
	Disp bbl/ft	0.0680	0.0672	0.0663	0.0653	0.0641	0.0629	0.0615	0.0600	0.0583	0.0565
8¾-in.	Wt lb/ft	199.0	196.8	194.3	191.5	188.3	184.8	181.0	176.8	172.3	167.4
	Disp bbl/ft	0.0724	0.0716	0.0707	0.0697	0.0685	0.0672	0.0658	0.0643	0.0697	0.0609
9-in.	Wt lb/ft	210.2	208.0	205.6	202.7	199.6	196.0	192.2	188.0	183.3	178.7
	Disp bbl/ft	0.0765	0.0757	0.0748	0.0738	0.0726	0.0714	0.0700	0.0685	0.0668	0.0651
10-in.	Wt lb/ft	260.9	258.8	256.3	253.4	250.3	246.8	242.9	238.8	234.3	229.4
	Disp bbl/ft	0.0950	0.0942	0.0933	0.0923	0.0911	0.0898	0.0884	0.0869	0.0853	0.0835

Spiral Drill Collars
Approx. Displacement of Spiral Drill Collar in bbl/ft

$$\frac{(OD^2 - ID^2) \times 2.56}{2{,}747}$$

TABLE 2.5—DRILL COLLARS CAPACITY AND DISPLACEMENT (WILD WELL CONTROL 2014)				
DC OD (in.)	DC ID (in.)	DC Capacity (bbl/ft)	Steel Displ. (bbl/ft)	Closed-End (bbl/ft)
3⅛	1.250	0.00152	0.0080	0.0095
3¾	1.500	0.00219	0.0115	0.0137
4⅛	2.000	0.00389	0.0126	0.0165
4¾	2.000	0.00389	0.0181	0.0219
6	2.250	0.00492	0.0301	0.0350
6¼	2.500	0.00607	0.0318	0.0379
6½	2.500	0.00607	0.0350	0.0410
8	2.813	0.00768	0.0545	0.0622
8¼	2.875	0.00803	0.0589	0.0661
8½	2.875	0.00803	0.0622	0.0629
9	2.875	0.00803	0.0707	0.0787
9½	2.875	0.00803	0.0796	0.0877
10	2.875	0.00803	0.0891	0.0971
10½	2.875	0.00803	0.0991	0.1071
11	2.875	0.00803	0.1095	0.1175
11½	2.875	0.00803	0.1204	0.1285
12	2.875	0.00803	0.1319	0.1399

TABLE 2.6—PREMIUM CONNECTION TUBING (WILD WELL CONTROL 2014)

| Tubing Size | Connection Data | | | Grade | Tube Data | | | | | | | | | | | | | | |
	Outer Dia. (in.)	Inner Dia. (in.)	Make-Up Torque		Outer Dia. (in.)	Inner Dia. (in.)	Drift	Wall Thick	Cross Section	100% Yield	Ult. Strength	Depth 100%	Pull 100%	PSI Burst 100%	Collapse 100%	Cap. (gal/1,000 ft)	Disp.	Capacity (bbl/ft)	Disp.
¾-in. CS HYDRIL 1.5# P-110	1.327	0.687	300	P-110	1.050	0.742	0.648	0.154	0.433	110,000	125,000	31,700	47,600	32,200	26,200	22.5	15.3	0.00054	0.00036
1-in. CS HYDRIL 2.25# C-75	1.600	0.864	400	C-75	1.315	0.957	0.848	0.179	0.639	75,000	95,000	21,300	48,000	20,400	17,600	37.4	34.4	0.00089	0.00082
1-in. CS HYDRIL 2.25# N-80/L-80	1.600	0.864	400	N-L-80	1.315	0.957	0.848	0.179	0.639	80,000	100,000	22,600	51,000	21,800	18,800	37.4	34.4	0.00089	0.00082
1-in. CS HYDRIL 2.25# T-95	1.600	0.864	400	T-95	1.315	0.957	0.848	0.179	0.639	95,000	105,000	27,000	60,700	25,900	22,300	37.4	34.4	0.00089	0.00082
1-in. CS HYDRIL 2.25# P-110	1.600	0.864	400	P-110	1.315	0.957	0.848	0.179	0.639	110,000	125,000	31,200	70,300	29,900	25,900	37.4	34.4	0.00089	0.00082
1-in. CS HYDRIL 2.25# S-135	1.600	0.864	400	S-135	1.315	0.957	0.848	0.179	0.639	135,000	145,000	38,300	86,200	36,700	31,700	37.4	34.4	0.00089	0.00082
1¼-in. CS HYDRIL 3.02# C-75	1.927	1.218	600	C-75	1.660	1.278	1.184	0.191	0.881	75,000	95,000	21,800	66,000	17,200	15,200	66.6	46.2	0.00159	0.00110
1¼-in. CS HYDRIL 3.02# N-80/L-80	1.927	1.218	600	N-L-80	1.660	1.278	1.184	0.191	0.881	80,000	100,000	23,500	71,000	18,400	16,200	66.6	46.2	0.00159	0.00110
1¼-in. CS HYDRIL 3.02# T-95	1.927	1.218	600	T-95	1.660	1.278	1.184	0.191	0.881	95,000	105,000	27,700	83,700	21,900	19,300	66.6	46.2	0.00159	0.00110
1¼-in. CS HYDRIL 3.02# P-110	1.927	1.218	600	P-110	1.660	1.278	1.184	0.191	0.881	110,000	125,000	32,000	96,600	25,300	22,400	66.6	46.2	0.00159	0.00110
1¼-in. CS HYDRIL 3.02# S-135	1.927	1.218	600	S-135	1.660	1.278	1.184	0.191	0.881	135,000	145,000	39,400	119,000	31,000	27,500	66.6	46.2	0.00159	0.00110
1½-in. CS HYDRIL 3.64# N-80/L-80	2.162	1.440	800	N-L-80	1.900	1.500	1.406	0.200	1.068	80,000	100,000	23,300	85,000	16,800	15,000	91.8	55.7	0.00219	0.00133
1½-in. CS HYDRIL 3.64# P-110	2.162	1.440	800	P-110	1.900	1.500	1.406	0.200	1.068	110,000	125,000	32,300	117,500	23,000	20,700	91.8	55.7	0.00219	0.00133
1½-in. CS HYDRIL 3.64# S-135	2.162	1.440	800	S-135	1.900	1.500	1.406	0.200	1.068	135,000	145,000	39,600	144,199	28,421	25,429	91.8	55.7	0.00219	0.00133
2¼-in. CS HYDRIL 3.25# N-80/L-80	2.330	1.700	900	N-L-80	2.063	1.751	1.657	0.156	0.935	80,000	100,000	23,000	75,000	12,100	11,200	125.0	49.7	0.00298	0.00118
2⅜-in. EUE 8RD 4.7# N-80/L-80	3.063	1.995	1500	N-L-80	2.375	1.995	1.901	0.190	1.304	80,000	100,000	22,200	104,300	12,800	11,770	162.3	71.9	0.00386	0.00171

TABLE 2.6—PREMIUM CONNECTION TUBING (WILD WELL CONTROL 2014) (Continued)

	Connection Data			Tube Data															
Tubing Size	Outer Dia. (in.)	Inner Dia. (in.)	Make-Up Torque	Grade	Outer Dia. (in.)	Inner Dia. (in.)	Drift	Wall Thick	Cross Section	100% Yield	Ult. Strength	Depth 100%	Pull 100%	PSI Burst 100%	Collapse 100%	Cap. (gal/1,000 ft)	Disp. (gal/1,000 ft)	Capacity (bbl/ft)	Disp. (bbl/ft)
2⅜-in. PH-6 HYDRIL 5.95# N-80/L-80	2.906	1.805	2,200	N-L-80	2.375	1.867	1.773	0.254	1.692	80,000	100,000	22,700	135,000	17,100	15,300	142.2	91.0	0.00339	0.00217
2⅜-in. PH-6 HYDRIL 5.95# RY-85	2.906	1.805	2,200	RY-85	2.375	1.867	1.773	0.254	1.692	85,000	100,000	24,100	143,800	18,200	16,240	142.2	91.0	0.00339	0.00217
2⅜-in. PH-6 HYDRIL 5.95# T-95	2.906	1.805	2,200	T-95	2.375	1.867	1.773	0.254	1.692	95,000	110,000	27,000	160,740	19,665	17,595	142.2	91.0	0.00339	0.00217
2⅜-in. PH-6 HYDRIL 5.95# P-110	2.906	1.805	2,700	P-110	2.375	1.867	1.773	0.254	1.692	105,000	120,000	29,900	178,000	22,500	20,060	142.2	91.0	0.00339	0.00217
2⅞-in. EUE 8RD 6.5# N-80/L-80	3.668	2.441	2,300	N-L-80	2.875	2.441	2.347	0.217	1.812	80,000	100,000	22,300	145,000	12,100	11,160	243.0	99.5	0.00579	0.00237
2⅞-in. PH-6 HYDRIL 8.7# N-80/L-80	3.500	2.200	3,000	N-L-80	2.875	2.259	2.165	0.308	2.484	80,000	100,000	22,800	198,700	17,140	15,300	208.1	133.1	0.00495	0.00317
2⅜-in. PH-6 HYDRIL 7.9# N-80/L-80	3.437	2.265	3,000	N-L-80	2.875	2.323	2.229	0.276	2.254	80,000	100,000	22,800	180,000	15,300	13,900	220.0	120.9	0.00524	0.00288
2⅜-in. PH-6 HYDRIL 7.9# T-95	3.437	2.265	3,200	T-95	2.875	2.323	2.229	0.276	2.254	95,000	110,000	27,098	214,082	18,000	16,000	220.0	120.9	0.00524	0.00288
2⅜-in. PH-6 HYDRIL 7.9# P-110	3.437	2.265	3,500	P-110	2.875	2.323	2.229	0.276	2.254	105,000	120,000	29,900	236,000	20,100	18,200	220.0	120.9	0.00524	0.00288
3½-in. EUE 8RD 9.3# N-80/L-80	4.500	2.992	2,400–3,200	N-L-80	3.500	2.992	2.867	0.254	2.590	80,000	100,000	22,200	207,200	11,600	10,700	365.2	134.5	0.00870	0.00320
3½-in. EUE 8RD 9.3# P-110	4.500	2.992	3,000–4,000	P-110	3.500	2.992	2.867	0.254	2.590	110,000	125,000	30,600	284,900	15,900	14,800	365.2	134.5	0.00870	0.00320
3½-in. PH-6 HYDRIL 12.95# N-80/L-80	4.312	2.687	5,500	N-L-80	3.500	2.750	2.625	0.375	3.682	80,000	100,000	22,700	294,500	17,100	15,310	308.4	198.1	0.00734	0.00472
3½-in. PH-6 HYDRIL 12.95# T-95	4.313	2.687	6,000	T-95	3.500	2.750	2.625	0.375	3.682	95,000	105,000	27,000	386,600	20,300	18,100	308.4	198.1	0.00734	0.00472
3½-in. PH-6 HYDRIL 12.95# P-110	4.312	2.687	7,000	P-110	3.500	2.750	2.625	0.375	3.682	105,000	120,000	29,800	386,600	22,500	20,090	308.4	198.1	0.00734	0.00472
4½-in. PH-6 HYDRIL 15.50# P-110	5.125	3.765	8,500	P-110	4.500	3.826	3.701	0.337	4.407	110,000	125,000	31,300	485,000	16,480	14,340	598.0	229.2	0.01424	0.00546

TABLE 2.7—API TUBING (WILD WELL CONTROL 2014)

Tubing Size Nominal (in.)	Normal Weight OD (in.)	Normal Weight T&C Non-Upset (lb/ft)	Normal Weight T&C Upset (lb/ft)	Grade	Wall Thick. (in.)	Inside Dia. (in.)	Drift Dia (in.)	Threaded Coupling — Coupling Outside dia. Non-Upset (in.)	Upset Rea. (in.)	Upset Spec. (in.)	Collapse Resistance PSI	Internal Yield Pressure PSI	Joint Yield Strength T&C Non-Upset (lb)	Joint Yield Strength T&C Upset (lb)	Capacity (bbl/ft)	Displacement T&C Non-Upset (bbl/ft)	Displacement T&C Upset (bbl/ft)
2⅜	2.375	4.00		H-40	0.167	2.041	1.947	2.875			4.880	4.920	30.130		0.00405	0.00146	
	2.375	4.60	4.70	H-40	0.190	1.995	1.901	2.875	3.063	2.910	5.520	5.600	35.960	52.170	0.00387	0.00167	0.00171
	2.375	4.00		J-55	0.167	2.041	1.947	2.875			6.340	6.770	41.430		0.00405	0.00146	
	2.375	4.60	4.70	J55	0.190	1.995	1.901	2.875	3.063	2.910	7.180	7.700	49.450	71.730	0.00387	0.00167	0.00171
	2.375	4.00		C-75	0.167	2.041	1.947	2.875			8.150	9.230	56.500		0.00405	0.00146	
	2.375	4.60	4.70	C-75	0.190	1.995	1.901	2.875	3.063	2.910	9.380	10.500	67.430	97.820	0.00387	0.00167	0.00171
	2.375	5.80	5.95	C-75	0.254	1.867	1.773	2.875	3.063	2.910	12.180	14.040	96.560	126.940	0.00339	0.00211	0.00216
	2.375	4.00		N80	0.167	2.041	1.947	2.875			8.660	9.840	50.260		0.00405	0.00146	
	2.375	4.60	4.70	N80	0.190	1.995	1.901	2.875	3.063	2.910	9.940	11.200	71.930	104.340	0.00387	0.00167	0.00171
	2.375	5.80	5.95	N80	0.254	1.867	1.773	2.875	3.063	2.910	12.890	14.970	102.990	135.400	0.00339	0.00211	0.00216
	2.375	4.60	4.70	P105	0.190	1.995	1.901	2.875	3.063	2.910	13.250	14.700	94.410	136.940	0.00387	0.00167	0.00171
	2.375	5.80	5.95	P105	0.254	1.867	1.773	2.875	3.063	2.910	17.190	19.650	135.180	177.710	0.00339	0.00211	0.00216
2⅞	2.875	6.40	6.50	H-40	0.217	2.441	2.347	3.500	3.668	3.460	5.230	5.280	52.780	72.480	0.00579	0.00233	0.00236
	2.875	6.40	6.50	J-55	0.217	2.441	2.347	3.500	3.668	3.460	6.800	7.260	72.580	99.660	0.00579	0.00233	0.00236
	2.875	6.40	6.50	C-75	0.217	2.441	2.347	3.500	3.668	3.460	8.900	9.910	98.970	135.900	0.00579	0.00233	0.00236
	2.875	8.60	8.70	C-75	0.308	2.259	2.165	3.500	3.668	3.460	12.200	14.060	149.360	185.290	0.00496	0.00313	0.00317
	2.875	6.40	6.50	N-80	0.217	2.441	2.347	3.500	3.668	3.460	9.420	10.570	105.570	144.960	0.00579	0.00233	0.00236
	2.875	8.60	8.70	N-80	0.308	2.259	2.165	3.500	3.668	3.460	12.920	15.000	159.310	198.710	0.00496	0.00313	0.00317
	2.875	6.40	6.50	P-105	0.217	2.441	2.347	3.500	3.668	3.460	12.560	13.870	138.560	190.260	0.00579	0.00233	0.00236
	2.875	8.60	8.70	P-105	0.308	2.259	2.165	3.500	3.668	3.460	17.220	19.690	209.100	260.810	0.00496	0.00313	0.00317
3½	3.500	7.70		H-40	0.216	3.068	2.943	4.250			4.070	4.320	65.070		0.00914	0.00280	
	3.500	9.20	9.30	H-40	0.254	2.992	2.867	4.250	4.500	4.180	5.050	5.080	79.540	103.810	0.00870	0.00335	0.00338
	3.500	10.20		H-40	0.289	2.922	2.797	4.250			5.680	5.780	92.550		0.00829	0.00371	
	3.500	7.20		J-55	0.215	3.068	2.943	4.250			5.290	5.940	89.470		0.00914	0.00262	

TABLE 2.7—API TUBING (WILD WELL CONTROL 2014) (Continued)

| Tubing Size | Normal Weight | | | | | | | Threaded Coupling | | | | | Joint Yield Strength | | | Displacement | |
Nominal (in.)	OD (in.)	T&C Non-Upset (lb/ft)	T&C Upset (lb/ft)	Grade	Wall Thick. (in.)	Inside Dia. (in.)	Drift Dia. (in.)	Non-Upset (in.)	Upset Rea. (in.)	Upset Spec. (in.)	Collapse Resistance PSI	Internal Yield Pressure PSI	T&C Non-Upset (lb)	T&C Upset (lb)	Capacity (bbl/ft)	T&C Non-Upset (bbl/ft)	T&C Upset (bbl/ft)
3½	3.500	9.20	9.30	J-55	0.254	2.992	2.867	4.250	4.500	4.180	6.560	6.980	109.370	142.460	0.00870	0.00335	0.00338
	3.500	10.20		J-55	0.289	2.922	2.797	4.250			7.390	7.950	127.250		0.00829	0.00371	
	3.500	7.70		C-75	0.216	3.068	2.943	4.250			6.690	8.100	122.010		0.00914	0.00280	
	3.500	9.20	9.30	C-75	0.254	2.992	2.867	4.250	4.500	4.180	8.530	9.520	149.140	194.260	0.00870	0.00335	0.00338
	3.500	10.20		C-75	0.289	2.922	2.797	4.250			9.660	10.840	173.530		0.00829	0.00371	
	3.500	12.70	12.95	C-75	0.375	2.750	2.625	4.250	4.500	4.180	12.200	14.060	230.990	276.120	0.00735	0.00462	0.00471
	3.500	7.70		N-80	0.216	3.068	2.943	4.250			7.080	8.640	130.140		0.00914	0.00280	
	3.500	9.20	9.30	N-80	0.254	2.992	2.867	4.250	4.500	4.180	9.080	10.160	159.090	207.220	0.00870	0.00335	0.00338
	3.500	10.20		N-80	0.289	2.922	2.797	4.250			10.230	11.560	185.100		0.00829	0.00371	
	3.500	12.70	12.95	N-80	0.375	2.750	2.625	4.250	4.500	4.180	12.920	15.000	246.390	294.530	0.00735	0.00462	0.00471
	3.500	9.20	9.30	P-105	0.254	2.992	2.867	4.250	4.500	4.180	12.110	13.330	208.800	271.970	0.00870	0.00335	0.00338
	3.500	12.70	12.95	P-105	0.375	2.750	2.625	4.250	4.500	4.180	17.200	19.690	323.390	386.570	0.00735	0.00462	0.00471
4	4.000	9.50		H-40	0.226	3.548	3.423	4.750			3.580	3.960	72.000		0.01223	0.00346	
	4.000		11.00	H-40	0.262	3.476	3.351		5.000		4.420	4.580		123.070	0.01174		0.00400
	4.000	9.50		J-55	0.226	3.548	3.423	4.750			4.650	5.440	99.010		0.01223	0.00346	
	4.000		11.00	J-55	0.262	3.476	3.351		5.000		5.750	6.300		169.220	0.01174		0.00400
	4.000	9.50		C-75	0.226	3.548	3.423	4.750			5.800	7.420	135.010		0.01223	0.00346	
	4.000		11.00	C-75	0.262	3.476	3.351		5.000		7.330	8.600		230.750	0.01174		0.00400
	4.000	9.50		N-80	0.226	3.548	3.423	4.750			6.120	7.910	144.010		0.01223	0.00346	
	4.000		11.00	N-80	0.262	3.476	3.351		5.000		7.780	9.170		246.140	0.01174		0.00400
4½	4.500	12.60	12.75	H-40	0.271	3.958	3.833	5.200	5.563		3.930	4.220	104.360	144.020	0.01522	0.00458	0.00464
	4.500	12.60	12.75	J-55	0.271	3.958	3.833	5.200	5.563		5.100	5.800	143.500	198.030	0.01522	0.00458	0.00464
	4.500	12.60	12.75	C-75	0.271	3.958	3.833	5.200	5.563		6.430	7.900	195.680	270.040	0.01522	0.00458	0.00464
	4.500	12.60	12.75	N-80	0.271	3.958	3.833	5.200	5.563		6.810	8.430	208.730	288.040	0.01522	0.00458	0.00464

TABLE 2.7—API TUBING (WILD WELL CONTROL 2014) (Continued)

Tubing Size Nominal (in.)	Normal Weight OD (in.)	Normal Weight T&C Non-Upset (lb/ft)	Normal Weight T&C Upset (lb/ft)	Grade	Wall Thick. (in.)	Inside Dia. (in.)	Drift Dia. (in.)	Coupling Non-Upset (in.)	Coupling Upset Rea. (in.)	Coupling Upset Spec. (in.)	Collapse Resistance PSI	Internal Yield Pressure PSI	Joint Yield T&C Non-Upset (lb)	Joint Yield T&C Upset (lb)	Capacity (bbl/ft)	Displacement T&C Non-Upset (bbl/ft)	Displacement T&C Upset (bbl/ft)
¾	1.050	1.14	1.20	H-40	0.113	0.824	0.730	1.313	1.660		7.200	7.530	6.360	13.300	0.00066	0.00041	0.00044
	1.050	1.14	1.20	J-55	0.113	0.824	0.730	1.313	1.660		9.370	10.360	8.740	18.290	0.00066	0.00041	0.00044
	1.050	1.14	1.20	C-75	0.113	0.824	0.730	1.313	1.660		12.250	14.120	11.920	24.940	0.00066	0.00041	0.00044
	1.050	1.14	1.20	N-80	0.113	0.824	0.730	1.313	1.660		12.970	15.070	12.710	26.610	0.00066	0.00041	0.00044
1	1.315	1.70	1.80	H-40	0.133	1.049	0.955	1.660	1.900		6.820	7.080	10.960	19.760	0.00107	0.00062	0.00065
	1.315	1.70	1.80	J-55	0.133	1.049	0.955	1.660	1.900		8.860	9.730	15.060	27.160	0.00107	0.00062	0.00065
	1.315	1.70	1.80	C-75	0.133	1.049	0.955	1.660	1.900		11.590	13.270	20.540	37.040	0.00107	0.00062	0.00065
	1.315	1.70	1.80	N-80	0.133	1.049	0.955	1.660	1.900		12.270	14.160	21.910	39.510	0.00107	0.00062	0.00065
1¼	1.660			H-40	0.125	1.410	1.286				5.220	5.270			0.00193		
	1.660	2.30	2.40	H-40	0.140	1.380	1.286	2.054	2.200		5.790	5.900	15.530	26.740	0.00185	0.00084	0.00087
	1.660			J-55	0.125	1.410	1.286				6.790	7.250			0.00193		
	1.660	2.30	2.40	J-55	0.140	1.380	1.286	2.054	2.200		7.530	8.120	21.360	36.770	0.00185	0.00084	0.00087
	1.660	2.30	2.40	C-75	0.140	1.380	1.286	2.054	2.200		9.840	11.070	29.120	50.140	0.00185	0.00084	0.00087
	1.660	2.30	2.40	N-80	0.140	1.380	1.286	2.054	2.200		10.420	11.810	31.060	53.480	0.00185	0.00084	0.00087
1½	1.900			H-40	0.125	1.850	1.516				4.450	4.610			0.00332		
	1.900	2.75	2.90	H-40	0.145	1.610	1.516	2.200	2.500		5.290	5.340	19.090	31.980	0.00252	0.00100	0.00106
	1.900			J-55	0.125	1.650	1.516				5.790	6.330			0.00264		
	1.900	2.75	2.90	J-55	0.145	1.610	1.516	2.200	2.500		6.870	7.350	26.250	43.970	0.00252	0.00100	0.00106
	1.900	2.75	2.90	C-75	0.145	1.610	1.516	2.200	2.500		8.990	10.020	35.800	59.960	0.00252	0.00100	0.00106
	1.900	2.75	2.90	N-80	0.145	1.610	1.516	2.200	2.500		9.520	10.680	38.130	63.950	0.00252	0.00100	0.00106
2¹/₁₆	2.063			H-40	0.156	1.751					5.240	5.290			0.00298		
	2.063			J-55	0.156	1.751					6.820	7.280			0.00298		
	2.063			C-75	0.156	1.751					8.910	9.920			0.00298		
	2.063			N-80	0.156	1.751					9.440	10.590			0.00298		

TABLE 2.8—CASING STRENGTH (WILD WELL CONTROL 2014)

Casing OD (in.)	Weight (ppf)	Burst Pressure (psi)						Collapse Pressure (psi)					
		H40	J/K 55	C75	N80	C95	P110	H40	J/K 55	C75	N80	C95	P110
4½	9.5		4,380						3,310				
	11.6		5,350	7,290	7,780	9,240	10,690		4,960	6,100	6,350	7,030	7,580
	13.5		6,200	8,460	9,020	10,710	12,410		6,420	8,140	8,540	9,660	10,680
	15.1		7,210	9,830	10,480		14,420		7,620	10,390	11,080		14,350
5	11.5		4,240						3,060				
	13.0		4,870	6,640	7,090				4,140	4,990	5,140		
	15.0		5,700	7,770	8,290	9,840	11,400		5,500	6,970	7,250	8,090	8,830
	18.0		6,970	9,500	10,140	12,040	13,940		7,390	10,000	10,490	12,010	13,470
5½	14.0		4,270	5,820					3,120	3,560			
	15.5		4,810	6,560	7,000		9,620		3,860	4,860	4,990		5,620
	17.0		5,320	7,250	7,740	9,190	10,640		4,910	6,070	5,890	6,930	8,520
	20.0		6,310	8,610	9,190	10,910	12,640		6,610	8,440	8,830	10,000	11,100
	23.0		7,270	9,900	10,560	12,540	14,520		7,670	10,400	11,160	12,920	14,520
6⅝	20.0		4,180		6,090	7,230			3,060		3,480	3,830	
	24.0		5,110	6,970	7,440	8,830	10,230		4,560	5,550	5,550	6,310	6,730
	28.0		6,060	8,260	8,810	10,460	12,120		6,170	7,830	8,170	9,200	10,140
7	20.0	2,720	3,740	5,100				1,920	2,500	2,660			
	23.0		4,360	5,940	6,340	7,530			3,270	3,770	3,830	4,150	
	26.0		4,980	6,790	7,240	8,600	9,960		4,320	5,250	5,320	5,870	7,220
	29.0		5,610	7,650	8,160	9,690	11,220		5,400	6,760	7,020	7,820	8,510
	32.0		6,230	8,490	9,060	10,760	12,460		6,460	8,230	8,600	9,730	10,760
	35.0		6,850	9,340	9,960	11,830	13,700		7,270	9,710	10,180	11,640	13,020
7⅝	26.4		4,140	5,650	6,020	7,150	8,280		3,010	3,280	3,930	3,716	3,900
	29.7			6,450	6,890	8,180	9,470			4,670	4,790	5,120	6,180
	33.7		5,430	7,400	7,900	8,180	10,860		5,090	6,320	6,560	7,260	7,870
	39.0			8,610	9,180	9,380	12,620			8,430	8,820	9,980	11,060
8⅝	24.0	2,860	2,950					2,210	950				
	32.0		3,930	5,360	5,710	7,860	8,930		2,530	2,950	3,050		3,430
	36.0		4,460	6,090	6,490	7,710			3,450	4,020	4,470	4,360	4,700
	40.0		5,020	6,850	7,300	8,670	10,040		4,400	5,350	5,520	6,010	7,420

TABLE 2.8—CASING STRENGTH (WILD WELL CONTROL 2014) (Continued)

Casing OD (in.)	Weight (ppf)	Burst Pressure (psi)						Collapse Pressure (psi)					
		H40	J/K 55	C75	N80	C95	P110	H40	J/K 55	C75	N80	C95	P110
9⅝	36.0	2,560	3,520	4,800	5,120			1,710	2,220	2,320	2,370		2,470
	40.0		3,950	5,390	5,750	6,820	7,900		2,570	2,980	3,530	3,330	3,480
	43.5		4,350	5,930	6,330	7,510	8,700		3,250	3,750	3,810	4,130	4,760
	47.0		4,720	6,440	6,870	8,150	9,440		3,880	4,630	4,760	5,080	5,310
	53.5			7,430	7,930	9,410	10,900			6,380	6,620	7,330	7,930
10¾	40.5	2,280	3,130	4,270				1,420	1,730	1,720			
	45.5		3,580	4,880	5,210	7,160			2,090	2,410	2,480	3,490	2,610
	51.0		4,030	5,490	5,860	6,960	8,060		2,700	3,100	3,750	4,300	3,750
	55.5		4,430	6,040	6,450	7,660	8,860		3,320	3,950	4,020	5,566	4,630
	60.7		4,880	6,650	7,100	8,436	9,760		4,160	5,020	5,160	6,950	5,860
	65.7		5,330	7,260	7,750	9,200	10,650		4,920	6,080	6,300	8,470	7,490
	71.1					10,050	11,640						9,280
11¾	47.0		3,070	4,190					1,630	1,620			
	54.0		3,560	4,860					2,070	2,380			
	60.0		4,010	5,460	5,830	6,920	8,010		2,660	3,070	3,680	3,440	3,610
13⅜	48.0	1,730						770					
	54.5		2,730	3,980					1,140				
	61.0		3,090	4,220	4,500				1,540	1,660	1,670		
	68.0		3,450	4,710	5,020	5,970	7,400		1,950	2,220	2,270	2,330	
	72.0		3,700	5,040	5,380	6,390			2,230	2,590	2,880	2,820	2,880
	77.0			5,400	5,760					2,990	3,100		
	85.0			5,970	6,360	8,750				3,810	3,870	4,490	
16	65.0	1,640						670					
	75.0		2,630						1,010				
	84.0		2,980						1,410				
	109.0		3,950				7,890		2,560				3,470
18⅝	87.5	1,550	2,110					520	520				
	106.0		2,740						1,140				
20	94.0	1,530	2,110					520	520				
	106.5		2,410						770				
	133.0		3,060						1,500				
24	156.0	X-42	1,910					860					
26	202.0	X-42	2,120					1,100					
30	310.0	X-42	2,450					1,480					
36	374.0	X-42	2,040					1,010					

Chapter 3

Formation Evaluation

This chapter contains equations to obtain various formation and formation fluids characteristics and properties. It includes calculations for water saturation using different methods, such as Archie's, flushed zone, neutron logs, spontaneous potential logs, clean-sand model, laminated-sand model, and dual-water model. The chapter also includes methods for obtaining formation resistivity, density, and porosity using sonic data and core analysis. The many calculations for rock formation characteristics inferred from various well-logging parameters, such as porosity, Young's bulk, and shear modulus, are also presented. The formation damage aspect of the formation, or the so-called "skin calculations," are presented for various circumstances such as partial penetration, deviated wells, gravel packing, completion, non-Darcy flow, and fracture damage. The chapter also contains the horizontal influx flow equations for different flow behaviors and geometries. Finally, nomographs and plots are given at the end of the chapter to ease the calculation of many of the above parameters.

3.1 Archie's Water Saturation

$$S_w = \left(\frac{aR_w}{\phi^m R_t} \right)^{1/n}$$

S_w Water saturation
R_w Formation water resistivity, $\Omega \cdot m$
R_t Observed bulk resistivity, $\Omega \cdot m$
ϕ Porosity
a Tortuosity constant
n Saturation exponent
m Cementation exponent

Resistivity Index

$$I_R = \frac{R_t}{R_o}$$

R_t Observed bulk resistivity, $\Omega \cdot m$
R_o Resistivity of rock fully saturated with water, $\Omega \cdot m$

3.2 Formation Resistivity Factor

$$F = \frac{R_o}{R_w}$$

F Formation resistivity factor
R_o Resistivity of rock fully saturated with water, $\Omega \cdot m$
R_w Water resistivity, $\Omega \cdot m$

Formation Resistivity Factor and Porosity

$$F = \frac{a}{\phi^m}$$

F Formation resistivity factor
ϕ Porosity
m Cementation constant
a Tortuosity constant

3.3 Flushed Zone Water Saturation

$$S_{xo} = \left(\frac{aR_{mf}}{\phi^m R_{xo}} \right)^{\frac{1}{n}}$$

S_{xo} Water saturation of the flushed zone
R_{mf} Resistivity of the mud filtrate at formation temperature, $\Omega \cdot m$
R_{xo} Shallow resistivity, $\Omega \cdot m$
a Tortuosity constant
n Saturation exponent
ϕ Porosity
m Cementation constant

3.4 Porosity Calculations From Sonic data

Wyllie Time-Average

$$\phi_s = \frac{\Delta t_{log} - \Delta t_{matrix}}{\Delta t_f - \Delta t_{matrix}}$$

Raymer-Hunt-Gardner

$$\phi_s = \frac{5}{8} \times \left(\frac{\Delta t_{log} - \Delta t_{matrix}}{\Delta t_{log}} \right)$$

For Unconsolidated Formations

$$\phi_s = \left(\frac{\Delta t_{log} - \Delta t_{matrix}}{\Delta t_f - \Delta t_{matrix}} \right) \times \frac{1}{C_p} \qquad C_p = \frac{\Delta t_{sh} \times C}{100}$$

ϕ_s Sonic porosity, fraction
Δt_{log} Measured interval travel time from sonic log, μs/ft
Δt_{matrix} Interval travel time of the rock matrix, μs/ft
Δt_f Interval travel time of the saturating fluid, μs/ft
Δt_{sh} Interval travel time of the shale beds, μs/ft
C_p Compaction factor
C Constant, normally = 1

3.5 Young's Modulus

Basic Equation

$$E = \frac{9K\rho v_s^2}{3K + \rho v_s^2}$$

Equation in Well-Logging Terms

$$E = \left(\frac{\rho}{\Delta t_s^2} \right) \left(\frac{3\Delta t_s^2 - 4\Delta t_c^2}{\Delta t_s^2 - \Delta t_c^2} \right) \times 13400$$

3.6 Bulk Modulus

Basic Equation

$$K = \rho\left(v_p^2 - \frac{4}{3}v_s^2\right)$$

Equation in Well-Logging Terms

$$K = \rho\left(\frac{3\Delta t_s^2 - 4\Delta t_c^2}{3\Delta t_s^2 - \Delta t_c^2}\right)\times 13400$$

3.7 Shear Modulus

Basic Equation

$$\mu = \rho v_s^2$$

Equation in Well-Logging Terms

$$\mu = \frac{\rho}{\Delta t_s^2}\times 13400$$

3.8 Poisson's Ratio

Basic Equation

$$\sigma = \frac{1}{2}\frac{\left(\dfrac{v_p^2}{v_s^2}\right) - 2}{\left(\dfrac{v_p^2}{v_s^2}\right) - 1}$$

Equation in Well-Logging Terms

$$\sigma = \frac{1}{2}\left(\frac{\Delta t_s^2 - 2\Delta t_c^2}{\Delta t_s^2 - \Delta t_c^2}\right)$$

v_s Shear wave velocity, ft/sec
v_p Compressional wave velocity, ft/sec
ρ Bulk density, lb/ft^3
Δt_s Shear sonic log travel time, μs/ft
Δt_c Compressional sonic log travel time, μs/ft

3.9 D-exponent

$$d_{\exp} = \frac{\log\left(\dfrac{R}{60N}\right)}{\log\left(\dfrac{12W}{1000d_b}\right)}$$

Corrected D-exponent

$$d_c = d_{\exp}\frac{\rho_n}{\rho_e}$$

R Penetration rate, ft/hr
N Rotary speed, rev/min
W Weight on bit, Mlbf

d_b Bit diameter, in.
ρ_n Mud density equivalent to a normal formation pore pressure
ρ_e Equivalent mud density at the bit while circulating

3.10 Porosity/Bulk Density

$$\phi = \frac{\rho_{ma} - \rho_b}{\rho_{ma} - \rho_{fl}}$$

ϕ Porosity
ρ_{ma} Matrix density, g/cm^3
ρ_b Formation bulk density, g/cm^3
ρ_{fl} Fluid density, g/cm^3

Porosity From Core Analysis

$$\phi_c = \phi_e + V_{cl}\phi_{cl} = \phi_e + V_{sh}\phi_{sh}$$

ϕ_c Core porosity
ϕ_e Effective porosity
ϕ_{cl} Clay porosity
ϕ_{sh} Shale porosity
V_{cl} Clay content
V_{sh} Shale content

Effective Porosity

$$\phi_e = \frac{\phi_D \times \phi_{Nsb} - \phi_N \times \phi_{Dsb}}{\left(\phi_{Nsb} - \phi_{Dsb}\right) \times \left(\phi_N - \phi_D\right)}$$

ϕ_D Density porosity
ϕ_N Neutron porosity
ϕ_{Dsb} Density porosity of extraneous materials
ϕ_{Nsb} Neutron porosity of extraneous materials

3.11 Saturation

Clean-Sand Model

$$S_w = \left(\frac{R_o}{R_t}\right)^{1/n}$$

n Saturation exponent
R_t Observed bulk resistivity, $\Omega \cdot m$
R_o Resistivity of rock fully saturated with water, $\Omega \cdot m$

Laminated-Sand/Shale Model

$$\frac{1}{R_t} = \frac{V_{sh}}{R_{sh}} + \frac{1 - V_{sh}}{R_{sd}}$$

$$R_{sd} = \frac{R_w}{\phi_{sd}^m S_{wsd}^n}$$

$$\phi_e = \phi_{sd}\left(1 - V_{sh}\right)$$

$$S_{we} = S_{wsd}$$

R_t True resistivity of uninvaded, deep formation, $\Omega \cdot m$
R_{sh} Shale resistivity, $\Omega \cdot m$

R_{sd} Clean-sand resistivity, $\Omega \cdot m$
R_w Connate-brine resistivity, $\Omega \cdot m$
V_{sh} Shale content, %BV
ϕ_e Effective porosity, %BV
ϕ_{sd} Sand porosity, %BV
S_{we} Water saturation of the effective porosity, %PV
S_{wsd} Sand water saturation, %PV

Poupon-Leveaux (Indonesia) Model

$$S_w = \left\{ \left[\left(\frac{V_{sh}^{2-V_{sh}}}{R_{sh}} \right)^{1/2} + \left(\frac{\phi_e^m}{R_w} \right)^{1/2} \right]^2 R_t \right\}^{-1/n}$$

S_W Water saturation, %PV
V_{sh} Shale content, %BV
R_{sh} Shale resistivity, $\Omega \cdot m$
R_w Connate-brine resistivity, $\Omega \cdot m$
R_t True resistivity of uninvaded, deep formation, $\Omega \cdot m$
ϕ_e Effective porosity, %BV
m Cementation exponent
n Saturation exponent

Waxman-Smits-Thomas Model

$$\frac{1}{R_t} = \phi_t^{m^*} S_{wt}^{n^*} \left(\frac{1}{R_w} + \frac{BQ_V}{S_{wt}} \right)$$

R_t True resistivity of uninvaded, deep formation, $\Omega \cdot m$
ϕ_t Total porosity, %BV
S_{wt} Water saturation of the total porosity, %PV
R_w Connate-brine resistivity, $\Omega \cdot m$
B Specific cation conductance, $\left[(1/\Omega \cdot m)/(mEq/mL) \right]$
Q_V Cation-exchange capacity of total PV, mEq / mL
m^* Waxman-Smith-Thomas cementation exponent
n^* Waxman-Smith-Thomas saturation exponent

Dual-Water Model

$$\frac{1}{R_t} = \phi_t^{m_o} S_{wt}^{n_o} \left[\frac{1}{R_{wf}} + \frac{S_{wb}}{S_{wt}} \left(\frac{1}{R_{wb}} - \frac{1}{R_{wf}} \right) \right]$$

$$\phi_e = \phi_t \left(1 - S_{wb} \right)$$

$$S_{we} = \frac{S_{wt} - S_{wb}}{1 - S_{wb}}$$

R_t True resistivity of uninvaded, deep formation, $\Omega \cdot m$
R_{wb} Clay-bound water resistivity, $\Omega \cdot m$
R_{wf} Free-formation-water resistivity, $\Omega \cdot m$
ϕ_t Total porosity, %BV
ϕ_e Effective porosity, %BV
S_{wt} Water saturation of the total porosity, %PV
S_{wb} Saturation of clay-bound water in the total porosity, %PV
S_{we} Water saturation of the effective porosity, %PV

Saturation From Neutron Logs

$$S_w = \frac{\left(\sum_{log} - \sum_{ma}\right) - \phi\left(\sum_h - \sum_{log}\right)}{\phi\left(\sum_w - \sum_h\right)}$$

S_w Water saturation

$\sum_{log}$ Capture cross section of log response, cm^2/cm^3

$\sum_{ma}$ Capture cross section of rock, cm^2/cm^3

$\sum_h$ Capture cross section of hydrocarbon, cm^2/cm^3

$\sum_w$ Capture cross section of water, cm^2/cm^3

ϕ Porosity, fraction

Saturation From SP Logs

$$\left(E_{SP}\right)_{QL} = \left(E_{SP}\right)_{log} - K \log\left(S_w / S_{xo}\right)^n$$

$\left(E_{SP}\right)_{QL}$ Quick look spontaneous potential, mV

$\left(E_{SP}\right)_{log}$ Log spontaneous potential, mV

S_w Water saturation

S_{xo} Flushed zone saturation

n Saturation exponent

K Coefficient, $= 61.3 + 0.133 T_f$

T_f Formation temperature, °F

Fertl and Hammack Equation

$$S_w = \left(\frac{0.81 R_w}{\phi^2 R_t}\right)^{1/2} - \left(\frac{V_{sh} R_w}{0.4 \phi R_{sh}}\right)$$

S_w Water saturation

R_w Resistivity of water, $\Omega \cdot m$

R_t Total resistivity, $\Omega \cdot m$

ϕ Porosity, fraction

V_{sh} Shale content, fraction

R_{sh} Shale resistivity, $\Omega \cdot m$

3.12 Skin Calculations

Skin Pressure Drop and Skin Factor

$$\Delta p_s = 141.2 \frac{qB\mu}{kh}\left(\frac{k}{k_s} - 1\right)\ln\left(\frac{r_s}{r_w}\right)$$

$$s = \left(\frac{k}{k_s} - 1\right)\ln\left(\frac{r_s}{r_w}\right) = \frac{kh\Delta p_s}{141.2 qB\mu}$$

Δp_s Additional pressure drop due to skin, psi

s Skin factor, dimensionless

q Flow rate at surface, STB/D

B Formation volume factor, res vol/surface vol

μ Viscosity, cp

h Net formation thickness, ft

k Permeability, md

k_s Permeability of damaged zone, md

r_w Wellbore radius, ft
r_s Outer radius of the damaged zone, ft

Skin With Apparent Wellbore Radius

$$s = -\ln\left(r_{wa}/r_w\right)$$

s Skin factor, dimensionless
r_{wa} Apparent or effective wellbore radius, ft
r_w Wellbore radius, ft

Skin in Incompletely Perforated Interval

$$s = \left(h/h_p\right)s_d + s_p$$

$$s_p = \left(\frac{1}{h_{pD}} - 1\right)\ln\frac{\pi}{2r_D} + \frac{1}{h_{pD}}\ln\left[\frac{h_{pD}}{2+h_{pD}}\left(\frac{A-1}{B-1}\right)^{\!1/2}\right]$$

$$A = \frac{1}{h_{1D} + h_{pD}/4}$$

$$h_{pD} = h_p/h$$

$$h_{1D} = h_1/h$$

$$B = \frac{1}{h_{1D} + 3h_{pD}/4}$$

s Skin factor, dimensionless
s_d Skin caused by formation damage, dimensionless
s_p Skin resulting from an incompletely perforated interval, dimensionless
h Net formation thickness, ft
h_p Perforated interval thickness, ft
h_1 Distance from top of formation to top of perforations, ft
r_D Dimensionless radius $= r/r_w$

Skin in Deviated Wells

$$s = s_d + s_\theta$$

$$s_\theta = \left(\frac{\theta'_w}{41}\right)^{2.06} - \left(\frac{\theta'_w}{56}\right)^{1.865}\log\left(\frac{h_D}{100}\right)$$

$$\theta'_w = \tan^{-1}\left(\sqrt{\frac{k_v}{k_h}}\tan\theta_w\right)$$

$$h_D = \frac{h}{r_w}\sqrt{\frac{k_h}{k_v}}$$

s Skin factor, dimensionless
s_d Skin caused by formation damage, dimensionless
s_θ Skin resulting from well inclination, dimensionless
θ_w Well angles from the vertical
θ_w Wellbore radius, ft
h Net formation thickness, ft
k_h Horizontal permeability, md
k_v Vertical permeability, md

Gravel Pack Skin

$$s_{gp} = \frac{khL_g}{2nk_{gp}r_p^2}$$

s_{gp} Skin factor from Darcy flow through gravel pack, dimensionless
h Net formation thickness, ft
k Reservoir permeability, md
k_{gp} Reservoir permeability, md
L_g The length of the flow path through the gravel pack, ft
n The number of perforations open
r_p The radius of the perforation tunnel, ft

Completion Skin

$$s = s_d + s_p + s_{dp}$$

$$s_{dp} = \left(\frac{h}{L_p n}\right)\left(\ln\frac{r_{dp}}{r_p}\right)\left(\frac{k}{k_{dp}} - \frac{k}{k_d}\right)$$

s_d Skin caused by formation damage, dimensionless
s_p Skin resulting from an incompletely perforated interval, dimensionless
s_{dp} Perforation damage skin, dimensionless
h Net formation thickness, ft
k Reservoir permeability, md
k_d Permeability of the damaged zone around the wellbore, md
k_{dp} Permeability of the damaged zone around perforation tunnels, md
L_p The length of perforation tunnel, ft
n The number of perforations open
r_p The radius of the perforation tunnel, ft
r_{dp} The radius of the damaged zone around the perforation tunnel, ft

Non-Darcy Flow Skin

$$s' = s + D|q_g|$$

s' Apparent skin factor, dimensionless
s True skin because of damage or stimulation, dimensionless
D Non-Darcy flow coefficient, D/Mscf
q_g Gas flow rate, Mscf/D

Skin Factor for Multiphase Flow Test Analysis Using Semilog Plots

$$s = 1.151\left[\frac{\Delta p_{1hr}}{-m} - \log\left(\frac{\lambda_t}{\phi c_t r_w^2}\right) + 3.23\right]$$

$$\lambda_t = \frac{k_o}{\mu_o} + \frac{k_w}{\mu_w} + \frac{k_g}{\mu_g}$$

Δp_{1hr} Pressure change from start of test to 1 hour elapsed time, psi
m   Slope of middle-time line, psi/cycle
λ_t Total mobility, md/cp
k_o Permeability of oil, md
k_w Permeability of gas, md
k_g Permeability of water, md
μ_o Oil viscosity, cp
μ_g Gas viscosity, cp

μ_w Water viscosity, cp

ϕ Porosity, dimensionless

c_t Total compressibility, psi^{-1}

Fracture Damage

Chocked-Fracture Skin

$$s = \frac{\pi k L_s}{k_{fs} w_f}$$

k Reservoir permeability, md

k_{fs} Reduces Permeability near wellbore, md

L_s Length of damaged zone in fracture, ft

w_f Fracture width, ft

Fracture-Face Skin

$$s = \frac{\pi w_s}{2 L_f}\left(\frac{k}{k_s} - 1\right)$$

k Reservoir permeability, md

k_s Permeability of altered zone, md

L_f Fracture half-length, ft

w_s Width of damaged zone around fracture face, ft

3.13 Horizontal Flow Influx Equations

Early-Radial Flow

$$p_i - p_{wf} = \frac{162.6qB\mu}{\sqrt{k_x k_z} L_w}\left[\log_{10}\left(\frac{\sqrt{k_x k_z}\, t}{\phi \mu c_t r_w^2}\right) - 3.227 + 0.868 s_d\right]$$

End of Early-Radial Flow

$$t_{\text{Eerf}} = \frac{1800 d_z^2 \phi \mu c_t}{k_z}$$

$$t_{\text{Eerf}} = \frac{125 L_w^2 \phi \mu c_t}{k_y}$$

Skin for Early-Radial Flow

$$s_d = 1.151\left[\frac{\Delta p_{1hr}}{|m_{erf}|} - \log\left(\frac{\sqrt{k_x k_z}}{\phi \mu c_t r_w^2}\right) + 3.23\right]$$

p_i Initial reservoir pressure, psi

p_{wf} Flowing bottomhole pressure, psi

q Flow rate at surface, STB/D

B Formation volume factor, res vol/surface vol

μ Viscosity, cp

k_x Permeability in x-direction, md

k_y Permeability in y-direction, md

k_z Permeability in z-direction, md

L_w Completed length of horizontal well, ft

d_z Shortest distance between horizontal well and z boundary, ft

t Elapsed time, hr
c_t Total compressibility, psi^{-1}
r_w Wellbore radius, ft
s_d Skin caused by formation damage, dimensionless
$\Delta p_{1\,hr}$ Pressure change from start of test to 1 hour elapsed time, psi
m_{erf} Slope of semilog plot of early-radial flow, psi/log cycle

Hemiradial Flow

$$p_i - p_{wf} = \frac{325.2qB\mu}{\sqrt{k_x k_z} L_w} \left[\log_{10} \left(\frac{\sqrt{k_x k_z}\, t}{\phi \mu c_t r_w^2} \right) - 3.227 + 0.868 s_d \right]$$

Start of Hemiradial Flow

$$t_{Shrf} \cong \frac{1800 d_z^2 \phi \mu c_t}{k_z}$$

End of Hemiradial Flow

$$t_{Eerf} = \frac{1800 D_z^2 \phi \mu c_t}{k_z}$$

$$t_{Eerf} = \frac{125 L_w^2 \phi \mu c_t}{k_y}$$

Skin for Hemiradial Flow

$$s_d = 2.303 \left[\frac{\Delta p_{1hr}}{|m_{hrf}|} - \log \left(\frac{\sqrt{k_x k_z}}{\phi \mu c_t r_w^2} \right) + 3.23 \right]$$

p_i Initial reservoir pressure, psi
p_{wf} Flowing bottomhole pressure, psi
q Flow rate at surface, STB/D
B Formation volume factor, res vol/surface vol
μ Viscosity, cp
k_x Permeability in x-direction, md
k_y Permeability in y-direction, md
k_z Permeability in z-direction, md
L_w Completed length of horizontal well, ft
d_z Shortest distance between horizontal well and z boundary, ft
D_z Longest distance between horizontal well and z boundary, ft
t Elapsed time, hr
c_t Total compressibility, psi^{-1}
r_w Wellbore radius, ft
s_d Skin caused by formation damage, dimensionless
$\Delta p_{1\,hr}$ Pressure change from start of test to 1 hour elapsed time, psi
m_{hrf} Slope of semilog plot of hemiradial flow, psi/log cycle

Early Linear Flow

$$p_i - p_{wf} = \frac{8.128qB}{hL_w} \sqrt{\frac{\mu t}{k_x \phi c_t}} + \frac{141.2qB\mu}{L_w \sqrt{k_x k_z}} \left(s_c + s_d \right)$$

Start of Early Linear Flow

$$t_{Self} = \frac{1800 D_z^2 \phi \mu c_t}{k_z}$$

End of Early Linear Flow

$$t_{Eelf} = \frac{160 L_w^2 \phi \mu c_t}{k_y}$$

Horizontal Permeability Perpendicular to the Well

$$\sqrt{k_x} = \frac{8.128 qB}{\left| m_{elf} \right| L_w h} \sqrt{\frac{\mu}{\phi c_t}}$$

Altered Permeability Skin for Early Linear Flow

$$s_d = \frac{L_w \sqrt{k_x k_z}}{141.2 qB\mu} \Delta p_{t=0} - s_c$$

$$s_c = \ln\left(\frac{h}{r_w}\right) + 0.25 \ln\left(\frac{k_x}{k_z}\right) - \ln\left[\sin\left(\frac{\pi d_z}{h}\right)\right] - 1.838$$

p_i Initial reservoir pressure, psi
p_{wf} Flowing bottomhole pressure, psi
q Flow rate at surface, STB/D
μ Viscosity, cp
k_x Permeability in x-direction, md
k_y Permeability in y-direction, md
k_z Permeability in z-direction, md
L_w Completed length of horizontal well, ft
d_z Shortest distance between horizontal well and z boundary, ft
D_z Longest distance between horizontal well and z boundary, ft
t Elapsed time, hr
c_t Total compressibility, psi^{-1}
r_w Wellbore radius, ft
h Net formation thickness, ft
s_d Skin caused by formation damage, dimensionless
s_c Convergence skin, dimensionless
m_{elf} Slope of square-root-of-time plot for early-radial flow, psi/log cycle

Late Pseudoradial Flow

$$p_i - p_{wf} = \frac{162.6 qB\mu}{\sqrt{k_x k_z} h}\left[\log_{10}\left(\frac{k_y t}{\phi \mu c_t L_w^2}\right) - 2.303\right] + \frac{141.2 qB\mu}{L_w \sqrt{k_x k_z}}(s_c + s_d)$$

Start of Pseudoradial Flow

$$t_{Sprf} = \frac{1480 L_w^2 \phi \mu c_t}{k_y}$$

End of Pseudoradial Flow

$$t_{Eprf} = \frac{2000 \phi \mu c_t \left(L_w / 4 + d_y\right)^2}{k_y}$$

$$t_{Eprf} = \frac{1650 \phi \mu c_t d_x^2}{k_x}$$

Permeability in Horizontal Plane

$$\sqrt{k_x k_y} = \frac{162.6 q B \mu}{\left| m_{prf} \right| h}$$

Altered Permeability Skin for Pseudoradial Flow

$$s_d = \left(1.151 \sqrt{\frac{k_z}{k_y}} \frac{L_w}{h} \right) \left[\frac{\Delta p_{1hr}}{\left| m_{prf} \right|} - \log \left(\frac{k_y}{\phi \mu c_t L_w^2} \right) + 1.76 \right] - s_c$$

p_i	Initial reservoir pressure, psi
p_{wf}	Flowing bottomhole pressure, psi
q	Flow rate at surface, STB/D
A	Drainage area, ft^2
B	Formation volume factor, res vol/surface vol
μ	Viscosity, cp
k_x	Permeability in x-direction, md
k_y	Permeability in y-direction, md
k_z	Permeability in z-direction, md
L_w	Completed length of horizontal well, ft
d_x	Shortest distance between horizontal well and x boundary, ft
d_y	Shortest distance between horizontal well and y boundary, ft
t	Elapsed time, hr
c_t	Total compressibility, psi^{-1}
r_w	Wellbore radius, ft
h	Net formation thickness, ft
s_d	Skin caused by formation damage, dimensionless
s_c	Convergence skin, dimensionless
Δp_{1hr}	Pressure change from start of test to 1 hour elapsed time, psi
m_{prf}	Slope of semilog plot for pseudoradial flow, psi/log cycle

Late Linear Flow

$$p_i - p_{wf} = \frac{8.128 q B}{h b_H} \sqrt{\frac{\mu t}{k_x \phi c_t}} + \frac{141.2 q B \mu}{b_H \sqrt{k_x k_z}} \left(s_p + s_c + \frac{b_H}{L_w} s_d \right)$$

Start of Late Linear Flow

$$t_{Sllf} = \frac{4800 \phi \mu c_t \left(d_y + L_w / 4 \right)^2}{k_y}$$

$$t_{Sllf} = \frac{1800 \phi \mu c_t D_z^2}{k_z}$$

End of Late Linear Flow

$$t_{Ellf} = \frac{1650 \phi \mu c_t d_x^2}{k_x}$$

The Length of Drainage Area

$$b_H = \frac{8.128 q B}{\left| m_{llf} \right| h} \sqrt{\frac{\mu}{\phi c_t k_x}}$$

Altered Permeability Skin for Late Linear Flow

$$s_d = \frac{L_w}{b_H}\left(\frac{b_H\sqrt{k_x k_z}\left(\Delta p_{t=0}\right)}{141.2 q B \mu}\right) - s_c - s_p$$

p_i Initial reservoir pressure, psi

p_{wf} Flowing bottomhole pressure, psi

q Flow rate at surface, STB/D

A Drainage area, ft^2

B Formation volume factor, res vol/surface vol

μ Viscosity, cp

k_x Permeability in x-direction, md

k_y Permeability in y-direction, md

k_z Permeability in z-direction, md

L_w Completed length of horizontal well, ft

d_x Shortest distance between horizontal well and x boundary, ft

d_y Shortest distance between horizontal well and y boundary, ft

D_z Longest distance between horizontal well and z boundary, ft

t Elapsed time, hr

c_t Total compressibility, psi^{-1}

r_w Wellbore radius, ft

h Net formation thickness, ft

b_H Length in direction parallel to wellbore, ft

s_d Skin caused by formation damage, dimensionless

s_c Convergence skin, dimensionless

s_p Skin resulting from an incompletely perforated interval, dimensionless

m_{llf} Slope of square-root-of-time plot for late linear flow, psi/log cycle

Uniform Flux Equation (Babu-Odeh Method)

$$q = \frac{0.00708 b_H \sqrt{k_x k_z}\left(\overline{p} - p_{wf}\right)}{B\mu\left[\ln\left(\frac{A^{1/2}}{r_w}\right) + \ln C_H - 0.75 + s_p + \left(\frac{b_H}{L_w}\right)s_d\right]}$$

$$C_H = 6.28\frac{a_H}{h}\sqrt{\frac{k_z}{k_x}}\left[\frac{1}{3} - \frac{d_x}{a_H} + \left(\frac{d_x}{a_H}\right)^2\right] - \ln\left(\sin\frac{\pi d_z}{h}\right) - 0.5\ln\left[\left(a_H/h\right)\sqrt{k_z/k_x}\right] - 1.088$$

p_i Initial reservoir pressure, psi

p_{wf} Flowing bottomhole pressure, psi

$\overline{p}$ Volumetric average or static drainage-area pressure, psi

q Flow rate at surface, STB/D

A Drainage area, ft^2

B Formation volume factor, res vol/surface vol

μ Viscosity, cp

k_x Permeability in x-direction, md

k_z Permeability in z-direction, md

L_w Completed length of horizontal well, ft

d_x Shortest distance between horizontal well and x boundary, ft

d_z Shortest distance between horizontal well and z boundary, ft

t Elapsed time, hr

r_w Wellbore radius, ft

h Net formation thickness, ft

a_H Total width of reservoir perpendicular to the wellbore, ft

b_H Length in direction parallel to wellbore, ft
s_d Skin caused by formation damage, dimensionless
s_p Skin resulting from an incompletely perforated interval, dimensionless

Productivity Index

$$J = \frac{\overline{k}b_H}{887.22B\mu\left(p_D + \dfrac{b_H}{2\pi L_w}\sum s\right)}$$

$$p_D = \frac{b_H C_H}{4\pi h} + \frac{b_H}{2\pi L_w}s_c$$

$$s_c = \ln\left(\frac{h}{2\pi r_w}\right) - \frac{h}{6L_w} + s_e$$

$$s_e = \frac{h}{L_w}\left[\frac{2d_z}{h} - \frac{1}{2}\left(\frac{2d_z}{h}\right)^2 - \frac{1}{2}\right] - \ln\left[\sin\left(\frac{\pi d_z}{h}\right)\right]$$

p_D Dimensionless pressure as defined for constant-rate production
         $= 0.00708\,kh\left(p_i - p\right)/qB\mu$
μ Viscosity, cp
$\overline{k}$ Average permeability, md
L_w Completed length of horizontal well, ft
d_z Shortest distance between horizontal well and z boundary, ft
r_w Wellbore radius, ft
h Net formation thickness, ft
b_H Length in direction parallel to wellbore, ft
s_c Convergence skin, dimensionless
s_e Skin caused by eccentric effects, dimensionless
Σ_s Sum of damage skin, turbulence, and other pseudoskin factors

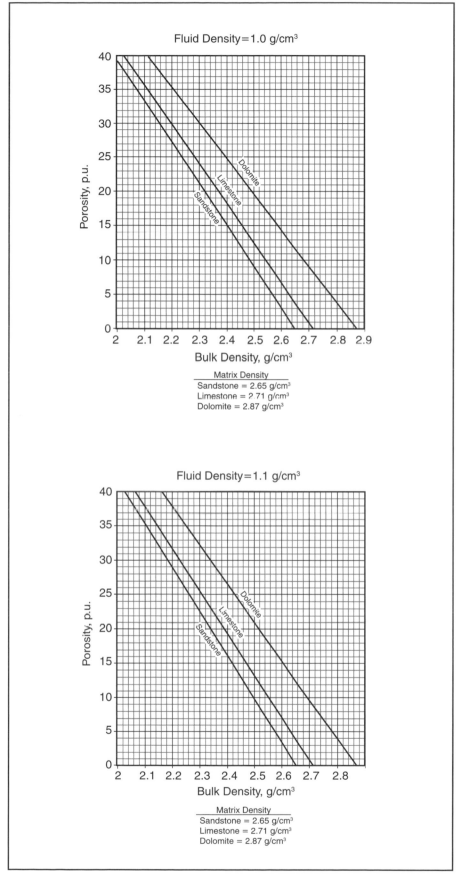

Fig. 3.1—Porosity determination from bulk density (Sperry-Sun 1996–1998).

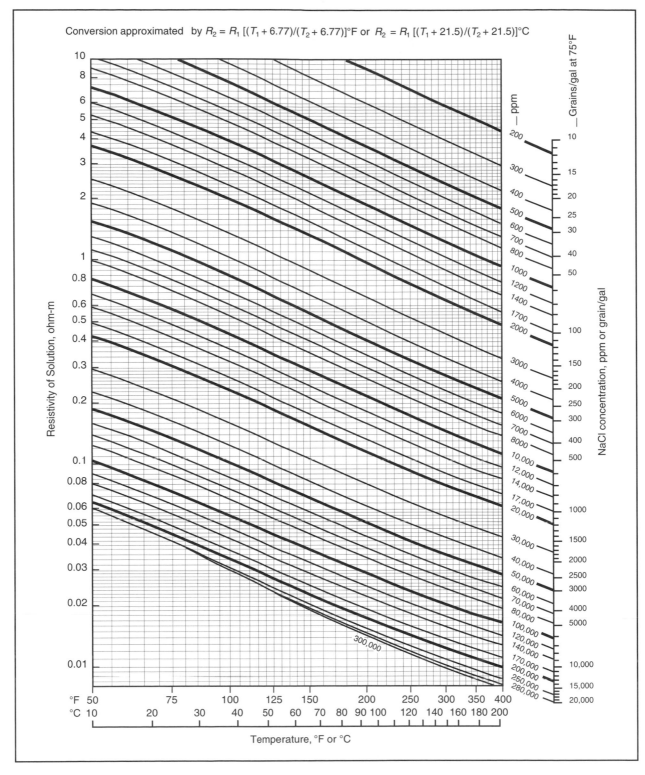

Fig. 3.2—Resistivity vs. temperature for NaCl solutions (Helander 1983). Courtesy of Schlumberger.

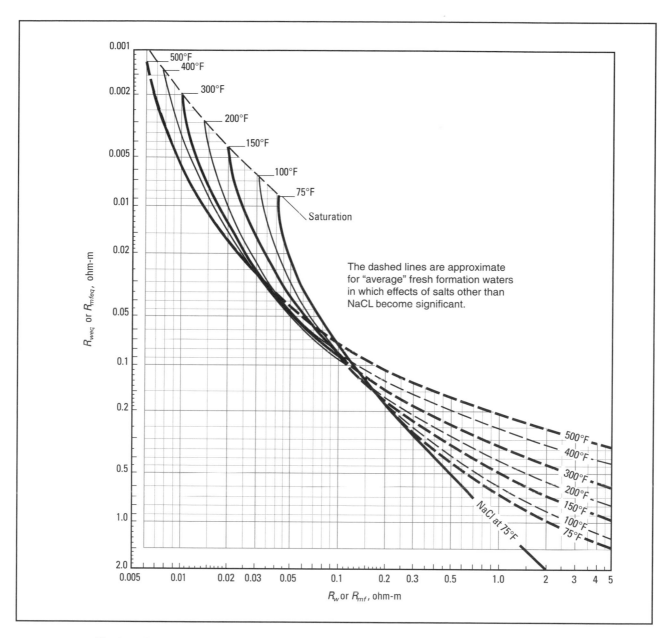

Fig. 3.3—R_w vs. R_{weq} and formation temperature (Helander 1983). Courtesy of Schlumberger.

Chapter 4

Production Engineering

This chapter contains equations to study different aspects of production engineering. The chapter includes the inflow and outflow of performance under steady-state, semisteady-state, and transient flow equations for oil and gas wells by introducing different methods to calculate inflow performance relationships. The fluid production and injection into and out of the well are facilitated by the equations for tubing design calculations considering its length change, stretch, hook load, axial load, burst, collapse, buckling effect, ballooning effect, etc. The flow efficiency is also provided for various perforation sizes and skin calculations for various flow conditions. Designs of different stimulation methods such as acidizing, fracturing, and sand control are also presented. Fluid filtration equations are also provided. Additionally, the chapter holds equations for diagnosing and analyzing well production problems. A section is devoted to coiled tubing design and different methods of artificial lifts, such as sucker rod pumping, gas lift, and electrical submersible pumps, chokes, and compressors. Finally, the problems of well production, such as low productivity, heavy oil, water coning, and excessive cumulative gas are also included.

4.1 Inflow/Outflow Performance

Radial Diffusivity Equation for a Slightly Compressible Liquid With a Constant Viscosity (Undersaturated Oil or Water)

$$\frac{1}{r}\frac{\partial}{\partial r}\left(r\frac{\partial p}{\partial r}\right) = \frac{\phi\mu c_t}{k}\left(\frac{\partial p}{\partial t}\right)$$

Traditional Pressure-Squared Equation for Real Gas

$$\frac{1}{r}\frac{\partial}{\partial r}\left(r\frac{\partial p^2}{\partial r}\right) = \frac{\phi\mu c_t}{k}\left(\frac{\partial p^2}{\partial t}\right)$$

General Pseudopressure Equation for Real Gas

$$\frac{1}{r}\frac{\partial}{\partial r}\left(r\frac{\partial p_p(p)}{\partial r}\right) = \frac{\phi\mu c_t}{k}\left(\frac{\partial\partial p_p(p)}{\partial t}\right)$$

p Pressure, psia
p_p Real gas pseudopressure, psia²/cp $= 2\int\frac{p}{\mu z}dp$
r Radius, ft
ϕ Porosity, fraction
μ Viscosity, cp
c_t Total compressibility, psia⁻¹
t Time, t
k Permeability, md

Steady-State Solution for Single-Phase Liquid Flow

$$q = \frac{kh\left(\bar{p}_R - p_{wf}\right)}{141.2 B\mu\left(\ln\dfrac{r_e}{r_w} - \dfrac{3}{4} + s\right)}$$

Steady-State Solution for Real Gas Flow (Pressure-Squared Form)

$$q = \frac{kh\left(\bar{p}_R^2 - p_{wf}^2\right)}{1422 \mu z T\left(\ln\dfrac{r_e}{r_w} - \dfrac{1}{2} + s\right)}$$

Steady-State Solution for Real Gas Flow (Pseudopressure Form)

$$q = \frac{kh\left[p_p\left(\bar{p}_R\right) - p_p\left(p_{wf}\right)\right]}{1422 T\left(\ln\dfrac{r_e}{r_w} - \dfrac{1}{2} + s\right)}$$

Semisteady-State Solutions for Real Gas Flow

$$q = \frac{kh\left(\bar{p}_R^2 - p_{wf}^2\right)}{1422 \mu z T\left(\ln\dfrac{r_e}{r_w} - \dfrac{3}{4} + s\right)}$$

$$q = \frac{kh\left[p_p\left(\bar{p}_R\right) - p_p\left(p_{wf}\right)\right]}{1422 T\left(\ln\dfrac{r_e}{r_w} - \dfrac{3}{4} + s\right)}$$

q	Flow rate, STB/D
$\bar{p}_R$	Average reservoir pressure, psia
p_{wf}	Bottomhole pressure, psia
p_p	Real gas pseudopressure, psia^2/cp
T	Temperature, °R
z	Gas compressibility factor, dimensionless
μ	Viscosity, cp
B	Formation volume factor, RB/STB
r_e	External drainage radius, ft
r_w	Wellbore radius, ft
k	Permeability, md
h	Formation thickness, ft
s	Skin factor, dimensionless

Gas Well Performance (Rawlins and Schellhard)

$$\frac{q_g}{q_{g,\,max}} = \left[1 - \left(\frac{p_{wf}}{\bar{p}_R}\right)^2\right]^n$$

$$\frac{q_g}{q_{g,\,max}} = \left[1 - \frac{p_p\left(p_{wf}\right)}{p_p\left(\bar{p}_R\right)}\right]^n$$

q_g	Gas flow rate, Mscf/D
$q_{g,\,max}$	Absolute Open Flow (AOF), maximum gas flow rate, Mscf/D

$\bar{p}_R$ Average reservoir pressure, psia

p_{wf} Bottomhole pressure, psia

p_p Real gas pseudopressure, psia^2/cp

Gas Well Performance (Houpert)

$$\bar{p}_R^2 - p_{wf}^2 = aq_g + bq_g^2$$

$$a = \frac{1422\mu zT\left(\ln\dfrac{r_e}{r_w} - \dfrac{3}{4} + s\right)}{kh}$$

$$b = \frac{1422\mu zT}{kh}D$$

$$p_p\left(\bar{p}_R\right) - p_p\left(p_{wf}\right) = aq_g + bq_g^2$$

$$a = \frac{1422T\left(\ln\dfrac{r_e}{r_w} - \dfrac{3}{4} + s\right)}{kh}$$

$$b = \frac{1422T}{kh}D$$

$$D = \frac{2.715\times10^{-15}\,\beta kMp_{sc}}{h\mu_g r_w T_{sc}}$$

$$\beta = 1.88\times10^{10}\,k^{-1.47}\phi^{-0.53}$$

q_g Gas flow rate, Mscf/D

$\bar{p}_R$ Average reservoir pressure, psia

p_{wf} Bottomhole pressure, psia

p_p Real gas pseudopressure, psia^2/cp

T Temperature, °R

z Gas compressibility factor, dimensionless

μ Viscosity, cp

μ_g Gas viscosity, cp

r_e External drainage radius, ft

r_w Wellbore radius, ft

k Permeability, md

h Formation thickness, ft

s Skin factor, dimensionless

a Laminar flow coefficient, psia^2/Mscf/D

b Turbulence coefficient, psia^2/(Mscf/D)^2

D Non-Darcy flow coefficient, D/Mscf

β Turbulence factor, ft^{-1}

ϕ Porosity, fraction

M Molecular weight, lbm/lbm-mole

p_{sc} Standard pressure, psia

T_{sc} Standard temperature, °R

Oilwell Inflow Performance Relationships

Vogel Method

$$\frac{q_o}{q_{o,\,\max}} = 1 - 0.2\left(\frac{p_{wf}}{\bar{p}_R}\right) - 0.8\left(\frac{p_{wf}}{\bar{p}_R}\right)^2$$

$$J = \frac{q_o}{\overline{p}_R - p_{wf}}, \qquad\qquad \overline{p}_R \geq p_{wf} \geq p_b$$

$$J = \frac{q_o}{\overline{p}_R - p_b + \dfrac{p_b}{1.8}\left[1.0 - 0.2\dfrac{p_{wf}}{p_b} - 0.8\left(\dfrac{p_{wf}}{p_b}\right)^2\right]}, \qquad\qquad \overline{p}_R \geq p_b \geq p_{wf}$$

Wiggins Method

$$\frac{q_o}{q_{o,\,max}} = 1 - 0.52\left(\frac{p_{wf}}{\overline{p}_R}\right) - 0.48\left(\frac{p_{wf}}{\overline{p}_R}\right)^2$$

$$\frac{q_w}{q_{w,\,max}} = 1 - 0.72\left(\frac{p_{wf}}{\overline{p}_R}\right) - 0.28\left(\frac{p_{wf}}{\overline{p}_R}\right)^2$$

Standing Method

$$\frac{q_o}{q_{o,\,max}} = \left(1 - \frac{p_{wf}}{\overline{p}_R}\right)\left[1 + 0.8\left(\frac{p_{wf}}{\overline{p}_R}\right)\right]$$

The Klins-Clark Method

$$\frac{q_o}{q_{o,\,max}} = 1 - 0.295\left(\frac{p_{wf}}{\overline{p}_R}\right) - 0.705\left(\frac{p_{wf}}{\overline{p}_R}\right)^d$$

$$d = \left[0.28 + 0.72\left(\frac{\overline{p}_R}{p_b}\right)\right](1.24 + 0.001p_b)$$

Fetkovich Method

$$q_o = \frac{0.00708kh}{\left[\ln\dfrac{r_e}{r_w} - 0.75 + s\right]} \int_{p_{wf}}^{\overline{p}_R} f(p)\,dp$$

$$f(p) = \frac{k_{ro}}{\mu_o B_o}$$

q_o	Oil flow rate, STB/D
$q_{o,\,max}$	Maximum oil flow rate, STB/D
q_w	Water flow rate, STB/D
$q_{w,\,max}$	Maximum water flow rate, STB/D
$\overline{p}_R$	Average reservoir pressure, psia
p_{wf}	Bottomhole pressure, psia
p_b	Bubblepoint pressure, psia
k_{ro}	Oil relative permeability, md
B_o	Oil formation volume factor, bbl/STB
μ_o	Oil viscosity, cp
J	Productivity index, STB/D/psia

Pressure Drop in Gas Wells

$$q = 200\left[\frac{Sd^5\left(p_{wf}^2 - e^S p_{wh}^2\right)}{\gamma_g T z L f_M\left(e^S - 1\right)}\right]$$

$$f_M = \left\{2\log\left[3.71/(\varepsilon/d)\right]\right\}^{-2}$$

$$S = \frac{0.0375\gamma_g L}{Tz}$$

q Flow rate, STB/D
d Pipe diameter, in.
p_{wf} Bottomhole pressure, psia
p_{wh} Wellhead pressure, psia
γ_g Gas specific gravity, dimensionless
L Length of pipe, psia
T Temperature, °R
z Gas compressibility factor, dimensionless
f_M Moody friction factor, dimensionless
ε Absolute pipe roughness, in.

Single-Phase Gas Flow Through a Choke

$$q_g = \frac{27.611 C_d p_{wh} d^2 T_{sc}}{p_{sc}\sqrt{\gamma_g T_{wh} z}}\left[\left(\frac{k}{k-1}\right)\left(y^{2/k} - y^{k+1/k}\right)\right]$$

$$y_c = \left(\frac{2}{k+1}\right)^{k/k-1}$$

q_g Gas flow rate, Mscf/D
p_{wh} Wellhead pressure, psia
T_{wh} Wellhead temperature, °R
C_d Discharge coefficient, dimensionless
d Pipe diameter, in.
γ_g Gas specific gravity, dimensionless
z Gas compressibility factor, dimensionless
T_{sc} Standard temperature, °R
p_{sc} Standard pressure, psia
k Specific heat capacity ratio, dimensionless, $= C_p/C_v$
C_p Specific heat capacity at constant pressure, $L^2/t^2–T$
C_v Specific heat capacity at constant volume, $L^2/t^2–T$
y Ratio of downstream pressure to upstream pressure, dimensionless, p_1/p_2
y_c Critical pressure ratio, dimensionless

4.2 Impact of Length and Force Changes to the Tubing String

Length Change Calculations

$$\Delta L_{\text{stretch}} = \Delta L_a + \Delta L_p + \Delta L_b + \Delta L_t$$

$\Delta L_{\text{stretch}}$ Total stretch or elongation of the drillpipe, ft
ΔL_a Stretch due to axial load, ft

$$= \frac{F_T \times L}{A \times E} + \frac{\Delta F_T \times L}{2 \times A \times E}$$

F_T Pressure area axial force, lb
ΔF_T Change in pressure area axial force over the component length, lb
A Cross-sectional area of the component, in.^{2}
E Young's modulus of the component material, psi
L Length, ft
ΔL_p Stretch due to the pressure effect (ballooning), ft

$$= \frac{-\upsilon \times L_p}{E \times \left(R^2 - 1\right)} \times \left[\left(\rho_s - R^2 \times \rho_a\right) \times L + 2 \times \left(P_s - R^2 \times P_a\right)\right]$$

L_p Length of the work string component element, ft
R Ratio of the component outside diameter to the inside diameter
υ Poisson's ratio of the component material
ρ_s Mud density inside the work string component, ppg
ρ_a Mud density in the annulus at the depth of the work string component, ppg
P_s Surface pressure on the drillstring side, psi
P_a Surface pressure in the annulus side, psi
ΔL_p Stretch due to buckling, ft

$$= \frac{-r^2}{4EI\omega}\left(F_2 - F_p\right)\left[0.3771F_2 - 0.3668F_p\right] \qquad \text{for } 2.8F_p > F_2 > F_p$$

$$= \frac{-r^2}{8EI\omega}\left[F_2^2 - F_1^2\right] \qquad \text{for } F > 2.8F_p$$

F_1, F_2 Buckling force, lb
F_p Paslay buckling force
ω Distributed buoyed weight of the casing
EI Pipe bending stiffness
r Radial annular clearance
ΔL_t Stretch due to temperature, ft

$$= a_t\left[\Delta t_0 + \frac{\Delta t}{\Delta z}\frac{L^2}{2}\right]$$

Δt_0 Initial average temperature change, °F
Δt Average temperature change, °F
Δz Change in measured depth, ft
L Measured calculation interval, ft
a_t Coefficient of thermal expansion defined as the fractional increase in length per unit rise in temperature, in./in./°F, $= 6.9 \times 10^{-6}$ for steel, 10.3×10^{-6} for aluminum, 4.9×10^{-6} for titanium

4.3 Tubing Design

Maximum Hydrostatic Test Pressure

$$p_h = \frac{2 \times \left(0.8 \times \sigma_y \times t\right)}{d_o}$$

The Internal Yield Pressure Rating for Tubing

$$p_{yi} = \frac{0.875 \times 2 \times \sigma_y \times t}{d_o}$$

P_h Hydrostatic test pressure, psi
P_{yi} Internal yield pressure, psi
σ_y Minimum yield strength of pipe, psi
t Tube thickness, in.
d_o Outside diameter, in.

Stretch in Tubing

$$\Delta L_t = \frac{12 \times L_p \times F}{E \times A_m}$$

ΔL_t Total axial stretch or contraction, in.
L_p Length of pipe, ft
F Superimposed tension or compression axial load, lbf

E Young's modulus of elasticity for steel, = 30 million psi
A_m Cross-section metal area of pipe, in.^{2}

Tubing Hook Load in Air

$$F_a = L_p \times w_n$$

F_a Tubing hook load in air, lbf
L_p Length of pipe, ft
w_n Weight per foot of tubing, lbm/ft

Tubing Hook Load in Fluid

$$F_f = F_a - F_b$$

F_f Tubing hook load in fluid, lbf
F_a Tubing hook load in air, lbf
F_b Axial buoyancy load, lbf

Axial Buoyancy Load

$$F_b = A_m - P_{bh}$$

F_b Axial buoyancy load, lbf
A_m Cross-section metal area of pipe, in.^{2}
P_{bh} Hydrostatic pressure at depth, psi

Hydrostatic Pressure at Depth

$$P_{bh} = D_{tV} \times g_f$$

P_{bh} Hydrostatic pressure at depth, psi
D_{tV} True vertical depth, ft
g_f Fluid gradient, psi/ft

Cross-Sectional Metal Area of Tubing

$$A_m = \frac{\pi \left(d_o^2 - d_i^2 \right)}{4}$$

A_m Cross-section metal area of pipe, in.^{2}
d_o Outside diameter, in.
d_i Inside diameter, in.

Design Factor in Air

$$D_t = F_j / F_a$$

D_t Design factor in tension, dimensionless
F_j Joint yield strength, lbf
F_a Tubing hook load in air, lbf

Design Factor in Fluid

$$D_t = F_j / F_f$$

D_t Design factor in tension, dimensionless
F_j Joint yield strength, lbf
F_f Tubing hook load in fluid, lbf

Maximum Allowed Internal Pressure

$$p_i = p_{yi}/D_b$$

p_i Initial pressure, psi
p_{yi} Internal yield pressure, psi
D_b Design factor in burst, dimensionless

Design Factor in Burst

$$D_b = p_{yi}/p_{wh}$$

D_b Design factor in burst, dimensionless
p_{yi} Internal yield pressure, psi
p_{wh} Wellhead pressure, psi

Design Factor in Burst

$$D_c = p_{cr}/p_{bh}$$

D_c Design factor in collapse, dimensionless
p_{cr} Minimum collapse pressure without axial stress, psi
p_{bh} Hydrostatic pressure at depth, psi

Collapse Differential Pressure

$$\Delta p_c = \left(g_a - g_t\right) \times D_{tV}$$

Δp_c Collapse differential, psi
g_a Gradient in the annulus, psi/ft
g_t Gradient in the tubing, psi/ft
D_{tV} True vertical depth, ft

Burst Differential Pressure

$$\Delta p_b = \left(g_t - g_a\right) \times D_{tV} + p_{wh}$$

Δp_b Burst differential, psi
g_a Gradient in the annulus, psi/ft
g_t Gradient in the tubing, psi/ft
D_{tV} True vertical depth, ft
p_{wh} Wellhead pressure, psi

Length of Tubing

$$L_p = \frac{\left[\left(p_{wh} - p_{br}\right)/D_b\right]}{g_a - g_t}$$

L_p Length of pipe, ft
p_{wh} Wellhead pressure, psi
p_{br} Burst pressure rating, psi
D_b Design factor in burst, dimensionless
g_a Gradient in the annulus, psi/ft
g_t Gradient in the tubing, psi/ft

Effect of Pressure and Temperature Changes on Tubing Sealed in a Packer

Hooke's Law Effect

$$\Delta L = \frac{L\Delta F}{EA_s}$$

$$\Delta F = \left(A_p - A_i\right)\Delta P_i - \left(A_p - A_i\right)\Delta P_o$$

ΔL Change in tubing length due to Hooke's law effect, in.

L Length of tubing, in.

F Force acting on bottom of tubing, lb

E Modulus of elasticity, 30×10^6 psi for steel

A_s Cross-sectional area of tubing, in.^{2}

A_i Area based on inside diameter of tubing, in.^{2}

A_o Area based on outside diameter of tubing, in.^{2}

A_p Area based on diameter of packer seal, in.^{2}

P_o Pressure at packer seal in annulus, psi

P_i Pressure at packer seal in tubing, psi

Buckling Effect

$$\Delta L = \frac{r^2 A_p^2 \left(\Delta P_i - \Delta P_o \right)^2}{8 E I \left(w_s + w_i - w_o \right)}$$

$$I = \frac{\pi}{64} \left(D^4 - d^4 \right)$$

ΔL Change in tubing length due to buckling, in.

r Radial clearance between tubing and casing, in.

w $= w_s + w_i - w_o$

w_s Weight of tubing, lb/in.

w_i Weight of fluid contained inside tubing, lb/in.

w_o Weight of annulus fluid displaced by bulk volume of tubing lb/in.

D Tubing outside diameter, in.

d Tubing inside diameter, in.

Ballooning Effect

$$\Delta L = \frac{\mu L^2}{E} \frac{\Delta \rho_i - R^2 \Delta \rho_o - \frac{1 + 2\mu}{2\mu} \delta}{R^2 - 1} + \frac{2 \mu L}{F} \left(\frac{\Delta p_i - R^2 \Delta \rho_o}{R^2 - 1} \right)$$

ΔL Change in length due to ballooning, in.

μ Poisson's ration (0.3 for steel)

R Tubing OD/Tubing ID

$\Delta \rho_i$ Change in density of fluid inside tubing, lb/in.^{3}

$\Delta \rho_o$ Change in density of fluid outside tubing, lb/in.^{3}

Δp_i Change in surface pressure inside tubing, psi

Δp_o Change in surface pressure outside tubing, psi

δ Pressure drop in tubing due to flow, psi/in. (usually considered 0)

Temperature Effect

$$\Delta L = L C \Delta T$$

ΔL Change in length due to temperature, in.

L Length of tubing string, in.

C Coefficient of expansion of steel per °F, $= 6.9 \times 10^{-6}$

ΔT Temperature change, °F

4.4 Perforating

Entrance Hole Size for High Velocity Jets

$$d = \left(2250 + \frac{4.2 x_r}{2250} + 4.2 x \right)^{0.5} d_r$$

d Entrance hole diameter in casing of interest, in.

d_r Entrance hole diameter in reference casing, in.

x Brinell hardness of casing of interest, 10-mm ball, 3000-kg load, dimensionless
x_r Brinell hardness of reference casing, 10-mm ball, 3000-kg load, dimensionless

Entrance Hole Size for Low Velocity Jets

$$d = \left(\frac{\sigma_{yr}}{\sigma_y}\right)^{0.5} d_r$$

d Entrance hole diameter in casing of interest, in.
d_r Entrance hole diameter in reference casing, in.
σ_y Yield strength of casing of interest, ksi
σ_{yr} Yield strength of reference casing, ksi

Penetration

$$\frac{L_p}{L_{pr}} = \exp\left[0.086\left(c_r - c\right)\right]$$

L_p Total target penetration in formation of interest, in.
L_{pr} Total target penetration in reference target, in.
c Compressive strength of formation of interest, ksi
c_r Compressive strength of Berea or reference target, ksi

$$L'_{API} = L_{API} - 3.5(\text{first} + \text{second string wall thickness})$$
$$-(\text{total cement thickness between first and third strings})$$

L'_{API} Total target penetration in Sec. 1 target, modified for effect of multiple casing strings, in.
L_{API} Total target penetration in Sec. 1 target, in.

$$s_e = p_{ob} - p_p$$

s_e Formation effective stress, psi
p_{ob} Overburden pressure, psi
p_p Reservoir or pore pressure, psi

$$L_p = L_{pc} - 0.5\left(d_{wb} - d_{ci}\right)$$

L_p Downhole perforation length in formation, in.
L_{pc} L_{API} corrected for formation strength and effective stress effects, in.
d_{wb} Wellbore diameter, in.
d_{ci} Casing ID, in.

Flow Efficiency of Perforated Systems

Well Flow Efficiency

$$J = \frac{q_p}{q_{oh}} = \frac{\ln\left(r_e / r_w\right)}{\left[\ln\left(r_e / r_w\right) + s_t\right]}$$

J Productivity ratio
q_p Flow from perforated system, B/D
q_{oh} Flow from ideal open hole, B/D
r_e Drainage radius, ft
r_w Wellbore radius, ft
s_t Total skin

Predicting the Well Performance

Oil Wells

$$\Delta p_p = A\left(\frac{q_o}{n}\right) + B\left(\frac{q_o}{n}\right)^2$$

$$A = \frac{141.2\mu_o B_o}{L_p k_{pd}} \ln\left(\frac{r_{pd}}{r_p}\right)$$

$$B = \frac{2.3\times10^{-14}\beta_{pd}B_o^2\rho_o}{L_p^2} \ln\left(\frac{1}{r_p} - \frac{1}{r_{pd}}\right)$$

Δp_p Pressure drop across perforations, psi
q_o Oil flow rate, B/D
n Number of perforations
μ_o Oil viscosity, cp
B_o Oil formation volume factor, STB/bbl
L_p Perforation length, ft
k_{pd} Perforation-damaged-zone permeability, md
r_{pd} Radius of perforation-damaged-zone, ft
r_p Perforation radius, ft
β_{pd} Velocity coefficient for flow through perforations damaged zone, 1/ft, $= 2.33\times10^{10}/k_{pd}^{1.201}$
ρ_o Oil density, lbm/ft³

$$\Delta p_R = Cq_o + Dq_o^2$$

$$C = \frac{141.2\mu_o B_o}{kh_t}\left[\ln\left(0.472\frac{r_e}{r_w}\right) + s_t\right]$$

$$D = \frac{2.3\times10^{-14}B_o^2\rho_o}{h_p^2}\left[\beta_{dd}\left(\frac{1}{r_w} - \frac{1}{r_{dd}}\right) + \beta_f\left(\frac{1}{r_{dd}} - \frac{1}{r_e}\right)\right]$$

Δp_R Pressure drop through reservoir, psi
q_o Oil flow rate, B/D
μ_o Oil viscosity, cp
B_o Oil formation volume factor, STB/bbl
k Formation permeability, md
h_t Total formation thickness, ft
h_p Perforated thickness, ft
r_e Drainage radius, ft
r_w Wellbore radius, ft
r_{dd} Drilling-damaged-zone radius, ft
s_t Total skin, $= s_d + s_{bf} + s_{\theta d}$
s_d Skin caused by damage
s_{bf} Skin caused by partial penetration of producing zone
$s_{\theta d}$ Skin resulting from well deviation
ρ_o Oil density, lbm/ft³
β_{dd} Velocity coefficient for flow through drilling damaged zone, 1/ft, $= 2.33\times10^{10}/k_{dd}^{-1.201}$
β_f Velocity coefficient for flow through formation, 1/ft, $= 2.33\times10^{10}/k^{-1.201}$

Gas Wells

$$p_{sf}^2 - p_{wb}^2 = A\left(\frac{q_g}{n}\right) + B\left(\frac{q_g}{n}\right)^2$$

$$A = \frac{1.424\times10^3\mu_g zT}{k_{pd}L_p}\left[\ln\left(\frac{r_{pd}}{r_p}\right)\right]$$

$$B = \frac{3.16 \times 10^{-12} \beta_{pd} \gamma_g z T}{L_p^2} \ln\left(\frac{1}{r_p} - \frac{1}{r_{pd}}\right)$$

p_{sf} Pressure at sandface, psi
p_{wb} Wellbore pressure, psi
q_g Gas flow rate, B/D
n Number of perforations
L_p Perforation length, ft
k_{pd} Perforation-damaged-zone permeability, md
r_{pd} Radius of perforation-damaged-zone, ft
r_p Perforation radius, ft
μ_g Gas viscosity, cp
z Gas compressibility factor
T Formation temperature, °R
β_{pd} Velocity coefficient for flow through perforations damaged zone, 1/ft, $= 2.33 \times 10^{10}/k_{pd}^{-1.201}$
γ_g Gas specific gravity, air = 1

$$p_R^2 - p_{sf}^2 = Cq_g + Dq_g^2$$

$$C = \frac{1.424 \times 10^3 \, \mu_g z T}{kh_t}\left[\ln\left(0.472\frac{r_e}{r_w}\right) + s_t\right]$$

$$D = \frac{3.16 \times 10^{-12} \gamma_g z T}{h_p^2}\left[\beta_{dd}\left(\frac{1}{r_w} - \frac{1}{r_e}\right) + \beta_f\left(\frac{1}{r_{dd}} - \frac{1}{r_e}\right)\right]$$

p_R Pressure drop through reservoir, psi
p_{sf} Pressure at sandface, psi
q_g Oil flow rate, B/D
μ_g Gas viscosity, cp
k Formation permeability, md
h_t Total formation thickness, ft
h_p Perforated thickness, ft
z Gas compressibility factor
T Formation temperature, °R
γ_g Gas specific gravity, air = 1
r_e Drainage radius, ft
r_w Wellbore radius, ft
r_{dd} Drilling-damaged-zone radius, ft
s_t Total skin, $= s_d + s_{bf} + s_{\theta d}$
s_d Skin caused by damage
s_{bf} Skin caused by partial penetration of producing zone
$s_{\theta d}$ Skin resulting from well deviation
β_{dd} Velocity coefficient for flow through drilling damaged zone, 1/ft, $= 2.33 \times 10^{10}/k_{dd}^{-1.201}$
β_f Velocity coefficient for flow through formation, 1/ft, $= 2.33 \times 10^{10}/k^{-1.201}$

Gravel Pack Completions

Oil Wells

$$\Delta p_G = 0.888\frac{L_T \mu_o B_o q_o}{k_g A_t} + 9.1 \times 10^{-13} \beta_g B_o^2 L_T \rho_o\left(\frac{q_o}{A_t}\right)^2$$

Δp_G Pressure drop through gravel-filled perforation tunnel, psi
L_T Perforation tunnel length, ft
q_o Oil flow rate, B/D
μ_o Oil viscosity, cp
B_o Oil formation volume factor, STB/bbl

k_g Tunnel material permeability, md
A_t Flow area, ft²
β_g Velocity coefficient, 1/ft, $= 1.47 \times 10^7 / k_g^{0.55}$
ρ_o Oil density, lbm/ft³

Gas Wells

$$\Delta p_G^2 = \frac{8.93 \times 10^3 \, \mu_g T z L_T q_g}{k_g A_t} + 1.247 \times 10^{-10} \beta_g \gamma_g z T L_T \left(\frac{q_g}{A_t} \right)^2$$

Δp_G Pressure drop through gravel-filled perforation tunnel, psi
L_T Perforation tunnel length, ft
q_g Oil flow rate, B/D
μ_g Oil viscosity, cp
z Gas compressibility factor
T Formation temperature, °R
γ_g Gas specific gravity, air = 1
A_t Flow area, ft²
k_g Tunnel material permeability, md
β_g Velocity coefficient, 1/ft, $= 1.47 \times 10^7 / k_g^{0.55}$

Skin Calculations

Total Skin

$$s_t = s_{bf} + \frac{1}{b_f} \left[\frac{1}{\gamma} s_p + \frac{1}{20} \left(9 + 11 b_f \right) s_{\theta d} \right]$$

s_t Total skin
s_{bf} Skin caused by partial penetration of producing zone
s_p Skin resulting from perforations
$s_{\theta d}$ Skin resulting from well deviation
b_f Fraction of formation open to flow
γ Correction factor

Combined Perforation Skin

$$s_p = s_H + s_V + s_{wb} + s_{pd}$$

s_p Skin resulting from perforations
s_H Horizontal skin
s_V Vertical skin
s_{wb} Wellbore effect skin
s_{pd} Perforation-damaged-zone skin

Horizontal Skin

$$s_H = \ln \left(r_w / 0.25 L_p \right) \quad \text{shot phasing} = 0$$

$$s_H = \ln \left[r_w / \alpha_\theta (L_p + r_w) \right] \quad \text{shot phasing} \neq 0$$

s_H Horizontal skin
r_w Wellbore radius, ft
L_p Perforation length, ft
α_θ Phasing parameter, Table

Vertical Skin

$$s_V = \left(10^a \right) \left(h_D^{b-1} \right) \left(r_{pD}^b \right)$$

$$a = a_1 \log_{10} r_{pD} + a_2 \qquad\qquad a_1, a_2 \text{ from Table}$$

$$b = b_1 r_{pD} + b_2 \qquad\qquad b_1, b_2 \text{ from Table}$$

$$h_D = \frac{h}{L_p} \sqrt{\frac{k_H}{k_V}}$$

$$r_{pD} = \frac{r_p}{2h}\left(1 + \sqrt{\frac{k_V}{k_H}}\right)$$

s_V Vertical skin
h_D Dimensionless perforation spacing
r_{pD} Dimensionless perforation radius
h Spacing between perforations, ft
L_p Perforation length
k_H Horizontal formation permeability, md
k_V Vertical formation permeability, md
r_p Perforation radius, ft

Wellbore Effect Skin

$$s_{wb} = c_1 \exp\left[c_2\left(\frac{r_w}{L_p + r_w}\right)\right] \qquad c_1, c_2 \text{ from Table}$$

s_{wb} Wellbore effect skin
L_p Perforation length
r_w Wellbore radius, ft

Perforation-Damaged-Zone Skin

$$s_{pd} = \frac{h}{L_p}\left(\frac{k}{k_{pd}} - 1\right)\ln\left(\frac{r_{pd}}{r_p}\right)$$

s_{pd} Perforation-damaged-zone skin
L_p Perforation length
h Spacing between perforations, ft
k Formation permeability, md
k_{pd} Perforation-damaged-zone permeability, md
r_{pd} Radius of perforation-damaged-zone, ft
r_p Perforation radius, ft

Drilling-Damaged-Zone Effect

$$s_p' = \left(\frac{k}{k_{dd}} - 1\right)\ln\left(\frac{r_{dd}}{r_w}\right) + \left(\frac{k}{k_{dd}}\right)\left(s_p + s_x\right)$$

$$L_p' = L_p - \left(1 - \frac{k_{dd}}{k}\right)L_{dd}$$

$$r_w' = r_w + \left(1 - \frac{k_{dd}}{k}\right)L_{dd}$$

s_p' Skin resulting from perforations modified to account for drilling-damage effect
L_p' Perforation length modified to account for drilling-damage effects, ft
r_w' Wellbore radius modified to account for drilling-damage effects, ft
L_p Perforation length
k Formation permeability, md

k_{dd} Drilling-damaged-zone permeability, md
L_{dd} Drilling-damaged-zone thickness, ft
r_{dd} Drilling-damaged-zone radius, ft
r_w Wellbore radius, ft
s_p Skin resulting from perforations
s_x Skin factor, from Table, negligible for $r_d \geq 1.5\left(r_w + L_p\right)$

Well Deviation Skin

$$s_{\theta d} = -\left(\frac{\theta'_d}{41}\right)^{2.06} - \left(\frac{\theta'_d}{56}\right)^{1.865} \log_{10}\left(\frac{h_{tD}}{100}\right)$$

$$\theta'_d = \tan^{-1}\left(\sqrt{\frac{k_V}{k_H}} \tan \theta_d\right)$$

$$h_{tD} = \left(\frac{h_t}{r_w}\right)\sqrt{\frac{k_H}{k_V}}$$

$s_{\theta d}$ Skin resulting from well deviation
θ'_d Adjusted well deviation, degree
θ_d Well deviation, degree
h_{tD} Dimensionless formation thickness
h_t Total formation thickness
r_w Wellbore radius, ft
k_H Horizontal formation permeability, md
k_V Vertical formation permeability, md

Partial Penetration Skin

$$s_{bf} = 1.35\left(\left(\frac{h_t}{h_p}-1\right)^{0.825}\left\{\ln\left(h_t\sqrt{\frac{k_H}{k_V}}+7\right)-\left[0.49+0.1\ln\left(h_t\sqrt{\frac{k_H}{k_V}}\right)\right]\ln\left(r_{wc}\right)-1.95\right\}\right)$$

$$r_{wc} = \left(r_w\right)\exp\left[0.2126\left(\frac{z_m}{h_t}+2.753\right)\right] \qquad \text{for } y > 0, \qquad r_{wc} = r_w \qquad \text{for } y = 0$$

$$z_m = y + \left(h_p/2\right)$$

s_{bf} Skin caused by partial penetration of producing zone
h_t Total formation thickness
h_p Perforated thickness, ft
k_H Horizontal formation permeability, md
k_V Vertical formation permeability, md
r_{wc} Wellbore radius corrected for partial penetration effect, ft
r_w Wellbore radius, ft
y Distance between top of sand and top of open interval, ft

Correction Factor for Total Skin

$$\gamma = \log_{10}\left(\frac{h_p}{r_w}\right)\left[0.66-0.62\left(\frac{r_{dd}}{h_p}\right)^{0.33}\right]+1.12\left(\frac{r_{dd}}{h_p}\right)^{0.33}$$

γ Correction factor
h_p Perforated thickness, ft
r_w Wellbore radius, ft
r_{dd} Drilling-damaged-zone radius, ft, when the open interval does not start at the top of the producing zone:
$\qquad r_{dd} = r_{ddc} = r_{wc}/r_w$

4.5 Acidizing

Fracture Gradient

$$FG = \frac{ISIP + 0.052\rho_f D}{D}$$

FG	Fracture gradient, psi/ft
$ISIP$	Instantaneous shut-in pressure obtained from a frac job, psi
ρ_f	Fluid density at the time of the ISIP, lb/gal
D	Datum depth (normally mid perforation), ft

Maximum Injection Rate

$$q_{i,\max} = \frac{4.917 \times 10^{-6} kh \left(p_{bd} - \overline{p}\right)}{\mu \ln \left(\dfrac{0.472 r_e}{r_w} + s\right)}$$

$q_{i,\max}$	Maximum injection rate, STB/D
p_{bd}	Breakdown pressure, psi
$\overline{p}$	Average reservoir pressure, psi
k	Permeability, md
h	Reservoir thickness, ft
μ	Viscosity, cp
r_e	Drainage radius, ft
r_w	Well radius, cp
s	Skin effects, dimensionless

Maximum Tubing Injection Pressure

$$p_{ti,\max} = p_{wf} - \Delta p_{PE} + \Delta p_F$$

$$p_{bd} = FG \times D$$

$$\Delta p_{PE} = 0.433 \times \gamma_F \times D$$

$$\Delta p_F = \frac{7.51 q_i^2 D \gamma_F}{d^5 N_{\mathrm{Re}}^{0.25}}$$

$$N_{\mathrm{Re}} = 132714.3 \frac{q_i \gamma_F}{d\mu}$$

q_i	Injection rate, bbl/min
$p_{ti,\max}$	Maximum tubing injection pressure, psi
p_{wf}	Flowing bottomhole pressure, psi
Δp_E	Potential energy pressure drop, psi
Δp_f	Frictional pressure drop, psi
N_{Re}	Reynolds number
FG	Fracture gradient, psi/ft
γ_F	Fluid specific gravity
μ	Viscosity, cp
D	Depth, ft
d	Tubular internal diameter, in.

Sandstone Acidizing Design

Acid Volume Calculations

$$N_{Ac,F} = \frac{\phi \beta_F C_{HF}^0 \rho_{\mathrm{acid}}}{(1-\phi) V_F^0 \rho_F}$$

$$\theta = \frac{\exp\left(N_{\mathrm{Da},S}\epsilon_f\right)-1}{N_{Ac,F}N_{\mathrm{Da},S}} + \epsilon_f$$

Linear Geometry

$$N_{\mathrm{Da},S} = \frac{(1-\phi)V_S^0 E_{f,S} S_S^* L}{u}$$

$$\theta = \frac{ut}{\phi L} \qquad \epsilon_f = \frac{x}{L}$$

Radial Geometry

$$N_{\mathrm{Da},S} = \frac{(1-\phi)V_S^0 E_{f,S} S_S^* \pi r_w^2 h}{q_i}$$

$$\theta = \frac{q_i t}{\pi r_w^2 h \phi} \qquad \epsilon_f = \frac{r^2}{r_w^2} - 1$$

Ellipsoidal Geometry

$$N_{\mathrm{Da},S} = \frac{2\pi(1-\phi)l_{\mathrm{perf}}^3 V_S^0 E_{f,S} S_S^*}{q_{\mathrm{perf}}}$$

$$\theta = \frac{q_{\mathrm{perf}} t}{2\pi l_{\mathrm{perf}}^3 \phi} \qquad \epsilon_f = \frac{1}{3}\bar{z}^3 - \bar{z} + \frac{2}{3} \qquad \bar{z} = \frac{z}{l_{\mathrm{perf}}}$$

$N_{Ac,F}$	Acid capacity number for fast-reacting minerals
$N_{\mathrm{Da},S}$	Damkohler number for slow-reacting minerals
C_{HF}^0	Initial concentration of HF in solution
ρ_{acid}	Density of acid
ρ_F	Density of fast-reacting minerals
β_F	Fluid dissolving power
ϕ	Porosity
V_F^0	Initial volume fraction of fast-reacting minerals
V_S^0	Initial volume fraction of slow-reacting minerals
$E_{f,S}$	Reaction rate constant
S_S^*	Specific surface area of slow-reacting minerals
θ	Location of the front
ϵ_f	Dimensionless position of the front
q_i	Injection rate, bbl/min
q_{perf}	Perforation rate, bbl/min
r	Radial distance, ft
r_w	Well radius, cp
l_{perf}	Perforation length, ft
z	Elevation, ft
L	Core length, in.
u	Acid flux, ft/min
t	Time
x	Distance, in.

Flow Distribution During Acidizing With Diverting Agents

$$c_{1,j} = \frac{s_{\mathrm{cake},j}}{\bar{V}_j} \frac{2.26 \times 10^{-16} C_{da} k_j}{r_w^2 (1-\phi_{\mathrm{cake}}) k_{\mathrm{cake}}}$$

$$\bar{V}_j < \bar{V}_{c,j}$$

$$a_{1,j} = \ln\left(\frac{r_e}{r_w}\right) + s_{0,j}$$

$$a_{2,j} = \left(c_1 - c_2\right)_j$$

$$a_{3,j} = \frac{2.066 \times 10^{-4}\left(p_{wf} - p_e\right)k_j}{\mu}$$

$$t_j = \frac{a_{1,j}\bar{V}_j + \left(a_{2,j}/2\right)\bar{V}_j^2}{a_{3,j}}$$

$$\bar{V}_j = \frac{-a_{1,j} + \sqrt{a_{1,j}^2 + 2a_{2,j}a_{3,j}t}}{a_{2,j}}$$

$$\bar{V}_j > \bar{V}_{c,j}$$

$$a_{1,j} = \ln\left(\frac{r_e}{r_w}\right)$$

$$a_{1,j} = c_{1,j}$$

$$a_{4,j} = -\left[a_{3,j}\left(t - t_{c,j}\right) + a_{1,j}\bar{V}_{c,j} + \left(a_{2,j}/2\right)\bar{V}_{c,j}^2\right]$$

$$t_j = t_{c,j} + \frac{a_{1,j}\left(\bar{V}_j - \bar{V}_{c,j}\right) + \left(a_{2,j}/2\right)\left(\bar{V}_j^2 - \bar{V}_{c,j}^2\right)}{a_{3,j}}$$

$$\bar{V}_j = \frac{-a_{1,j} + \sqrt{a_{1,j}^2 - 2a_{2,j}a_{4,j}}}{a_{2,j}}$$

$\bar{V}_j$	Volume of acid injected in layer j
$\bar{V}_{c,j}$	Volume of acid needed to reduce the skin effect to zero in layer j
k_j	Permeability of layer j, md
k_{cake}	Permeability of filter cake, md
ϕ_{cake}	Porosity of filter cake
s_{cake}	Skin effect of filter cake
μ	Viscosity, cp
r_e	Drainage radius, ft
r_w	Well radius, ft
p_{wf}	Flowing bottomhole pressure, psi
p_e	Drainage pressure, psi
$s_{0,j}$	Initial damage skin effect in layer j
t_j	Time of injection a given volume of acid in layer j
$t_{c,j}$	Time of injection when a volume of acid reduces the skin effect to zero in layer j
C_{da}	Concentration of diverting agent particles in the carrying solution, ft^3

HCl Preflush Design

$$\varepsilon_{HCl} = \frac{\theta}{1 + \left[\left(1-\phi\right)/\phi\right]V_{CO_3}^0 + \left(1/N_{Ac,HCl}\right)}$$

$$N_{Ac,HCl} = \frac{\phi\beta_{HCl}C_{HCl}^0\rho_{acid}}{\left(1-\phi\right)V_{CO_3}^0\rho_{CO_3}}$$

ε_{HCl} Dimensionless position of the HCl front

ϕ Initial porosity in the region contacted by HCl

$V_{\text{CO}_3}^0$ Initial volume fraction of the rock that is carbonate mineral

$N_{Ac,\text{HCl}}$ Acid capacity number for HCl

θ Location of the front

C_{HCl}^0 Initial concentration of HCl in solution

ρ_{acid} Density of acid

ρ_{CO_3} Density of the rock that is carbonate mineral

β_F Fluid dissolving power

Carbonate Acidizing Design

Radius of Wormhole Penetration With Daccord's Model

$$r_{wh} = \left[\frac{b N_{Ac} V}{\pi h \phi} D^{-2/3} \left(\frac{q}{h} \right)^{-1/3} \right]^{1/d_f}$$

r_{wh} Radius of wormhole penetration, ft

b Constant

d_f Fractal dimension

N_{Ac} Acid capacity number

V Cumulative volume of acid, ft^3

D Molecular diffusion coefficient

h Thickness, ft

μ Viscosity, cp

ϕ Porosity

q Injection rate, bbl/min

Skin Effect During Injection With a Damaged Zone

$$s = -\frac{k}{2k_s} \ln \left[\left(\frac{r_w}{r_s} \right)^2 + \frac{N_{Ac} V}{\eta \pi r_s^2 h \phi} \right] - \ln \frac{r_s}{r_w}$$

Skin Effect for Wormhole Beyond the Damaged Zone

$$s = -\frac{1}{2} \ln \left[1 + \frac{N_{Ac} V}{\eta \pi r_w^2 h \phi} \right]$$

s Skin effect

h Thickness, ft

μ Viscosity, cp

ϕ Porosity

r_w Well radius, ft

r_s Radius of damage zone, ft

N_{Ac} Acid capacity number

V Cumulative volume of acid, ft^3

k Permeability, md

k_s Permeability, md

η Wormholing efficiency

4.6 Fracturing

Basic Hydraulic Fracturing Equations

Breakdown Pressure

$$p_b = -\sigma_H + 3\sigma_h - T$$

Reopening Pressure

$$p_r = -\sigma_H + 3\sigma_h$$

Propagation Pressure

$$p_p = \sigma_h + \Delta p_k + \Delta p_p$$

Instantaneous Shut-In Pressure

$$ISIP = \sigma_h + \delta_p$$

Closure Pressure

$$p_c = \sigma_h$$

σ_H	Major geostatic horizontal stress
σ_h	Geostatic horizontal stress
Δp_k	Cohesive resistance of the material
Δp_p	Pressure drop in the fracture
δ_p	Extra pressure needed to keep the fracture open after shut-in

General Fracturing Treatment Formulas

Bottomhole Fracturing Pressure Gradient

$$G_F = \frac{P_s + P_h - P_{tf} - P_{pf}}{D}$$

Bottomhole Fracturing Pressure

$$P_F = G_F \times D$$

Instantaneous Shut-Down Pressure

$$P_i = P_F - P_h$$

Total Surface Pressure

$$P_S = P_F + P_{tf} + P_{pf} - P_h$$

Hydraulic Horsepower

$$HHP = 0.0245 \times P_S \times Q$$

P_h	Total hydrostatic pressure, psi
P_{pf}	Perforation friction pressure, psi
P_{tf}	Total tubular friction pressure, psi
Q	Injection rate, bbl/min
D	Depth of producing interval, ft

The Minimum Horizontal Stress for a Vertical Fracture

$$\sigma_{min} \cong \frac{v}{1-v}\left(\sigma_1 - \alpha p_p\right) + \alpha p_p + \sigma_{ext}$$

σ_{min}	The minimum horizontal stress, m/Lt^2
v	Poisson's ratio
σ_1	Overburden stress, m/Lt^2
α	Biot's constant

p_p Reservoir fluid pressure or pore pressure, m/Lt^2

σ_{ext} Tectonic stress, m/Lt^2

Near-Wellbore Pressure Drop Caused by Perforation Friction

$$p_{pfr} = \frac{0.2369 i_{pf}^2 \rho}{d_{pf}^4 \alpha^2}$$

p_{pfr} Perforation friction pressure drop, psi

i_{pf} Specific injection rate, bbl/min-perforation

ρ Fracturing fluid density, m/L^3

α Discharge coefficient, usually 0.9

d_{pf} Perforation diameter, in.

Near-Wellbore Pressure Drop Caused by Tortuosity

$$\Delta p_\tau = a \times Q^{0.5}$$

Δp_τ Near-wellbore pressure drop caused by tortuosity, m/Lt^2

a Constant

Q Injection rate, L^3/t

Net Pressure

$$p_n = p_f - \sigma_{min}$$

p_n Net pressure, m/Lt^2

p_f Actual pressure in the fracture, m/Lt^2

σ_{min} The minimum horizontal stress, m/Lt^2

Fracture Propagation—Perkins, Kern, Nordgren (PKN) Geometry

Fluid Flow Down an Elliptical Tube

$$\frac{\partial p}{\partial x} = \frac{64}{\pi} - \frac{Qu}{Hw^3}$$

PKN Fracture Mechanics Equation

$$w_{(x,t)} = \frac{(1-v)H\Delta p_{(x,t)}}{G}$$

PKN Width Equation

$$w_{(0,t)} = 2.52 \left[\frac{(1-v)Q\mu L}{G} \right]^{1/4}$$

Δp Change in net pressure in the fracture, m/Lt^2

x Distance, L

Q Injection rate, L^3/t

u Viscosity, cp

H Fracture height, L

w Fracture width, L

μ Fluid viscosity, m/Lt

L Fracture half-length, L

G Shear modulus, m/L^3

v Poisson's ratio, dimensionless

t Time, t

Dimensionless Fracture Conductivity

$$C_{fD} = \frac{k_f w}{k x_f}$$

C_{fD} Dimensionless fracture conductivity
k_f Fracture permeability, md
k Permeability, md
w Width, ft
x_f Productive fracture half-length, ft

Optimum Fracture Conductivity

$$C_{fD} = 31.4159 k L_f$$

C_{fD} Dimensionless fracture conductivity
k Formation permeability, md
L_f Fracture half-length, ft

Fracture Productivity Index

$$\frac{J}{J_o} = \frac{\ln\left(\dfrac{r_e}{r_w}\right)}{\ln\left(\dfrac{r_e}{0.5 L_f}\right)}$$

J Productivity index, STB/D/psi
J_o Productivity index of unfractured well, STB/D/psi
r_e Drainage radius, ft
r_w Wellbore radius, ft
L_f Fracture half-length, ft

Fluid-Loss Rate From a Fracture

$$q_L \approx \frac{2 C_L A}{\sqrt{t - \tau}}$$

q_L Fluid-loss rate, bbl/min
C_L Fluid-loss coefficient, ft/min$^{1/2}$
A An element of the fracture area, ft^2
τ Time when each small area element of a fracture is created or opened, min
t Time measured from the start of pumping, min

Relation Between Fracture Variables and Design Goals

$$L \cong \frac{q_i t_p}{6 C_L h_L \sqrt{t_p} + 4 h_L S_p + 2 \bar{w} h_f}$$

L Fracture half-length, ft
q_i Injection rate, bbl/min
t_p Pumping time for a treatment, hr
C_L Fluid-loss coefficient, ft/min$^{1/2}$
h_L Fluid-loss height, ft
$\bar{w}$ Average fracture width, ft
h_f Fracture height, ft

Net Pressure Equation

$$p_{net} \approx \left[\frac{E'^3}{h_f^4} \{ \kappa \mu q_i L \} + p_{tip}^4 \right]^{1/4}$$

p_{net} Net pressure, psi
E' Plane strain modulus, psi
h_f Fracture height, ft
κ Constant
μ Fluid viscosity, m/Lt
q_i Injection rate, bbl/min
L Fracture half-length, ft
p_{tip} Net pressure at fracture tip for extension, psi

Effective Propped Width

$$w_{p-eff} = w_f \times F - w_{lost}$$

$$F = \frac{C}{\left(8.33 \times \gamma_{prop} + C \right) \times \left(1 - \phi \right)}$$

w_{p-eff} Effective propped width, ft
w_f Fracture width, ft
w_{lost} Proppant volume lost to the fracture width, ft
C Proppant concentration, ft³/ft³
γ_{prop} Specific gravity of proppant
ϕ Porosity, fraction

Fracture-Face Surface Area

$$A_f = \frac{q_i t}{\overline{w} + 2C_L \sqrt{2t}}$$

A_f Fracture-face surface area, ft²
q_i Injection rate, bbl/min
t Time, t
$\overline{w}$ Average fracture width, ft
C_L Fluid-loss coefficient, ft/min$^{1/2}$

Pressure for Propagation of a Radial Fracture

$$P_{net} = \left(\frac{2\pi^3 \gamma_F^3 E^2}{3\left(1 - v^2 \right)^2 V} \right)^{1/5}$$

p_{net} Net pressure, psi
γ_F Fracture surface energy
E Young's modulus, psi
v Poisson's ratio
V Fracture volume, ft³

Fracture Radius

$$R = \left(\frac{9q_i^2 t^2}{128\pi\gamma_F \left(1 - v^2 \right)} \right)^{1/5}$$

R Fracture radius, ft
q_i Injection rate, bbl/min
t Time, t
γ_F Fracture surface energy
v Poisson's ratio

Fracture Maximum Width

$$w = \frac{2P_{net}h_f\left(1-v^2\right)}{E}$$

w Fracture width, ft
p_{net} Net pressure, psi
E Young's modulus, psi
v Poisson's ratio
h_f Fracture height, ft

Leakoff Velocity—Combined Mechanisms

$$u_L = \frac{C_t}{\sqrt{t}} = \sqrt{\frac{k_{cake}\alpha\Delta p_{cake}}{2\mu_{fil}\left(t-t_{sp}\right)}} = \sqrt{\frac{k_{fil}\phi\Delta p_v}{2\mu_{fil}t}} = \sqrt{\frac{k_r\phi c_t}{\pi\mu_r t}}\Delta p_c$$

$$C_t = C_{wcv} = \frac{2C_cC_vC_w}{C_vC_w + \sqrt{C_w^2C_v^2 + 4C_c^2\left(C_v^2 + C_w^2\right)}}$$

u_L Leakoff velocity, ft/sec
k_{cake} Filter-cake permeability, md
k_{fil} Filtrate permeability, md
k_r Reservoir permeability, md
α Constant
ϕ Porosity, fraction
c_t Total compressibility, psi^{-1}
Δp_{cake} Pressure drop across the filter cake, psi
Δp_v Pressure drop across the filtrate invaded zone, psi
Δp_c Pressure drop between filtrate interface and reservoir, psi
μ_{fil} Viscosity of fracturing fluid filtrate, cp
μ_r Relative viscosity, cp
t Time, s
t_{sp} Spur time, s
C_t Combined fluid-loss coefficient, ft/min$^{1/2}$
C_{wcv} Total leakoff coefficient, ft/min$^{1/2}$
C_c Compressibility control leakoff coefficient, ft/min$^{1/2}$
C_v Viscosity controlled leakoff coefficient, ft/min$^{1/2}$
C_w Wall or filter-cake fluid-loss coefficient, ft/min$^{1/2}$

Effect of Proppant on Fracturing Fluid Rheology

$$\mu_r = \frac{\mu_{slurry}}{\mu_{base}} = \frac{1}{\left(1-f_v/f_{vM}\right)^{2.5n}}$$

μ_r Relative viscosity, cp
μ_{slurry} Slurry viscosity, cp
μ_{base} Base fracturing viscosity, cp
f_v Proppant volume fraction
f_{vM} Maximum fraction for a mobile slurry
n Power-law index

Stress Intensity Factor for a 2D Crack

$$K_I = \sqrt{\pi L} \, p_{net}$$

K_I Stress intensity factor, psi/in.$^{1/2}$
p_{net} Net internal pressure opening the crack, psi
L Crack length, in.

Stress Intensity Factor for a Radial Crack

$$K_I = 2\sqrt{\frac{R}{\pi}} \, p_{net}$$

K_I Stress intensity factor, psi/in.$^{1/2}$
p_{net} Net internal pressure opening the crack, psi
R Crack radius, in.

Fracture Toughness

$$K_{lc} = 2\sqrt{\frac{2E\gamma_F}{1-v^2}}$$

K_{lc} Critical stress intensity factor, psi/in.$^{1/2}$
γ_F Fracture surface energy
v Poisson's ratio
E Young's modulus, psi

Perforation Friction

$$\Delta p_{pf} = 0.2369 \frac{q^2 \rho}{n^2 D_p^4 C^2}$$

Δp_{pf} Pressure drop due to perforation friction, psi
q Total flow rate, B/D
ρ Fluid density, lbm/ft^3
n Number of perforations
D_p Perforation diameter, in.
C Discharge coefficient

Tortuosity for a Newtonian Fluid

$$R = \lambda \sqrt{\frac{E^3 \mu q}{h_f}} \left(\frac{1}{\sigma_{h,min} (\kappa - 1)} \right)^2$$

R Radius of curvature R of the reorientation path
λ Experimental coefficient
q Total flow rate, B/D
μ Fluid viscosity, cp
E Young's modulus, psi
κ Ratio between the stress against which the fracture in opening and the minimum stress
h_f Fracture height, ft
$\sigma_{h,min}$ Minimum horizontal stress, psi

Mass Dissolving Power of an Acid

$$X_C = \frac{\rho_C \beta C}{\rho_{CaCO_3}}$$

$$\beta = \frac{(\text{molecular weight of rock})(\text{rock stoichiometric coefficient})}{(\text{molecular weight of acid})(\text{acid stoichiometric coefficient})}$$

X_C Dissolving power of acid
β Dissolving power coefficient
ρ_C Density of acid solution, lbm/ft³
ρ_{CaCO_3} Density of calcium carbonate, lbm/ft³
C Weight fraction concentration

Effect of Acid Fracturing on Fluid Temperature

$$\Delta T_{fl} = \frac{\Delta \bar{C} \Delta H}{\rho_f C_{pfl}}$$

ΔT_{fl} Change in fluid temperature
$\Delta \bar{C}$ Average change in acid concentration
ΔH Heat of reaction
ρ_f Fluid density
C_{pfl} Fluid heat capacity

Acid Reaction Model

$$K_r \left(C_{wall} - C_{eqm} \right)^m = \left(K_g + u_L \right) \left(\bar{C} - C_{wall} \right)$$

K_r Reaction rate
K_g Mass transfer coefficient
C_{wall} Surface acid concentration
C_{eqm} Equilibrium concentration
$\bar{C}$ Average acid concentration
u_L Leakoff velocity
m Reaction rate order

Hydraulic Power

$$H_h = 0.0245 p_s q_t$$

H_h Hydraulic power, hp
p_s Surface injection pressure, psi
q_t Flow rate, bbl/min

Surface Injection Pressure

$$p_s = p_t + \Delta p_f + \Delta p_p + \Delta p_s$$

p_t Bottomhole fracture treating pressure, $= G_f D$
Δp_f Frictional pressure drop in the pipe
Δp_p Pressure drop in the perforation
Δp_s Hydrostatic pressure
D Depth
G_f Fracture gradient

Hydrostatic Pressure

$$\rho = 8.34 \gamma + \frac{\chi}{1 + 0.0456 \chi}$$

$$\gamma_T = \gamma_{60} \left[1 - \beta \left(T - 60 \right) \right]$$

$$\Delta p_s = 0.052 \rho_T D$$

ρ Density of the fluid-sand mix, ppg
γ Specific gravity of fluid
χ Concentration of sand, ppg
β Thermal coefficient of expansion fluid
T Temperature, °F

Rock Mechanics

Lab Measurements of Rock Properties Under Statics Conditions

$$T = \frac{2\sigma_3 b^2 - p_1\left(a^2 + b^2\right)}{b^2 - a^2}$$

T Rock tensile strength, psi
b Diameter of rock core, in.
a Diameter of hole in rock, in.
σ_3 Confining pressure, psi
p_1 Borehole pressure to cause failure, psi

Lab Measurements of Rock Properties Under Dynamic Conditions

$$V_p = \left[\frac{E_d\left(1-v_d\right)}{\rho\left(1+v_d\right)\left(1-2v_d\right)}\right]^{0.5}$$

$$V_s = \left[\frac{E_d}{2\rho\left(1-v_d\right)}\right]^{0.5}$$

V_p Compressional wave velocity
V_s Shear wave velocity
E_d Dynamic Young's modulus
v_d Dynamic Poisson's ratio
ρ Density of the rock

4.7 Sand Control

Completion Success

$$S_B = \frac{n_B}{T - \sum_{i-1}^{B} \frac{n_{i-1}^i}{S_{i-1}}}$$

S_B Fractional success at B barrels of production
T Total jobs
n_B Number of jobs that have produced at least B barrels
i Production increments
n_{i-1}^i Number of jobs that have produced at least $i-1$ but have not yet had the opportunity to produce i increments of production
S_{i-1} Fractional success at $i-1$ increments of production

Linear Pressure Drop Through a Single Perforation With Non-Darcy Turbulent Liquid flow

$$\Delta p_L = 0.888\left(\mu qL / kA\right) + 9.1\times10^{-13}\beta\rho\left(q/A\right)^2 L$$

Linear Pressure Drop Through a Single Perforation With Gas Flow

$$p_2 = 14.7\left\{\left(\frac{p_1}{14.7}\right) - \left[\left(2.57\times10^{-12}\times\frac{q_g\gamma\beta}{d^2\mu} + \frac{1}{k}\right)\times0.33\times\frac{zT\mu Lq_g\gamma}{d^2}\right] / \left(\gamma 28.964\right)\right\}^{1/2}$$

Δp_L Pressure drop, psi
μ Viscosity, cp

q Flow rate per perforation, B/D

A Cross-sectional flow area of perforation tunnel, ft^2

L Length of perforation tunnel, ft

k Permeability of tunnel fill material, darcies

β Beta factor (inertia coefficient for sandstone), $= 10^{(6.5-9.5\log k)}$, 1/ft

ρ Fluid density, lbm/ft^3

q_g Gas rate per perforation, scf/D

γ Gas specific gravity, (air = 1.0)

d Perforation diameter, in.

T Temperature, °K

z Gas compressibility factor

Filter Design Process

Base Soil Categories Summary

Base soil category	% finer than No. 200 sieve (0.075 mm) (After regrading where applicable)	Base soil description
1	> 85	Fine silt, clays
2	40–85	Sands, silts, clays, silty and clayey sands
3	15–39	Silty and clayey sands, gravel
4	<15	Sands, gravel

Filtering Criteria—Maximum D_{15}

Base soil category	Filtering criteria
1	$\leq 9 \times d_{85}$, but not less than 0.2 mm
2	≤ 0.7 mm
3	$\left(\dfrac{40 - A}{40 - 15}\right)\left[\left(4 \times d_{85}\right) - 0.7\text{mm}\right] + 0.7\text{mm}$ A = % passing No. 200 sieve after regrading (If $4 \times d_{85}$ is less than 0.7 mm, use 0.7 mm)
4	$\leq 4 \times d_{85}$ of base soil after regrading

Permeability Criteria

Base soil category	Minimum D_{15}
All categories	$\geq 4 \times d_{15}$ of the base soil before regrading, but not less than 0.1 mm

Maximum and Minimum Particle Size Criteria

Base soil category	Maximum D_{100}	Minimum D_5 (mm)
All categories	< 3 inches	0.075 mm
	(75 mm)	(No. 200 sieve)

[The minus No. 40 (0.425 mm) material for all filters must be nonplastic as determined according to ASTM D4318]

Segregation Criteria

Base soil category	If D_{10} is (mm)	Then maximum D_{90} is (mm)
All categories	< 0.5	20
	0.5–1.0	25
	1.0–2.0	30
	2.0–5.0	40
	5.0–10	50
	>10	60

Criteria for Filters Used Adjacent to Perforated Collector Pipe

For noncritical drains where surging or gradient reversal is not anticipated, the filter D85 must be greater than or equal to the perforation size.

For critical drains, or where surging or gradient reversal is anticipated, the filter D15 must be greater than or equal to the perforation size.

Other Filter Design Criteria

To prevent gap-graded filters:

The width of the designed filter band should be such that the ratio of the maximum diameter to the minimum diameter at any given percent passing value less than or equal to 60 percent is less than or equal to 5. Both sides of the design filter band will have a coefficient of uniformity (CU), defined as

$$CU = \frac{D_{60}}{D_{10}} \le 6$$

Initial design filter bands by these steps have CU value of 6. For final design, filter bands may be adjusted so that CU values less than 6 results. This is acceptable as long as other filter and permeability criteria are satisfied.

4.8 Well Production Problems

Low Productivity

Identifying Flow Regimes

Radial Flow Regime

(Horizontal Radial Flow, Vertical Radial Flow, Horizontal Pseudoradial Flow)

$$p' = \frac{d\Delta p}{d\ln(t)} = \frac{qB\mu}{4\pi \overline{k} H_R}$$

Linear Flow Regime

$$p' = \frac{d\Delta p}{d\ln(t)} = \frac{qB}{4hx_f}\sqrt{\frac{\mu t}{\pi\phi c_t k_y}}$$

Pseudolinear Flow Regime

$$p' = \frac{d\Delta p}{d\ln(t)} = \frac{qB}{2L(h - z_w)}\sqrt{\frac{\mu t}{\pi\phi c_t k_y}}$$

p'	Diagnostic pressure derivative
Δp	Pressure difference for drawdown tests = $p_i - p_{wf}$ for pressure buildup tests = $p_{sw} - p_{wfe}$
p_i	Initial reservoir pressure
p_{wf}	Flowing bottomhole pressure
p_{sw}	Ship-in bottomhole pressure
p_{wfe}	Flowing bottomhole pressure at the end of flow (before shut-in)
t	Flow time
q	Volumetric liquid production rate
B	Formation volume factor
μ	Fluid viscosity
c_t	Total reservoir compressibility
ϕ	Initial reservoir pressure
$\overline{k}$	Average permeability in the flow plane ($k_h = \sqrt{k_x k_y}$ or $k_{yz} = \sqrt{k_y k_z}$)
H_R	Thickness of the radial flow (h or L)
x_f	Fracture half-length
h	Pay zone thickness

k_y Permeability in the direction perpendicular to the fracture face
z_w Distance between the horizontal well and the z boundary

Determine Permeability Based on Flow Regime

Radial Flow

$$\bar{k} = -\frac{qB\mu}{4\pi H_R m_R}$$

Linear Flow

$$k_y = \frac{\mu}{\pi\phi c_t}\left(\frac{qB}{m_L H_L X_L}\right)^2$$

q Volumetric liquid production rate
B Formation volume factor
μ Fluid viscosity
c_t Total reservoir compressibility
ϕ Initial reservoir pressure
m_R Slope of plot of bottomhole pressure vs. time on a semilog scale
m_L Slope of plot of bottomhole pressure vs. square root of time
H_R Thickness of the radial flow (h or L)
H_L For linear flow = h, for pseudolinear flow = $h - z_w$
X_L For linear flow = $2x_f$, for pseudolinear flow = L
z_w Distance between the horizontal well and the z boundary
L Length of the horizontal well

Skin Effect

$$S = S_D + S_{C+\theta} + S_P + \sum S_{PS}$$

S General expression of the skin factor
S_D Damage skin during cementing, well completion, fluid injection, and oil and gas production
$S_{C+\theta}$ Skin component due to partial completion and deviation angle
S_P Skin component due to the nonideal flow condition around the perforations associated with cased-hole completion
$\sum S_{PS}$ Pseudoskin components due to non-Darcy flow effect, multiphase effect, and flow convergence near the wellbore

Excessive Cumulative Gas (ECG) Production

$$ECG = \sum_{t=t_b}^{t=t_c}\left[(GOR)_t - (GOR)_i\right]q_{ot}\Delta t$$

$(GOR)_i$ Initial gas/oil ratio
$(GOR)_t$ Gas/oil ratio at time t
t_c Coning-turn-channeling time
t_b Gas breakthrough time
q_{ot} Oil rate at time t
Δt Timestep or time interval

Critical Coning Rate

$$q_{oc} = 2.46\times10^{-5}\frac{\rho_w - \rho_o}{B_o \ln(r_e/r_w)}\frac{K_o}{\mu_o}\left(h^2 - D^2\right)$$

q_{oc} Critical coning rate, STB/D
K_o Reservoir permeability related to oil, md
h Reservoir thickness, ft
μ_o Oil viscosity, cp
D Drainage width or half distance between two horizontal well lines, ft
ρ_w Water density, lb/ft^3
ρ_o Oil density, lb/ft^3
B_o Oil formation volume factor, bbl/STB
r_e Drainage radius, ft
r_w Wellbore radius, ft

Liquid Loading of Gas Wells

$$Q_{gslMM} = \frac{3.06 p v_{sl} A}{Tz}$$

Q_{gslMM} Minimum gas flow rate, MMscf/D
P Pressure, psia
v_{sl} Terminal slip velocity, ft/sec
A Area, ft^2
T Gas temperature, °R
z Gas compressibility factor

Coiled Tubing

Hydrostatic Pressure Test

$$P = \frac{2 \times f \times Y \times t_{min}}{D}$$

Internal Yield Pressure

$$P = \frac{2 \times Y \times t_{min}}{D}$$

Torsional Yield Strength

$$T_f = \frac{Y \times \left[D^4 - \left(D - 2t_{min}\right)^4 \right]}{7.113 \times D}$$

T_f Torsional yield strength, ft
P Hydrostatic test pressure, psi
f Test factor, = 0.80
Y Specified minimum yield strength, psi
t_{min} Minimum specified wall thickness of the thinnest wall segment of tubing on the spool, mm or in., $\approx 0.95t$
D Specified outside diameter, in.

Pipe Body Yield Load

$$L_y = 3.1416 \left(D - t_{min}\right) t_{min} Y$$

L_y Pipe body yield load, lb
Y Specified minimum yield strength, psi
D Specified outside diameter, in.
t_{min} Minimum wall thickness, in.

Pressure Losses

Inside Casing and Tubing

$$\Delta P_i = \frac{L\rho^{0.8}V^{1.8}\mu^{0.2}}{3212923D^{1.2}} = \frac{L\rho^{0.8}Q^{1.8}\mu^{0.2}}{10141D^{4.8}}$$

In Annulus

$$\Delta P_a = \frac{L\rho^{0.8}V^{1.8}\mu^{0.2}}{2519939\left(D_o - D_i\right)^{1.2}} = \frac{L\rho^{0.8}Q^{1.8}\mu^{0.2}}{7952\left(D_o + D_i\right)^{1.8}\left(D_o - D_i\right)^3}$$

L	Length, ft
V	Circulation velocity, ft/min
Q	Flow rate, gpm
D	Inner diameter, in.
D_o, D_i	Outer and inner diameter, in.
μ	Dynamic viscosity, cp
ρ	Density of fluid, ppg

Water Coning

Schols Critical Production Rate

$$q_c = \left(\frac{\left(\rho_w - \rho_o\right)k\left(h^2 - D^2\right)}{2049\mu_o B_o}\right)\left(0.432 + \frac{\pi}{\ln\left(r_e / r_w\right)}\right)\left(\frac{h}{r_e}\right)^{0.14}$$

q_c	Critical production rate, STB/D
ρ_w	Density of water, g/cm^3
h	Density of oil, g/cm^3
D	Penetration, ft
k	Permeability, md
μ_o	Oil viscosity, cp
B_o	Oil formation volume factor, bbl/STB
r_e	Drainage radius, ft
r_w	Wellbore radius, ft

Heavy Oil Production

Frictional Pressure Drop

$$\Delta P_f = \frac{705\times10^{-4}}{\left(D+d\right)\left(D-d\right)^3}\times Q\times\mu_f\times L\times\frac{1}{\ln\mu_s/\mu_f}\left(\frac{\mu_s}{\mu_f}-1\right)$$

Resistant Torque Generated by the Viscosity

$$\Gamma_v = 0.165\times10^{-8}\times\mu_f\times L\times N\times\frac{d^3}{D-d}\left(\frac{\mu_s}{\mu_f}-1\right)\frac{1}{\ln\mu_s/\mu_f}\left(\frac{\mu_s}{\mu_f}-1\right)$$

ΔP_f	Pressure drop due to friction, kPa
Γ_v	Resistant torque, m.daN
D	Inside diameter of the tubing, cm
d	Drive string diameter, cm
N	Rotating speed, rev/min
Q	Pumped flow rate, m^3/d
μ_f	Viscosity of the effluent at the inlet temperature, mPa.s
μ_s	Viscosity of the effluent at the surface, mPa.s
L	Length of the tubing

4.9 Artificial Lifts

Sucker Rod Pumping

$$PRL_{max} = W_f + (0.9 + F_1)W_r$$

$$PRL_{min} = (0.9 - F_2)W_r$$

$$W_f = S_f(62.4)\frac{DA_p}{144}$$

$$W_r = \frac{\gamma_s DA_r}{144}$$

$$F_1 = \frac{SN^2\left(1 \pm \dfrac{c}{h}\right)}{70471.2} \qquad \text{For conventional and air-balanced units}$$

$$F_2 = \frac{SN^2\left(1 \mp \dfrac{c}{h}\right)}{70471.2} \qquad \text{For conventional and air-balanced units}$$

$$C = 0.5W_f + W_r\left(0.9 \pm \frac{SN^2}{70471.2}\frac{c}{h}\right) \qquad \text{For conventional and air-balanced units}$$

$$T = \frac{1}{4}S\left(W_f + \frac{2SN^2 W_r}{70471.2}\right)$$

$$N_{limit} = \frac{187.7}{\sqrt{S\left(1 \mp \dfrac{c}{h}\right)}} \qquad \text{For conventional and air-balanced units}$$

$$q = 0.1484\frac{A_p N S_p E_v}{B_o}$$

$$\delta l_r = \frac{W_f D_r}{A_r E}$$

$$S_p = S - \frac{12D}{E}\left[W_f\left(\frac{1}{A_r} + \frac{1}{A_t}\right) - \frac{SN^2\left(1 \pm \dfrac{c}{h}\right)}{70471.2}\frac{W_r}{A_r}\right]$$

$$q_s = \frac{k_p}{\mu}\frac{(d_b - d_p)^{2.9}(d_b + d_p)}{d_b^{0.1}}\frac{p}{L_p}$$

$$P_{pm} = F_s(P_h + P_f)$$

$$P_f = 6.31 \times 10^{-7} W_r SN$$

$$P_h = 7.36 \times 10^{-6} q\gamma_l L_N$$

$$L_N = H + \frac{p_{tf}}{0.433\gamma_l}$$

PRL_{max} Maximum polish rod load, lb
PRL_{min} Minimum polish rod load, lb
W_f Fluid load, lb
W_r Weight of the rod string in air, lb

S_f	Specific gravity of fluid in tubing
S	Polished rod stroke length, in.
k_p	Constant
T	Peak torque, lb
q	Pump deliverability (liquid production rate), B/D
q_s	Slippage rate, B/D
D	Length of sucker rod string, ft
D_r	Length of rod string, ft
d_b	Plunger outside diameter, in.
d_p	Barrel inside diameter, in.
L_p	Length of plunger, in.
L_N	Net lift, ft
Δp	Barrel inside diameter, in.
P_h	Hydraulic power, hp
P_{pm}	Prime mover power, hp
P_f	Power to overcome friction losses, hp
p_{tf}	Flowing tubing head pressure, psi
F_s	Safety factor, = 1.25 to 1.5
N_{limit}	Speed limit of pumping stroke
C	Counter-balance load, lb
γ_s	Specific weight of steel, (490 lb/ft^3)
γ_l	Liquid specific gravity, water = 1
A_p	Gross plunger cross-sectional area, in.^{2}
A_r	Sucker rod cross-sectional area, in.^{2}
A_t	Tubing cross-sectional area, in.^{2}
N	Number of pumping strokes per minute
c	Length of crank arm, ft
μ	Viscosity, cp
H	Depth to the average fluid level in the annulus, ft
h	Length of pitman arm, ft
S_p	Effective plunger stroke length, in.
E_v	Volumetric efficiency of the plunger
E	Modulus of elasticity of steel, (30 × 10^6 lb/in.^{2})
B_o	Formation volume factor of the fluid, STB/bbl

Gas Lift

Gas Lift Potential (GLP)

$$GLR_{\text{opt},o} = GLR_{fm} + \frac{q_{g,\text{inj}}}{q_o}$$

$GLR_{\text{opt},o}$	Optimum GLR at operating flow rate, scf/STB
GLR_{fm}	Formation oil GLR, scf/STB
$q_{g,\text{inj}}$	Lift gas injection rate, scf/D
q_o	Expected operating liquid flow rate, scf/D

Gas Flow Rate Requirement

$$q_{g,\text{total}} = S_f \sum_{i=1}^{N_w} \left(q_{g,\text{inj}} \right)_i$$

$q_{g,\text{total}}$	Total output gas flow rate of the compression station, scf/D
S_f	Safety factor, =1.5 or higher
N_w	Number of wells

Output Gas Pressure Requirement

$$p_{out} = S_f p_L$$

p_{out} Output pressure of the compression station, psia
p_L Pressure at the inlet of the gas distribution line, psia
S_f Safety factor, = 1.5 or higher

Injection Pressure at Valve Depth

$$p_{c,v} = p_{t,v} + \Delta p_v$$

$p_{c,v}$ Casing pressure at valve depth, psia
$p_{t,v}$ Tubing pressure at valve depth, psia
Δp_v Pressure differential across the operating valve (orifice)

Injection Pressure at Surface

$$p_{c,s} = p_{c,v} \exp\left(-0.01875 \frac{\gamma_g D_v}{\bar{z}\bar{T}}\right)$$

$p_{c,s}$ Casing pressure at surface, psia $\cong p_{dn}$
p_{dn} Pressure downstream the choke, psia
$p_{c,v}$ Casing pressure at valve depth, psia
γ_g Gas specific gravity, air = 1.0
$\bar{z}$ Average gas compressibility factor
$\bar{T}$ Average temperature, °R
D_v Valve depth, ft

Pressure Upstream the Choke

Sonic Flow

$$q_{gM} = 879 C_c A p_{up} \sqrt{\left(\frac{k}{\gamma_g T_{up}}\right)\left(\frac{2}{k+1}\right)^{\frac{k+1}{k-1}}}$$

Subsonic Flow

$$q_{gM} = 1248 C_c A p_{up} \sqrt{\left(\frac{k}{(k-1)\gamma_g T_{up}}\right)\left[\left(\frac{p_{dn}}{p_{up}}\right)^{\frac{2}{k}} - \left(\frac{p_{dn}}{p_{up}}\right)^{\frac{k+1}{k}}\right]}$$

q_{gM} Gas flow rate, Mscf/D
p_{up} Pressure upstream the choke, psia
p_{dn} Pressure downstream the choke, psia
C_c Choke flow coefficient
A Cross-sectional area of choke, in.^{2}
γ_g Gas specific gravity related to air
T_{up} Upstream temperature, °R
k Constant, = 1.28 for natural gas

Pressure of the Gas Distribution Line

$$p_L = \sqrt{p_{up}^2 + \left(\frac{q_{gM}p_b}{0.433T_b}\right)^2 \frac{\gamma_g \bar{T}\bar{z}L_g}{D^{16/3}}}$$

p_L Pressure at the inlet of gas distribution line, psia
p_{up} Pressure upstream the choke, psia

q_{gM} Gas flow rate, Mscf/D
p_b Base pressure, psi
T_b Base temperature, °R
γ_g Gas specific gravity, air = 1.0
$\bar{z}$ Average gas compressibility factor
$\bar{T}$ Average temperature, °R
L_g Length of distribution line, mile
D Distribution line diameter, in.

Volumetric Efficiency of Compressor Performance

$$E_v = 0.97 - \left[\left(\frac{z_s}{z_d}\right)r^{1/k} - 1\right]C_l - e_v$$

E_v Volumetric efficiency, fraction
r Cylinder compression ratio
C_l Clearance, fraction
z_s Gas deviation factor at suction of the cylinder
z_d Gas deviation factor at discharge of the cylinder
e_v Correction factor
k Constant, = 1.28 for natural gas

Isentropic Horsepower

$$w = \frac{k}{k-1}\frac{53.241}{\gamma_g}T_1\left[\left(\frac{p_2}{p_1}\right)^{(k-1)/k} - 1\right]$$

w Theoretical shaft work required to compress the gas, ft-lbf/lbm
p_1 Suction pressure of the gas, psia
p_2 Pressure of the gas at discharge point, psia
T_1 Suction temperature of the gas
γ_g Gas specific gravity, air = 1.0
k Constant, = 1.28 for natural gas

Centrifugal Compressor Horsepower

$$Hp_g = \frac{q_1 p_1}{229E_p}\left(\frac{z_1 + z_2}{2z_1}\right)\left(\frac{r^{R_p} - 1}{R_p}\right)$$

Hp_g Constant, = 1.28 for natural gas
E_p Polytropic efficiency
R_p Polytropic ratio, = $(n-1)/n$
n Polytropic exponent
p_1 Inlet pressure, psia
q_1 Gas flow rate at inlet condition, scf/D
z_1 Gas compressibility at inlet condition
z_2 Gas compressibility at discharge condition
r Compression raio, = p_2/p_1

Unbalanced Bellow Valve

$$P_{vo} = \frac{1}{1-R}P_d + S_t - \frac{R}{1-R}P_t$$

Fluid-Operated Valve

$$P_{vo} = \frac{1}{1-R}P_d + S_t - \frac{R}{1-R}P_c$$

P_{vo} Valve opening pressure, psig
P_d Pressure in the dome, psig
S_t Equivalent pressure caused by spring tension, psig
P_t Tubing pressure at valve depth when the valve opens, psi
P_c Casing pressure, psig
R Area ratio, $= A_p / A_b$
A_p Valve seat area, in.^{2}
A_b Total effective bellows area, in.^{2}

General Equation for Depth of Valve i in Continuous Gas Lift

$$D_i = \frac{p_{c,s} - \Delta p_{cm} - p_{hf,d} + \left(G_s - G_{fd}\right)D_{i-1}}{G_s - \dfrac{p_{c,s} - \Delta p_{cm}}{40000}}$$

D_i Depth of valve i, ft
D_{i-1} Depth of valve $i-1$, ft
G_{fd} Design unloading gradient, psi/ft
G_s Static (dead liquid) gradient, psi/ft
$p_{c,s}$ Casing pressure at surface, psia
Δp_{cm} Casing pressure margin, psi
$p_{hf,d}$ Design wellhead pressure, psi

Valve Testing

$$P_{tro} = \frac{P_d \text{ at } 60\,^\circ\text{F}}{1-R} + S_t$$

$$P_d \text{ at } 60\,^\circ\text{F} = \frac{520 z_{60\,^\circ\text{F}} P_d}{T_d z_d}$$

P_{tro} Test rack opening pressure, psi
P_d Pressure in the dome, psi
S_t Optional string pressure, psi
R Area ratio, $= A_p / A_b$
T_d Temperature at valve depth, °R
z_d Gas compressibility factor at valve depth condition

Electrical Submersible Pump (ESP)

$$h = \frac{\Delta p}{0.433}$$

h Pumping head, ft
Δp Pump pressure differential, psi

$$D_{pump} = D - \frac{p_{wf} - p_{suction}}{0.433 \gamma_L}$$

D_{pump} Minimum pump depth, ft
D Depth of production interval, ft
p_{wf} Flowing bottomhole pressure, psia

$p_{suction}$ Required suction pressure of pump, 150–300 psi
γ_L Specific gravity of production fluid, 1.0 for fresh water

Hydraulic Piston Pumping

$$q_{pump} = q_{eng} \frac{A_{pump}}{A_{eng}}$$

q_{pump} Flow rate of the produced fluid in the pump, B/D
q_{eng} Flow rate in the power fluid, B/D
A_{pump} Net cross-sectional area of pump piston, in.^{2}
A_{eng} Net cross-sectional area of engine piston, in.^{2}

$$P_{eng,i} - P_{eng,d} = \left(P_{pump,d} - P_{pump,i}\right)\left(P/E\right) + F_{pump}$$

$P_{eng,i}$ Pressure at engine inlet, psia
$P_{eng,d}$ Engine discharge pressure, psia
$P_{pump,d}$ Pump discharge pressure, psia
$P_{pump,i}$ Pressure intake pressure, psia
F_{pump} Pump friction-induced pressure loss, psia
P/E Proportionality factor, $= A_{pump} / A_{eng}$

$$F_{pump} = 50\gamma_L \left(0.99 + 0.01v_{pf}\right)\left(7.1e^{Bq_{total}}\right)^{N/N_{max}}$$

F_{pump} Pump friction-induced pressure loss, psia
γ_L Specific gravity of production liquid, 1.0 for H$_2$O
v_{pf} Viscosity of power fluid, centistokes
q_{total} Total liquid flow rate, B/D
N Pump speed, strokes/min
N_{max} Maximum pump speed, strokes/min
B = 0.000514 for 2 3/8-in. tubing
   = 0.000278 for 2 7/8-in. tubing
   = 0.000167 for 3 ½-in. tubing
   = 0.000078 for 4 ½-in. tubing

Progressive Cavity Pumping

$$P_s = \frac{L_r + 1}{L_r} P_r$$

P_s Pitch length of stator, ft
P_r Pitch length of rotor, ft
L_r Number of rotor lobes

$$V_0 = 0.028 D E P_s$$

V_0 Pump displacement, ft^3
D Rotor diameter, in.
E Rotor/stator eccentricity, in.
P_s Pitch length of stator, ft

$$Q_c = 7.12 D E P_s N - Q_s$$

Q_c Pump flow rate, B/D
N Rotary speed, rev/min
Q_s Leak rate, B/D

$$\Delta P = \left(2n_p - 1\right)\delta p$$

ΔP Pump head rating, psi
n_p Number of pitches of stator
δp Head rating developed into an elementary cavity, psi

$$T_m = \frac{144V_0\Delta P}{e_p}$$

T_m Mechanical resistant torque, lbf-ft
e_p Efficiency
ΔP Pump head rating, psi
V_0 Pump displacement, ft^3

$$F_b = \frac{\pi}{4}\left(2E + D\right)^2 \Delta P$$

F_b Axial load on thrust bearing, lbf
ΔP Pump head rating, psi
D Rotor diameter, in.
E Rotor/stator eccentricity, in.

Plunger Lift

$$GLR_{min} = 400\frac{D}{1000}$$

GLR_{min} Minimum required GLR by a rule of thumb, scf/bbl
D Depth of plunger, ft

$$p_c = p_{Lmax} + \frac{p_{sh}}{f_{sl}}$$

p_c Required casing pressure, psia
p_{Lmax} Maximum line pressure, psia
p_{sh} Slug hydrostatic pressure, psia
f_{sl} Slug factor, 0.5 to 0.6

$$P_{c,min} = \left[P_p + 14.7 + P_t + \left(P_{lh} + P_{lf}\right)\times V_{slug}\right]\left(1 + \frac{D}{K}\right)$$

$P_{c,min}$ Required minimum casing pressure, psia
P_p $= W_p / A_t$, psia
W_p Plunger weight, lbf
A_t Tubing inner cross-sectional area, in.^{2}
P_t Tubing head pressure, psia
P_{lh} Hydrostatic liquid gradient, psi/bbl slug
P_{lf} Fluid liquid gradient, psi/bbl slug
V_{slug} Slug volume, bbl
D Depth to plunger, ft
K Characteristic length for gas flow in tubing, ft

$$V_g = \frac{37.14F_{gs}P_{c,avg}V_t}{z\left(T_{avg} + 460\right)}$$

V_g Required gas per cycle, Mscf
F_{gs} Modified Foss and Gaul slippage factor, $= 1 + 0.02 \times \left(D / 1000\right)$

$P_{c,avg}$ Average casing pressure, $= P_{c,\min}(1 + A_t / 2A_a)$, psia
A_t Tubing cross-sectional area, in.^{2}
A_a Annulus cross-sectional area, in.^{2}
V_t Gas volume in tubing, $= A_t(D - V_{slug}L)$, Mscf
L Tubing inner capacity, ft/bbl
z Gas compressibility factor in average tubing condition
T_{avg} Average temperature in tubing, °F
V_{slug} Slug volume, bbl
D Depth to plunger, ft

$$N_{Cmax} = \frac{1440}{\dfrac{D}{V_r} + \dfrac{D - V_{slug}L}{V_{fg}} + \dfrac{V_{slug}L}{V_{fl}}}$$

N_{Cmax} The maximum number of cycles per day
V_{fg} Plunger falling velocity in gas, ft/min
V_{fl} Plunger falling velocity in liquid, ft/min
V_r Plunger rising velocity, ft/min
V_{slug} Slug volume, bbl
D Depth to plunger, ft

$$q_{Lmax} = N_{Cmax} V_{slug}$$

q_{Lmax} Maximum liquid production rate, bbl/day
N_{Cmax} The maximum number of cycles per day
V_{slug} Slug volume, bbl

$$GLR_{min} = \frac{V_g}{V_{slug}}$$

GLR_{min} Minimum required GLR, scf/bbl
V_g Required gas per cycle, Mscf
V_{slug} Slug volume, bbl

Hydraulic Jet Pumping

$$R = \frac{A_j}{A_t}$$

$$M = \frac{q_3}{q_1}$$

$$H = \frac{p_2 - p_3}{p_1 - p_2}$$

$$\eta = MH$$

$$q_1 = 1214.5 A_j \sqrt{\frac{p_1 - p_3}{\gamma_1}}$$

R Dimensionless nozzle area
M Dimensionless flow rate
H Dimensionless head
η Pump efficiency
p_1 Power fluid pressure, psia
q_1 Power fluid rate, B/D

p_2 Discharge pressure, psia

q_2 Total fluid rate in return column, $= q_1 + q_3$, B/D

p_3 Intake pressure, psia

q_3 Intake (produced) fluid rate, B/D

A_j Jet nozzle area, in.^{2}

A_s Net throat area, in.^{2}

A_t Total throat area, in.^{2}

γ_1 Specific gravity of the power fluid

Chapter 5

Facilities

This chapter contains equations to design various facilities, such as the design and calculations of horizontal separators and vertical vessels, water and gas treating units, calculation of parameters required to design hydrostatic and hydrodynamic pumps, centrifugal pumps, positive-displacement pumps, and compressors. A section is devoted for calculations and design of pipelines by considering different fluid flow equations and flow regimes inside the pipes, wall thickness, liquid and gas-line sizing using velocity considerations, and design of offshore pipelines. The chapter also includes calculations of parameters for different types of flowmeters and other flow measurement units and the design of different storage facilities. A series of calculations for different parameters in electrical systems is also provided. Finally, many nomographs and plots are given at the end of the chapter to ease the calculation of many of the above parameters.

5.1 Separation Units

Settling Theory

Horizontal Separators

Liquid Drops in Gas Phase

$$\frac{L_{\text{eff}}d^2F_g}{h_g} = 421\frac{TZQ_g}{P}\left[\left(\left|\frac{\rho_g}{\rho_l-\rho_g}\right|\right)\frac{C_D}{d_m}\right]^{1/2}$$

d Vessel internal diameter, in.
d_m Drop diameter, μm
h_g Gas-phase space height, in.
F_g Fractional gas cross-sectional area
L_{eff} Effective length of the vessel where separation occurs, ft
T Operating temperature, °R
Q_g Gas flow rate, MMscf/D
P Operating pressure, psia
Z Gas compressibility
ρ_l Liquid density, lbm/ft³
ρ_g Gas density, lbm/ft³
C_D Drag coefficient

Bubbles or Liquid Drops in Liquid Phase

$$\frac{L_{\text{eff}}d^2F_c}{h_c} = \frac{Q_c}{12}\left[\left(\left|\frac{\rho_c}{\rho_d-\rho_c}\right|\right)\frac{C_D}{d_m}\right]^{1/2}$$

d_m Bubble or drop diameter, μm
h_c Continuous liquid-phase space height, in.
F_c Fractional continuous-phase cross-sectional area

ρ_d Dispersed liquid-phase density, lbm/ft^3
ρ_c Continuous liquid-phase density, lbm/ft^3
Q_c Continuous liquid-phase flow rate, B/D

$$h_c = \frac{0.00129 t_{rc}\left(\Delta\gamma\right) d_m^2}{\mu_c}$$ for low Reynolds number flow

t_{rc} Continuous-phase retention time, min
μ_c Continuous-phase dynamic viscosity, cp
$\Delta\gamma$ Specific gravity difference (heavy/light) of continuous and dispersed phases

Vertical Vessels

Liquid Drops in Gas Phase

$$d^2 = 5054\frac{TZQ_g}{P}\left[\left(\left|\frac{\rho_g}{\rho_l - \rho_g}\right|\right)\frac{C_D}{d_m}\right]^{1/2}$$

Bubbles or Liquid Drops in Liquid Phase

$$d^2 = Q_c\left[\left(\left|\frac{\rho_c}{\rho_d - \rho_c}\right|\right)\frac{C_D}{d_m}\right]^{1/2}$$

$$d^2 = 6663\frac{Q_c\mu_c}{\left(\Delta\gamma\right)d_m^2}$$ for low Reynolds number flow

d Vessel internal diameter, in.
d_m Drop diameter, μm
T Operating temperature, °R
Q_g Gas flow rate, MMscf/D
P Operating pressure, psia
Z Gas compressibility
ρ_l Liquid density, lbm/ft^3
ρ_g Gas density, lbm/ft^3
C_D Drag coefficient
ρ_d Dispersed liquid-phase density, lbm/ft^3
ρ_c Continuous liquid-phase density, lbm/ft^3
Q_c Continuous liquid-phase flow rate, B/D
μ_c Continuous-phase dynamic viscosity, cp
$\Delta\gamma$ Specific gravity difference (heavy/light) of continuous and dispersed phases

Retention Time

Horizontal Vessels

$$d^2 L_{eff} = \frac{t_{ro}Q_o + t_{rw}Q_w}{1.4F_l}$$

Vertical Vessels

$$d^2\left(h_o + h_w\right) = \frac{t_{ro}Q_o + t_{rw}Q_w}{0.12}$$

d Vessel internal diameter, in.
L_{eff} Effective length of the vessel where separation occurs, ft
t_{ro} Oil retention time, min
t_{rw} Water retention time, min
h_o Oil pad height, in.

h_w Water pad height, in.
Q_o Oil flow rate, B/D
Q_w Water flow rate, B/D
F_l Fraction of vessel cross-sectional area filled by liquid

Demister Sizing

$$V_m = K_d \sqrt{\frac{\rho_l - \rho_g}{\rho_g}}$$

Horizontal Vessels

$$A_d = \frac{0.327 \dfrac{TZQ_g}{P}}{K_d \sqrt{\dfrac{\rho_l - \rho_g}{\rho_g}}}$$

Vertical Vessels

$$d^2 = \frac{60 \dfrac{TZQ_g}{P}}{K_d \sqrt{\dfrac{\rho_l - \rho_g}{\rho_g}}}$$

d Vessel internal diameter, in.
A_d Required demister area, in.
V_m Maximum velocity, ft/sec
K_d Maximum velocity, ft/sec
ρ_l Maximum velocity, ft/sec
ρ_g Maximum velocity, ft/sec

Seam-to-Seam Length

Horizontal Vessels

$$L_{ss} = L_{eff} + \frac{d}{12} \text{ (gas)} = \frac{4}{3} L_{eff} \text{ (liquid)}$$

Vertical Vessels

$$L_{ss} = \frac{h + \text{nozzle ID} + \text{demister height} + 54}{12} \quad \text{or}$$

$$L_{ss} = \frac{h + \text{nozzle ID} + d + \text{demister height} + 18}{12}$$

L_{ss} Seam-to-seam vessel length, ft
L_{eff} Effective length of the vessel where separation occurs, ft
d Vessel internal diameter, in.

5.2 Treating and Processing Units

Emulsion Treating

$$\mu_e / \mu_o = 1 + 2.5f + 14.1f^2$$

μ_e Viscosity of emulsion, cp
μ_o Viscosity of clean oil, cp
f Fraction of the dispersed phase

$$Q = 16\Delta T \left(0.5 q_o \gamma_o + q_w \gamma_w \right)$$

Q Required heat input for an insulted vessel, Btu/hr
ΔT Temperature increase, °F
q_o Oil flow rate, B/D
γ_o Specific gravity of oil
q_w Water flow rate, B/D
γ_w Specific gravity of water

$$v = \frac{\left(1.78 \times 10^{-6}\right) \Delta \gamma_{ow} d^2}{\mu_o}$$

v Downward velocity of the water droplet relative to the oil, ft/sec
d Diameter of the water droplet, μm
$\Delta \gamma_{ow}$ Specific gravity difference between the water and the oil (water/oil)
μ_o Dynamic viscosity of the oil, cp

$$C_{so} = 0.35 C_{sw} \gamma_w f_w$$

C_{so} Salt content of the oil, lbm/1000 bbl
C_{sw} Concentration of salt in produced water, ppm
γ_w Specific gravity of produced water
f_w Volume fraction of water in crude oil

$$h_{wd} = \left(h_{oo} - h_{ww}\right) \frac{\gamma_o}{\gamma_w} + h_{ww}$$

h_{wd} Height of water draw-off overflow nipple in the weir box above the tank bottom, ft
h_{oo} Height of clean oil outlet above the tank bottom, ft
h_{ww} Desired height of water wash in the tank above the tank bottom, ft
γ_o Specific gravity of oil
γ_w Specific gravity of water

$$F = \frac{70 \varepsilon E^2 r^6}{d_i^4}$$

F Dipolar attractive force between drops, N
ε Dielectric constant, C²/N·m²
E Electric field gradient, V/m
r Drop radius, m
d_i Interdrop distance, m

$$E_c \leq \varepsilon \left(\frac{\sigma}{d}\right)^{0.5}$$

E_c Critical voltage gradient as instability limit, V/m
ε Dielectric constant, C²/N·m²
σ Interfacial tension, N/m
d Droplet diameter, m

Inlet Spreader Design

$$q = A C_o \sqrt{2gh\left(\gamma_w - \gamma_o\right)}$$

Outlet Collectors Design

$$q = 19.65 C_o n D^2 \sqrt{h}$$

q Flow, ft³/sec
A Area of diffuser holes, ft2
C_o Orifice factor, = 0.6 to 0.7
g Gravitational constant, = 32.2 ft/sec²
h Head, ft
γ_w Specific gravity of brine
γ_o Specific gravity of oil
D Hole diameter, in
n Number of holes

Water Treating

Gravity Segregation

$$v = g_c \frac{\Delta \rho \left(d_p \right)^2}{18 \mu_L}$$

v Velocity of the droplet or particle rising or settling in a continuous phase, cm/s
$\Delta \rho$ Difference in density of the dispersed particle and the continuous phase, g/cm³
g_c Gravity acceleration constant, cm/s²
d_p Dispersed particle diameter, cm
μ_L Viscosity of the continuous phase (liquid), g/cm·s

Dispersion

$$d_{max} = 432 \left(\frac{t_r}{\Delta p} \right)^{2/5} \left(\frac{\sigma}{\rho_w} \right)^{3/5}$$

d_{max} Diameter of the droplet above which only 5% of the oil volume is contained, μm
t_r Retention time, min
Δp Pressure drop, psi
σ Surface tension, dynes/cm
ρ_w Density, g/cm³

Coalescence

$$t = \frac{\left(d_d \right)^4}{2 f_V K_s}$$

t Time for a small droplet to grow large in a quiet gravity-settling tank, seconds
d_d Droplet diameter, μm
f_V Volume fraction of the dispersed phase
K_s Empirical settling constant

Horizontal Pressure Vessel Sizing

$$d_i L_e = \frac{1000 q_w \mu_w}{\Delta \gamma_{ow} \left(d_d \right)^2}$$

$$t_r = 0.7 \frac{\left(d_i \right)^2 L_e}{q_w}$$

Vertical Cylindrical Vessel

$$\left(d_i\right)^2 = 6691F\,\frac{q_w\mu_w}{\Delta\gamma_{ow}\left(d_d\right)^2}$$

d_i Vessel internal diameter (ID), in.
L_e Effective length in which separation occurs, ft, (for design use of 75% seam-to-seam length)
q_w Water flow rate, BWPD
μ_w Water viscosity, cp
$\Delta\gamma_{ow}$ Difference in specific gravity between oil and water
d_d Oil-droplet diameter, μm
t_r Retention time, minutes
F A factor to account for turbulence and short circuiting

General Sizing Equation for Plate Coalescers

$$\left(d_d\right)^2 = \frac{4.7q_wL_p\mu_w}{Z_pB_pL\Delta\gamma_{ow}\cos\theta}$$

$$\left(q_w\right)_{max} = \frac{1562Z_pB_p}{L_p}$$

d_d Design oil-droplet diameter, μm
q_w Bulk water flow rate, BWPD
L_p Perpendicular distance between plates, in.
μ_w Water viscosity, cp
Z_p Height of the plate section perpendicular to the axis of water flow, ft
B_p Width of the plate section perpendicular to the axis of water flow, ft
L Length of the plate section parallel to the axis of water flow, ft
$\Delta\gamma_{ow}$ Difference in specific gravity between oil and water
θ Angle of the plate with the horizontal, degree

Skim Pile Sizing

$$\left(d_i\right)^2 L_{bs} = 19.1\left(q_w + 0.356A_dq_r + q_{WD}\right)$$

$$N_c = \frac{41.7\left(d_i\right)^2 L_{bs}}{q_wt}$$

d_i Pile internal diameter, in.
L_{bs} Length of baffle section, ft
q_w Produced water rate if it is disposed in pile, B/D
A_d Deck area, ft²
q_r Rainfall rate, in./hr
q_{WD} Washdown rate, B/D
N_c Number of nonflow cycles that a particle sees as it traverses the baffle section
t Time for the dump cycle, s

Separating Suspended Solids From Produced Water by Gravity Settling

$$b = \frac{36q_w\mu_w}{\Delta\gamma\left(d_p\right)^2 L_e}$$

$$v_w = 6.5\times10^{-5}\,\frac{q_w}{h_fb}$$

b Width (breath) of the flow channel, ft
q_w Water flow rate, B/D

μ_w Water viscosity, cp
d_p Dispersed particle diameter, in.
L_e Effective length, ft
v_w Velocity of water, ft/sec
h_f Height of the flume, ft

Separating Suspended Solids From Produced Water by Desanding Hydrocyclones

$$x_{98} = \frac{0.0094 D^{1.18} \exp(6.3c)}{Q_f^{0.45} (\rho_s - \rho_l)^{0.5}}$$

x_{98} Particle size at 98% efficiency, m
D Internal diameter of the cyclone, in.
c Solid concentration
Q_f Feed volumetric flow rate, m³/s
ρ_s Solid density, kg/m³
ρ_l Liquid density, kg/m³

Removing Dissolved Solids From Water by Membranes

$$Q_{pf} = K_f K_T K A \Delta p_{avg}$$

Q_{pf} Permeate flow, gal/D
K_f Fouling factor
K_T Membrane temperature-correction factor
K Permeate flow coefficient at standard temperature, gal/D-psi-ft²
A Membrane area, ft²
Δp_{avg} Average trans-membrane pressure drop, psi

Gas Treating

Estimating Solution Circulation Rate

Circulation rate : $US\ gal/min = 0.219 \times MW_a \times Q \times AG / (ML \times SG_a \times W_s)$

Acid gas pick up : $scf/gal = 31.72 \times ML \times SG_a \times W_s / MW_a$

MW_a Molecular weight of amine, lbm/mol
AG Percent acid gas, %
ML Mole loading, mol/mol
SG_a Specific gravity of amine
W_s Weight percent of solvent in solution, %

Contactor Design Consideration

$$V = K \left(\frac{\rho_l - \rho_g}{\rho_g} \right)^{0.5}$$

$$\rho_g = 2.70 \frac{P\gamma}{zT}$$

$$d = 7.75 \left(\frac{QTz}{PV} \right)^{0.5}$$

V Superficial gas velocity, ft/sec
K Coefficient
ρ_l Liquid density, lbm/ft³
ρ_g Gas density, lbm/ft³
P Pressure, psia

T Absolute temperature, °R
Q Gas flow rate, MMscf/d
z Gas compressibility factor, dimensionless
d Internal diameter, in.
γ Gas specific gravity, air = 1

Gas/Oil Ratio (GOR) at Primary Separator

GOR at primary separator, scf/sep bbl =
GOR for primary separator, scf/STB × Oil Shrinkage at primary separator, STB/sep bbl

5.3 Pumps

Hydrostatics

$$h = 2.31 p / \gamma$$

$$\gamma = \rho_f / \rho_w$$

h Height of the fluid column above a reference point
p Pressure
γ Specific gravity of the liquid
ρ_f Density of the liquid being pumped
ρ_w Density of water at standard conditions of temperature and pressure

Hydrodynamics

Bernoulli's Equation

$$v_1^2 / 2g + p_1 / \rho + Z_1 = v_2^2 / 2g + p_2 / \rho + Z_2 + h_f$$

Velocity Head

$$v^2 / 2g = 0.00259 Q^2 / d^4$$

v Average velocity of the liquid in the pipe
g Acceleration of gravity
p Pressure
ρ Density
Z Height above a datum
h_f Friction loss between points 1 and 2
d Inside pipe diameter
Q Flow rate

Suction Head

$$H_s = \left[\left(p_1 - p_{f1} \right) \times 2.31 \right] / \gamma + H_1$$

H_s Suction head of liquid being pumped
p_1 Suction-vessel operating pressure
p_{f1} Pressure drop resulting from friction in the suction pipe
γ Specific gravity of liquid, dimensionless
H_1 Height of liquid suction vessel above pump reference point

Discharge Head

$$H_d = \left[\left(p_2 + p_{f2} + P_c \right) \times 2.31 \right] / \gamma + H_2$$

H_s Discharge head of liquid being pumped
p_2 Discharge vessel operating pressure

p_{f2} Pressure drop resulting from friction in the discharge piping
γ Specific gravity of liquid, dimensionless
H_2 Operating or normal height of liquid in the discharge vessel above the pump reference
P_c Discharge flow-control-valve losses

Calculating Total Dynamic Head (TDH)

$$H_{td} = H_d - H_s = \left[\left(p_2 - p_1 + p_{f1} + p_{f2} + P_c\right)\times 2.31\right]/\gamma + H_2 - H_1$$

Power Requirements for Kinetic Energy Pumps

$$P_B = \left(q \times H_{td} \times \gamma\right)/3960e$$

Power Requirements for Positive-Displacement Pumps

$$P_B = \left(q \times \Delta p\right)/1714e$$

Energy Consumption

$$E/t = 17.9 P_B / e_m$$

P_B Brake horsepower, horsepower
e The pump efficiency factor obtained from the pump manufacture
H_{td} Total dynamic head, ft
q Pump capacity, gpm
γ Specific gravity of liquid, dimensionless
Δp Pressure difference, psi
E Electrical energy, kW-hr
e_m Motor efficiency, fraction

Centrifugal Pumps

Pump Specific Speed

$$N_s = \frac{N\sqrt{q}}{\left(H_{td}'\right)^{0.75}}$$

N_s Pump specific speed, dimensionless
N Pump rotative speed, rev/min
q Pump capacity, gpm
H_{td}' TDH per stage at the best efficiency point (BEP), ft

The Constant Portion of System Head Curves

$$H_{ws} = \left\{\left[\left(p_2 - p_1\right)\times 2.31\right]/\gamma\right\} + H_2 - H_1$$

H_{ws} The static difference between the suction and the discharge at zero flow, ft

The Variable Portion of System Head Curves

$$H_V = \left[\left(p_{f1} + p_{f2} + P_c\right)\times 2.31\right]/\gamma$$

H_V The head required to overcome friction as a result of flow, ft

Affinity Laws

$$q_2 = q_1\left(N_2 / N_1\right)$$

$$H_{td2} = H_{td1}\left(N_2 / N_1\right)^2$$

$$P_{B2} = P_{B1}\left(N_2 / N_1\right)^3$$

N_1 Old speed, rev/min
N_2 New speed, rev/min

$$q_2 = q_1\left(D_2 / D_1\right)$$

$$H_{td2} = H_{td1}\left(D_2 / D_1\right)^2$$

$$P_{B2} = P_{B1}\left(D_2 / D_1\right)^3$$

D_1 Old diameter, in.
D_2 New diameter, in.

$$q_2 = q_1\left(D_2 / D_1\right)\left(N_2 / N_1\right)$$

$$H_{td2} = H_{td1}\left(D_2 / D_1\right)^2 \left(N_2 / N_1\right)^2$$

$$P_{B2} = P_{B1}\left(D_2 / D_1\right)^3 \left(N_2 / N_1\right)^3$$

Positive-Displacement Pump

Cylinder Displacement of a Reciprocating Pump

$$s = \frac{A \times L_s \times N \times m}{231} \qquad \text{single acting cylinder}$$

$$s = \frac{\left(2A - a\right) \times L_s \times N \times m}{231} \qquad \text{double acting cylinder}$$

s Cylinder displacement, gpm
A Plunger or piston area, in.^{2}
a Piston-rod cross-sectional area, in.^{2}
L_s Stroke length, in.
N Speed, rev/min
m Number of pistons or plungers

Pump Capacity

$$q = \frac{s\left(100 - S\right)}{100}$$

q Pump capacity, gpm
s Cylinder displacement, gpm
S Slip, percent

5.4 Compressors

Isentropic (Adiabatic) Compression

$$P_1 V_1^k = P_2 V_2^k$$

Polytropic Compression

$$P_1 V_1^n = P_2 V_2^n$$

P_1 Specified absolute suction pressure, psia
V_1 Volume at pressure 1
P_2 Specified absolute discharge pressure, psia

V_2 Volume at pressure 2
k Ratio of specific heats, $= C_p / C_v$
n Polytropic exponent

Isentropic (Adiabatic) Head

$$H_{is} = 53.3 z_{avg} \left(T_s / S \right) \left[k / \left(k - 1 \right) \right] \left[\left(P_d / P_s \right)^{(k-1)/k} - 1 \right]$$

Polytropic Head

$$H_p = 53.3 z_{avg} \left(T_s / S \right) \left[k \eta_p / \left(k - 1 \right) \right] \left[\left(P_d / P_s \right)^{(k-1)/k \eta_p} - 1 \right]$$

H_{is} Isentropic head, ft-lbf/lbm
H_p Polytropic head, ft-lbf/lbm
z_{avg} Average compressibility factor, dimensionless
T_s Suction temperature, °R
S Gas specific gravity (standard atmospheric air = 1.00)
k Ratio of specific heats
P_d Discharge pressure, psia
P_s Suction pressure, psia
η_p Polytropic efficiency

Isentropic (Adiabatic) Efficiency

$$\eta_{is} = T_s \left[\left(P_d / P_s \right)^{(k-1)/k} - 1 \right] / \left(T_d - T_s \right)$$

Polytropic Efficiency

$$\eta_p = \left[\left(k - 1 \right) / k \right] \ln \left(P_d / P_s \right) / \ln \left(T_d / T_s \right)$$

η_{is} Isentropic efficiency
η_p Polytropic efficiency
T_s Suction temperature, °R
T_d Discharge temperature (actual or predicted), °R
P_d Discharge pressure, psia
P_s Suction pressure, psia
k Ratio of specific heats

Compressibility Factor

$$z = PV / nRT$$

z Compressibility factor
P Pressure
V Volume
T Temperature
n Number of moles
R Constant for a specific gas

Actual (Inlet) Volume Flow

Actual cubic feet per minute (ACFM) $= WRT_s z_s / 144 P_s MW$

Actual cubic feet per minute (ACFM) $= 19.6 T_s Q_g z_s / P_s$

W Mass flow, lbm/min
Q_g Standard volume flow, MMscf/D

R Universal gas constant, = 1545
MW Molecular weight
T_s Suction temperature, °R
P_s Absolute suction pressure, psia
z_s Compressibility at inlet

Power Requirement for Centrifugal Compressors

$$GHP = WH_p / 33000\eta_p$$

Power Requirement for Reciprocating Compressors

$$GHP = \left[(0.004367)(P_1 / V_1)(k / k - 1)(P_2 / P_1^{k-1/k} - 1)\right] / CE$$

GHP Gas horsepower, horsepower
W Mass flow, lbm/min
H_p Polytropic head, ft-lbf/lbm
η_p Polytropic efficiency
P_1 Inlet pressure, psia
V_1 Inlet volume, ACFM
P_2 Discharge pressure, psia
CE Compression efficiency, assume 0.85 for estimating purposes

Discharge Temperature for Compression

$$\ln(T_2 / T_1) = \left\{\left[\left((k-1)/k\right)\left(\ln(P_2 / P_1)\right)\right]\right\} / \eta_p$$

T_2 Estimated absolute discharge temperature, °R
T_1 Specified absolute suction temperature, °R
P_1 Specified absolute suction pressure, psia
P_2 Specified absolute discharge pressure, psia
k Ratio of specific heats
η_p Assumed polytropic efficiency
   ≈ 0.72 to 0.85 for centrifugal compressors
   ≈ 1.00 for reciprocating compressors

$$R_{\text{sect}} = \left(P_2 / P_1\right)^{1/n}$$

R_{sect} Compression ratio per section
n Number of sections

Reciprocating Compressors

Compressor Capacity

$$q_a = E_v (PD)$$

$$q_g = 35.4\left[(q_a P_s) / (T_s Z_s)\right]$$

$$Q_g = 0.051\left[(q_a P_s) / (T_s z_s)\right]$$

q_a Inlet capacity of the cylinder at actual inlet conditions, acf/min
E_v Volumetric efficiency
PD Piston displacement, acf/min
q_g Inlet capacity of the cylinder, scf/min
Q_g Inlet capacity of the cylinder, MMscf/D
T_s Suction temperature, °R
P_s Absolute suction pressure, psia
z_s Compressibility at inlet

Piston Displacement for Single-Acting Cylinder (Head-End Displacement)

$$PD = \left(d_c^2 SN \right) / 2200$$

Piston Displacement for Single-Acting Cylinder (Crank-End Displacement)

$$PD = \left[\left(d_c^2 - d_r^2 \right) SN \right] / 2200$$

Piston Displacement for Double-Acting Cylinder

$$PD = \left[\left(2d_c^2 - d_r^2 \right) SN \right] / 2200$$

PD Piston displacement, acf/min
S Stroke, in.
N Compressor speed, rev/min
d_c Cylinder diameter, in.
d_r Rod diameter, in.

Clearance Volume for Single-Acting Cylinder (Head-End Clearance)

$$\%C = 127 \left[C_{HE} / \left(d_c^2 S \right) \right]$$

Clearance Volume for Single-Acting Cylinder (Crank-End Clearance)

$$\%C = 127 \left[C_{HE} / \left(\left(d_c^2 - d_r^2 \right) S \right) \right]$$

Clearance Volume for Double-Acting Cylinder (Head-End and Crank-End Clearance)

$$\%C = 127 \left[\left(C_{HE} + C_{CE} \right) / \left(d_c^2 + \left(d_c^2 - d_r^2 \right) S \right) \right]$$

$\%C$ Cylinder clearance, %
C_{HE} Head-end clearance, in.^{3}
C_{CE} Crank-end clearance, in.^{3}
d_c Cylinder inside diameter, in.
d_r Rod diameter, in.
S Stroke length, in.

Volumetric Efficiency

$$E_v = 96 - R - C \left[\left(R^{1/k} \right) \left(z_s^2 / z_d^2 - 1 \right) \right] - L$$

E_v Volumetric efficiency
R Compression ratio
C Cylinder clearance, % of piston-swept volume
z_s Inlet compressibility factor
z_d Discharge compressibility factor
k Volumetric efficiency
L Slippage of gas past piston rings, % (1% for high-speed separable, 5% for nonlubricated compressors and 4% for propane service)

Rod Load for Single-Acting Cylinder (Head-End)

$$RL_c = a_p \left(P_d - P_u \right) + a_r P_u$$

$$RL_t = a_p \left(P_u - P_s \right) - a_r P_u$$

Rod Load for Single-Acting Cylinder (Crank-End)

$$RL_c = a_p \left(P_u - P_s \right) + a_r P_s$$

$$RL_t = a_p \left(P_d - P_u \right) - a_r P_d$$

Rod Load for Double-Acting Cylinder

$$RL_c = a_p \left(P_d - P_s \right) + a_r P_s$$

$$RL_t = a_p \left(P_d - P_s \right) - a_r P_d$$

RL_c	Rod load in compression, lbf
RL_t	Rod load in tension, lbf
a_p	Cross-section area of piston, in.^{2}
a_r	Cross-section area of rod, in.^{2}
P_d	Discharge pressure, psia
P_s	Suction pressure, psia
P_u	Pressure in unloaded end, psia

Piping Vibration

$$f_p = \left(N / 60 \right)^n$$

f_p	Compressor pulsation frequency, cycles/sec
N	Compressor speed, rev/min
n	Cylinder factor, = 1 for single-acting cylinder, = 2 for double-acting cylinder

5.5   Pipelines

Pressure Drop Equations

Bernoulli's Equation

$$Z_1 + \frac{144 P_1}{\rho_1} + \frac{V_1^2}{2g} = Z_2 + \frac{144 P_2}{\rho_2} + \frac{V_2^2}{2g} + H_L$$

$$H_L = \frac{fLV^2}{2Dg} \qquad \text{from Darcy's}$$

$$\Delta P = 0.0013 \frac{f \rho L V^2}{d} \qquad \text{from Darcy's}$$

Z	Elevation head, ft
P	Pressure, psi
ρ	Density, lbm/ft^3
V	Velocity, ft/sec
g	Gravitational constant, ft/sec^2
H_L	Head loss, ft
f	Moody friction factor, dimensionless
L	Pipe length, ft
D	Pipe diameter, ft
ΔP	Pressure drop, psi
d	Pipe inside diameter, in.

Reynolds Number for Liquids

$$\text{Re} = \frac{92.1 \left(SG \right) Q_l}{d \mu}$$

Reynolds Number for Gases

$$\text{Re} = \frac{20100 S Q_g}{d\mu}$$

μ Viscosity, cp
d Pipe inside diameter, in.
SG Specific gravity of liquid relative to water, (water=1)
S Specific gravity of gas at standard conditions relative to air (molecular weight divided by 29)
Q_l Liquid flow rate, B/D
Q_g Gas flow rate, MMscf/D

Pressure Drop for Liquid Flow

$$d^5 = \left(11.5 \times 10^{-6}\right) \frac{f L Q_l^2 (SG)}{\Delta P}$$

d Pipe inside diameter, in.
f Moody friction factor, dimensionless
L Pipe length, ft
SG Specific gravity of liquid relative to water
Q_l Liquid flow rate, B/D
ΔP Pressure drop, psi (total pressure drop)

Hazen-Williams Equation (Water in Turbulent Flow at 60 °F)

$$H_L = 0.00208 \left(\frac{100}{C}\right)^{1.85} \left(\frac{\text{gpm}}{d^{2.63}}\right)^{1.85} \qquad L = 0.015 \frac{Q_l^{1.85} L}{d^{4.87} C^{1.85}} \qquad \Delta P = 0.43 H_L$$

H_L Head loss because of friction, ft
L Pipe length, ft
C Friction factor constant, dimensionless
d Pipe inside diameter, in.
Q_l Liquid flow rate, B/D
gpm   Liquid flow rate, gpm
ΔP Pressure drop, psi

Pressure Drop for Gas Flow (General)

$$w^2 = \left[\frac{144 g A^2}{V_1'\left(\frac{fL}{D} + 2\log_e \frac{P_1}{P_2}\right)}\right] \times \left[\frac{P_1^2 - P_2^2}{P_1}\right]$$

Simplified Practical Equation

$$P_1^2 - P_2^2 = 25.2 \left[\frac{S Q_g^2 z T f L}{D^5}\right]$$

w Rate of flow, lbm/sec
g Acceleration of gravity, 32.2 ft/sec^2
A Cross-sectional area of pipe, ft^2
V_1' Specific volume of gas at upstream conditions, ft^3/lbm
f Friction factor, dimensionless
L Length, ft
D Diameter of the pipe, in.
P_1 Upstream pressure, psia

P_2 Downstream pressure, psia
S Specific gravity of gas
Q_g Gas flow rate, MMscf/D
z Compressibility factor for gas, dimensionless
T Flowing temperature, °R

Weymouth Equation

$$Q_g = 1.1 d^{2.67} \left[\frac{P_1^2 - P_2^2}{LSzT_1} \right]^{1/2}$$

Q_g Gas flow rate, MMscf/D
d Inside diameter of the pipe, in.
P_1 Upstream pressure, psia
P_2 Downstream pressure, psia
L Length, ft
z Compressibility factor for gas, dimensionless
T_1 Temperature of the gas at inlet, °R
S Specific gravity of gas

Panhandle Equation

$$Q_g = 0.028 E \left[\frac{P_1^2 - P_2^2}{L_m S^{0.961} z T_1} \right]^{0.51} d^{2.53}$$

Q_g Gas flow rate, MMscf/D
d Inside diameter of the pipe, in.
P_1 Upstream pressure, psia
P_2 Downstream pressure, psia
L_m Length, miles
z Compressibility factor for gas, dimensionless
T_1 Temperature of the gas at inlet, °R
S Specific gravity of gas
E Efficiency factor (new pipe: 1.0; good operating conditions: 0.95; average operating conditions: 0.85)

Spitzglass Equation

$$Q_g = 0.09 \left[\frac{\Delta h_w d^5}{SL(1 + 3.6/d + 0.03d)} \right]^{1/2}$$

Assumptions: $f = (1 + 3.6/d + 0.03d)(1/100)$, $T = 520°R$, $P_1 = 15$ psia, $z = 1.0$, $\Delta P \le 10\% \, P_1$

Q_g Gas flow rate, MMscf/D
d Pipe ID, in.
Δh_w Pressure loss, in. of water
L Length, ft
S Specific gravity of gas

Two-Phase Pressure Drop

$$\Delta P = \frac{3.4 \times 10^{-6} \, f L w^2}{\rho_M d^5}$$

ΔP Friction pressure drop, psi
f Friction factor, dimensionless
L Length, ft

W Rate of flow of mixture, lbm/hr
ρ_M Density of the mixture, lbm/ft^3
d Pipe ID, in.

$$W = 3180Q_g S + 14.6Q_l\left(SG\right)$$

Q_g Gas flow rate, MMscf/D
Q_l Liquid flow rate, B/D
S Specific gravity of gas at standard conditions, lbm/ft^3 (air = 1)
SG Specific gravity of liquid, relative to water, lbm/ft^3

$$\rho_M = \frac{12409\left(SG\right)P + 2.7RSP}{198.7P + RTz}$$

P Operating pressure, psia
R Gas/liquid ratio, ft^3/bbl
T Operating temperature, °R
S Specific gravity of gas at standard conditions, lbm/ft^3 (air = 1)
SG Specific gravity of liquid, relative to water, lbm/ft^3
z Compressibility factor for gas, dimensionless

Pressure Drop Duo to Changes in Elevation

$$\Delta P_Z \approx 0.433\left(SG\right)\Delta Z$$

ΔP_Z Pressure drop because of elevation increase in the segments, psi
SG Specific gravity of liquid in the segment, relative to water, lbm/ft^3
ΔZ Increase in elevation for segment, ft

Pressure Drop Caused by Valves and Fittings

Resistance Coefficient

$$H_L = K_r \frac{V^2}{2g}$$

H_L Head loss, ft
K_r Resistance coefficient, dimensionless
V Velocity, ft/sec
D Pipe ID, ft
g Gravity acceleration, ft/sec^2

Flow Coefficients

$$C_V = \frac{29.9d^2}{K_r^{1/2}}$$

$$\Delta P = 8.5\times10^{-4}\left(\frac{Q_L}{C_V}\right)^2\left(SG\right)$$

ΔP Pressure drop, psi
C_V Flow coefficient for liquid
Q_L Liquid flow rate, B/D
SG Liquid specific gravity relative to water
d Pipe ID, in.
K_r Resistance coefficient, dimensionless

Equivalent Lengths

$$L_e = \frac{K_r D}{f} \qquad L_e = \frac{K_r D}{12 f} \qquad L_e = \frac{K_r d^5}{f C_V^2}$$

K_r Resistance coefficient, dimensionless
d Pipe ID, in.
D Diameter of the pipe, ft
f Moody friction factor, dimensionless
C_V Flow coefficient for liquids

Pipe Wall Thickness

Basic Formula for Thin Wall Cylinder

$$t = \frac{P d_o}{2(H_s + P)}$$

H_s Hoop stress in pipe wall, psi
t Pipe wall thickness, in.
L Length of pipe, ft
P Internal pressure of the pipe, psi
d_o Outside diameter of pipe, in.

Wall Thickness Calculations—Using B31.3 Code

$$t = t_e + t_{th} + \left[\frac{P d_o}{2(SE + PY)}\right]\left[\frac{100}{100 - T_{ol}}\right]$$

t Minimum design wall thickness, in.
t_e Corrosion allowance, in.
t_{th} Thread or groove depth, in.
P Allowable internal pressure in pipe, psi
d_o Outside diameter of pipe, in.
S Allowable stress for pipe, psi
E Longitudinal weld-joint factor [1.0 seamless, 0.95 electric fusion weld, double butt, straight or spiral seam APL 5L, 0.85 electric resistance weld (ERW), 0.6 furnace butt weld]
Y Derating factor (0.4 for ferrous materials operating below 900 °F)
T_{ol} Manufacturers' allowable tolerance, % (12.5 pipe up to 20 in. OD, 10 pipe > 20 in. OD, API 5L)

Wall Thickness Calculations—Using B31.4 Code

$$t = \frac{P d_o}{2(FES_Y)}$$

t Minimum design wall thickness, in.
P Internal pressure in pipe, psi
d_o OD of pipe, in.
S_Y Minimum yield stress for pipe, psi
F Designing factor, 0.72 for all locations
E Longitudinal weld-joint factor [1.0 seamless, ERW, double submerged arc weld and flash weld; 0.80 electric fusion (arc) weld and electric fusion weld, 0.60 furnace butt weld]

Wall Thickness Calculations—Using B31.8 Code

$$t = \frac{P d_o}{2(FETS_Y)}$$

t Minimum design wall thickness, in.
P Internal pressure in pipe, psi

d_o OD of pipe, in.
S_Y Minimum yield stress for pipe, psi **(Table 5.1)**
F Designing factor **(Table 5.2)**
E Longitudinal weld-joint factor **(Table 5.3)**
T Temperature derating factor **(Table 5.4)**

TABLE 5.1—SPECIFIED MINIMUM YIELD STRENGTH FOR STEEL PIPE COMMONLY USED IN PIPE SYSTEMS (Reprinted from ASME B31.8-2003 by permission of The American Society of Mechanical Engineers. All rights reserved.)

Spec. No.	Grade	Type [Note (1)]	SMYS, psi
API 5L [Note (2)]	A25	BW, ERW, S	25,000
API 5L [Note (2)]	A	ERW, S, DSA	30,000
API 5L [Note (2)]	B	ERW, S, DSA	35,000
API 5L [Note (2)]	X42	ERW, S, DSA	42,000
API 5L [Note (2)]	X46	ERW. S, DSA	46,000
API 5L [Note (2)]	X52	ERW, S, DSA	52,000
API 5L [Note (2)]	X56	ERW, S, DSA	56,000
API 5L [Note (2)]	X60	ERW, S, DSA	60,000
API 5L [Note (2)]	X65	ERW, S, DSA	65,000
API 5L [Note (2)]	X70	ERW, S, DSA	70,000
API 5L [Note (2)]	X80	ERW, S, DSA	80,000
ASTM A 53	Type F	BW	25,000
ASTM A 53	A	ERW, S	30,000
ASTM A 53	B	ERW, S	35,000
ASTM A 106	A	S	30,000
ASTM A 106	B	S	35,000
ASTM A 106	C	S	40,000
ASTM A 134		EFW	[Note (3)]
ASTM A 135	A	ERW	30,000
ASTM A 135	B	ERW	35,000
ASTM A 139	A	EFW	30,000
ASTM A 139	B	EFW	35,000
ASTM A 139	C	EFW	42,000
ASTM A 139	D	EFW	45,000
ASTM A 139	E	EFW	52,000
ASTM A 333	1	S, ERW	30,000
ASTM A 333	3	S, ERW	35,000
ASTM A 333	4	S	35,000
ASTM A 333	6	S, ERW	35,000
ASTM A 333	7	S, ERW	35,000
ASTM A 333	8	S, ERW	75,000
ASTM A 333	9	S, ERW	46,000
ASTM A 381	Class Y-35	DSA	35,000
ASTM A 381	Class Y-42	DSA	42,000
ASTM A 381	Class V-46	DSA	46,000

TABLE 5.1—SPECIFIED MINIMUM YIELD STRENGTH FOR STEEL PIPE COMMONLY USED IN PIPE SYSTEMS (Reprinted from ASME B31.8-2003 by permission of The American Society of Mechanical Engineers. All rights reserved.) (Continued)

Spec. No.	Grade	Type [Note (1)]	SMYS, psi
ASTM A 381	Class Y-48	DSA	48,000
ASTM A 381	Class Y-50	DSA	50,000
ASTM A 381	Class Y-52	DSA	52,000
ASTM A 381	Class Y-56	DSA	56,000
ASTM A 381	Class Y-60	DSA	60,000
ASTM A 381	Class Y-65	DSA	65,000

GENERAL NOTE:
This table is not complete. For the minimum specified yield strength of other grades and grades in other approved specifications, refer to the particular specification.

NOTES:
(1) Abbreviations: BW—furnace butt-welded; ERW—electric resistance welded; S—seamless; FW—flash welded; EFW-electric fusion welded; DSA—double submerged-arc welded.
(2) Intermediate grades are available in API 5L.
(3) See applicable plate specification tor SMYS.

(For additional information see *ANSI/ASME B31.8*, Appendix D)

TABLE 5.2—BASIC DESIGN FACTOR (*F*) FOR STEEL-PIPE CONSTRUCTION OF NATURAL-GAS SERVICE PIPELINES (Reprinted from ASME B31.8-2003 by permission of The American Society of Mechanical Engineers. All rights reserved.)

Facility	Location Class				
	1		2	3	4
	Div. 1	Div. 2			
Pipelines, mains, and service lines [see para. 840.2(b)]	0.80	0.72	0.60	0.50	0.40
Crossings of roads, railroads without casing:					
(a) Private roads	0.80	0.72	0.60	0.50	0.40
(b) Unimproved public roads	0.60	0.60	0.60	0.50	0.40
(c) Roads, highways, or public streets, with hard surface and railroads	0.60	0.60	0.50	0.50	0.40
Crossings of roads, railroads with casing:					
(a) Private roads	0.80	0.72	0.60	0.50	0.40
(b) Unimproved public roads	0.72	0.72	0.60	0.50	0.40
(c) Roads, highways, or public streets, with hard surface and railroads	0.72	0.72	0.60	0.50	0.40
Parallel encroachment of pipelines and mains on roads and railroads:					
(a) Private roads	0.80	0.72	0.60	0.50	0.40
(b) Unimproved public roads	0.80	0.72	0.60	0.50	0.40
(c) Roads, highways, or public streets, with hard surface and railroads	0.60	0.60	0.60	0.50	0.40
Fabricated assemblies (see para. 841.121)	0.60	0.60	0.60	0.50	0.40
Pipelines on bridges (see para. 841.122)	0.60	0.60	0.60	0.50	0.40
Compressor station piping	0.50	0.50	0.50	0.50	0.40
Near concentration of people in Location Classes 1 and 2 [see para. 840.3(b)]	0.50	0.50	0.50	0.50	0.40

TABLE 5.3—BASIC DESIGN LONGITUDINAL JOINT FACTOR (E) FOR STEEL PIPELINES IN NATURAL-GAS SERVICE (Reprinted from ASME B31.8-2003 by permission of The American Society of Mechanical Engineers. All rights reserved.)

Spec. No.	Pipe Class	E Factor	Spec. No.	Pipe Class	E Factor
ASTM A 53	Seamless	1.00	ASTM A 671	Electric Fusion Welded	
	Electric Resistance Welded	1.00		Classes 13, 23, 33, 43, 53	0.80
	Furnace Butt Welded — Continuous Weld	0.60		Classes 12, 22, 32, 42, 52	1.00
ASTM A 106	Seamless	1.00	ASTM A 672	Electric Fusion Welded	
ASTM A 134	Electric Fusion Arc Welded	0.80		Classes 13, 23, 33, 43, 53	0.80
ASTM A 135	Electric Resistance Welded	1.00		Classes 12, 22, 32, 42, 52	1.00
ASTM A 139	Electric Fusion Welded	0.80			1.00
ASTM A 211	Spiral Welded Steel Pipe	0.80	API 5L	Seamless	1.00
ASTM A 333	Seamless	1.00		Electric Resistance Welded	1.00
	Electric Resistance Welded	1.00		Electric Flash Welded	1.00
ASTM A 381	Double Submerged-Arc-Welded	1.00		Submerged Arc Welded	1.00
				Furnace Butt Welded	0.60

GENERAL NOTE:
Definitions for the various classes of welded pipe are given in para 804.243
For additional information, see *ANSI Standard B31.8.*

TABLE 5.4—BASIC DESIGN TEMPERATURE DERATING FACTORS (T) FOR STEEL PIPELINE IN NATURAL-GAS SERVICE (Reprinted from ASME B31.8-2003 by permission of The American Society of Mechanical Engineers. All rights reserved.)

−20 to 250°F	T = 1.000
300°F	T = 0.967
350°F	T = 0.933
400°F	T = 0.900
450°F	T = 0.867

For additional information, see *ANSI/ASME Standard B31.8*

Velocity Considerations

Liquid-Line Sizing

$$V = 0.012 \frac{Q_L}{d}$$

V Flow velocity, ft/sec
Q_L Fluid flowrate, B/D
d Pipe ID, in.

Gas-Line Sizing

$$V_g = 60 \frac{Q_g Tz}{d^2 P}$$

V_g Gas velocity, ft/sec
Q_g Gas flow rate, MMscf/D
T Gas flowing temperature, °R
P Flowing pressure, psia
z Compressibility factor, dimensionless
d Pipe ID, in

Multiphase-Line Sizing

$$V_e = \frac{C}{\rho_M^{1/2}}$$

$$\rho_M = \frac{(12409)(SG)P + (2.7)RSP}{(198.7)P + zRT}$$

V_e Erosional velocity of the mixture, ft/sec
C Empirical constant
ρ_M Average density of the mixture at flowing conditions, lbm/ft^3
SG Liquid specific gravity relative to water
S Specific gravity of the gas relative to air
T Gas/liquid flowing temperature, °R
P Flowing pressure, psia
z Compressibility factor, dimensionless
R Gas/liquid ratio, ft^3/bbl

Determining the Pipe Size

$$d = \left[\frac{\left(11.9 + \dfrac{zTR}{16.7P}\right)Q_L}{1000V}\right]^{1/2}$$

d Pipe ID, in.
z Compressibility factor, dimensionless
R Gas/liquid ratio, ft^3/bbl
T Gas/liquid flowing temperature, °R
P Flowing pressure, psia
V Maximum allowable velocity, ft/sec
Q_L Liquid flowrate, B/D

Offshore Pipeline Design

Minimum Bending Radius of Concrete Coated Pipe

$$R = EC / S_B$$

R Bending radius, in.
E Modulus of elasticity for concrete = 3000000 psi
C Pipe radius + enamel thickness + concrete thickness, in.
S_B 2500 psi

Minimum Bending Radius of Steel Pipe

$$R = EC / fS_Y - PD / 4t$$

R Bending radius, in.
P Design pressure, psi
D Pipe OD, in.
t Pipe wall thickness, in.
E Modulus of elasticity for concrete = 30000000 psi
C Pipe radius, in.
S_Y Pipe specified minimum yield strength, psi
f Stress factor: use 75 to 85% for offshore design

Pipeline Pigging

Slug Catchers

$$Q_L = 5000Q_g Tz / P$$

Q_L Liquid flow rate in front of the pig, B/D
Q_g Gas flow rate behind the pig, MMscf/D
T Temperature, °R
P Line pressure, psi
z Compressibility factor, dimensionless

$$(\text{Vol})_{SC} = (\text{Vol}) - Q_d T_R$$

$(\text{Vol})_{SC}$ Volume of slug catcher, bbl
Vol Volume of liquid holdup, bbl
Q_d Design liquid dump rate from the slug catcher, B/D
T_R Time during which slug is processed, days, $= \text{Vol} / Q_L$
Q_L Liquid flow rate in front of the pig, B/D

5.6 Flow Measurements Units

Differential Pressure Flowmeters

$$q_v = \frac{C}{\sqrt{1-\beta^4}} \cdot \varepsilon \cdot \frac{\pi}{4} d^2 \frac{\sqrt{2\rho_1 \Delta p}}{\rho}$$

q_v Volume flow rate
C Coefficient of discharge
β Diameter ratio, $= d / D$
d Orifice diameter
D Pipe internal diameter
ε Expansion factor (for compressible media, only)
d Inside diameter of the orifice plate
ρ_1 Density at the upstream pressure tapping cross section
ρ Density of the fluid at the appropriate conditions of pressure and temperature
Δp Differential pressure

Variable Area Flowmeters

$$q_v = \frac{\alpha}{\rho_m} D_s \sqrt{g m_s \rho_m (1 - \rho_m / \rho_s)}$$

q_v Volume flow rate
ρ_m Density of the measuring medium
α Flow coefficient, $= \sqrt{1 / c_w}$
c_w Resistance coefficient
D_s Diameter of the float at the reading edge
m_s Mass of the float
ρ_m Density of the measuring medium
ρ_s Density of the float
g Gravitational acceleration

Electromagnetic Flowmeters

$$q_v = K \frac{U_0}{U_{\text{Ref}}}$$

q_v Volume flow rate
K Calibration factor
U_0 Signal Voltage
U_{Ref} Voltage generated in the sensor/transmitter

Ultrasonic Flowmeters

$$q_{adm} = q_b + q_t + \sum_{i=1}^{n} \left(\frac{\overline{v}_{ai} + \overline{v}_{ai+1}}{2} \left[A(z_{i+1}) - A(z_i) \right] \right)$$

q_{adm} Total discharge
q_b Flow rate in the bottom section with the bottom velocity obtained from the lowest path velocity by correction for bottom friction
q_t Flow rate at the highest active section with velocity v_{top} interpolated from the velocity profile
$\overline{v}_{ai}$ Mean velocity along the i_{th} acoustic path
$A(z_i)$ Cross section below the i_{th} path

Vortex Shedding Flowmeters

$$q_v = \left(\frac{\rho_f}{\rho_b} \right) \times \frac{f}{K}$$

q_v Volume flow rate
ρ_f Fluid density at flowing conditions
ρ_b Base density
f Vortex shedding frequency
K K factor

Thermal Mass Flowmeters

$$q_m = \frac{(P - L) \times C}{c_p \times \Delta T}$$

q_m Mass flow rate
P Constant electrical heating power
L Thermal power dissipation
C Device constant
ΔT Resultant temperature difference
c_p Heat capacity

Basic Orifice Meter

$$q_m = C_d E_v Y (\pi / 4) d^2 \left(2 g_c \rho_{t,p} \Delta P \right)^{0.5}$$

q_m Mass flow rate, lbm/sec
C_d Orifice plate coefficient of discharge, dimensionless
E_v Velocity of approach factor, dimensionless
Y Expansion factor, dimensionless
d Orifice plate bore diameter calculated at flowing temperature T_f, ft
g_c Dimensional conversion constant, lbm-ft/lbf-sec^2
$\rho_{t,p}$ Density of the fluid at flowing conditions (P_f, T_f), lbm/ft^3
ΔP Orifice differential pressure, lbf/in.^{2}

Orifice Meter Equation for Natural Gas

$$q_v = 218.573 C_d E_v Y_t d^2 (T_b / P_b) \sqrt{\frac{P_{fl} Z_{bair} h_w}{G_r Z_{fl} T_f}}$$

q_v Volume flow rate, scf/hr
C_d Orifice plate coefficient of discharge, dimensionless
E_v Velocity of approach factor, dimensionless

Y_l Expansion factor (upstream tap), dimensionless
d Orifice plate bore diameter calculated at flowing temperature T_f, in.
G_r Real gas relative density (specific gravity)
h_w Orifice differential pressure of water at 60 °F, in.
P_b Base pressure, psia
P_{fl} Flowing pressure (upstream tap), psia
T_b Base temperature, °R
T_f Flowing temperature, °R
Z_{bair} Compressibility at base conditions (P_b, T_b)
Z_{fl} Compressibility (upstream flowing conditions P_{fl}, T_f)

Transit-Time Ultrasonic Meters

$$q_v = V_m \left(\frac{\pi D^2}{4} \right) = K \left(\frac{t_{du} - t_{ud}}{t_{du} \times t_{ud}} \right)$$

q_v Volume flow rate
t_{du} Transit time from transducer D to U $= L / (C - V_m \cos\theta)$
t_{ud} Transit time from transducer U to D $= L / (C + V_m \cos\theta)$
L Distance between transducers U and D (path length)
C Velocity of sound in the gas
V_m Mean velocity of the flowing gas
θ Angle between acoustic path and meter axis
D Diameter of the meter bore
K Constant for a specific meter application

Turbine Meter Equation for Gas

$$q_b = q_f M_f \left(\frac{P_f T_b Z_b}{P_b T_f Z_f} \right)$$

q_b Flow rate at base conditions
q_f Flow rate at operating conditions (meter reading)
M_f Meter factor to correct meter output based on calibration
P_f Pressure flowing conditions
P_b Base pressure set by agreement near atmospheric pressure
T_b Base temperature set by agreement at 60 °F
T_f Temperature at flowing conditions
Z_b Compressibility at base pressure and temperature
Z_f Compressibility at flowing pressure and temperature

Turbine Meter Equation for Liquid

$$q_b = q_f M_f F_t F_p$$

q_b Flow rate at base conditions
q_f Flow rate at operating conditions (meter reading)
M_f Meter factor to correct meter output based on calibration
F_t Factor to control fluid from flowing temperature to base temperature
F_p Factor to correct fluid from flowing pressure to base pressure

5.7 Storage Facilities

Minimum Thickness of Shell Plates

$$t_d = \frac{2.6D(H-1)G}{S_d} + CA$$

$$t_t = \frac{2.6D(H-1)}{S_t}$$

Bottom-Course Thickness

$$t_{1d} = \left(1.06 - \frac{0.463D}{H}\sqrt{\frac{HG}{S_d}}\right)\left(\frac{2.6DHG}{S_d}\right) + CA$$

$$t_{1t} = \left(1.06 - \frac{0.463D}{H}\sqrt{\frac{H}{S_t}}\right)\left(\frac{2.6DH}{S_t}\right)$$

Upper-Course Thickness

Lowest Value Obtained From the Following

$$x_1 = 0.61(rt_u)^{0.5} + 3.84CH$$

$$x_2 = 12CH$$

$$x_3 = 1.22(rt_u)^{0.5}$$

Minimum Thickness for Upper Shell Courses

$$t_{dx} = \frac{2.6D\left(H - \dfrac{x}{1000}\right)G}{S_d} + CA$$

$$t_{tx} = \frac{2.6D\left(H - \dfrac{x}{1000}\right)}{S_t}$$

t_d Design shell thickness, in.
t_t Hydrostatic test shell thickness, in.
t_{1d} Design bottom-course thickness, in.
t_{1t} Hydrostatic bottom-course thickness, in.
t_{dx} Design Upper shell course thickness, in.
t_{tx} Hydrostatic upper shell course thickness, in.
D Nominal tank diameter, ft
H Design liquid level
G Design specific gravity of the liquid to be stored, as specified by the Purchaser
CA Corrosion allowance, in., as specified by the Purchaser
S_d Allowable stress for the design condition, lbf/in.^{2}
S_t Allowable stress for the hydrostatic test condition, lbf/in.^{2}
t_u Thickness of the upper course at the girth joint, exclusive of any corrosion allowance, in.
C $= \left[K^{0.5}(K-1)\right]/\left(1+K^{1.5}\right)$
K $= t_L / t_u$
t_L Thickness of the lower course at the girth joint, exclusive of any corrosion allowance, in.
r Nominal tank radius, in.

Minimum Width of the Tank-Bottom Reinforcing Plate

$$t_b = \frac{h^2}{14,000} + \frac{b}{310}\sqrt{HG}$$

t_b Minimum thickness of the bottom reinforcing plate, in.
h Vertical height of clear opening, in.
b Horizontal width of clear opening, in.
H Maximum design liquid level, ft
G Specific gravity, not less than 1.0

Minimum Section Modulus of the Stiffening Ring

$$Z = 0.0001 D^2 H_2 \left(\frac{V}{120} \right)^2$$

Z Required minimum section modulus, in.^{3}
D Nominal tank diameter, ft
H_2 Height of the tank shell, ft
V Design wind speed (3-sec gust), mph

Maximum Height of the Unstiffened Shell

$$H_1 = 600,000 t \sqrt{\left(\frac{t}{D} \right)^3 \left(\frac{120}{V} \right)^2}$$

H_1 Vertical distance, ft
t As-built thickness of the thinnest shell course, in.
D Nominal tank diameter, ft
V Design wind speed (3-sec gust), mph

Allowable Stress on Roof-Supporting Columns

$$F_a = \frac{\dfrac{\left[1 - \dfrac{(l/r)^2}{2C_c^2} \right]}{\dfrac{5}{3} + \dfrac{3(l/r)}{8C_c} - \dfrac{(l/r)^3}{8C_c^3}}}{\left[1.6 - \dfrac{l}{200r} \right]} \qquad l/r \le C_c$$

$$F_a = \frac{\left[\dfrac{12\pi^2 E}{23(l/r)^2} \right]}{\left[1.6 - \dfrac{l}{200r} \right]} \qquad l/r > C_c$$

$$C_c = \sqrt{\frac{2\pi^2 E}{F_y}}$$

F_a Allowable compression stress, lbf/in.^{2}
F_y Yield stress of material, lbf/in.^{2}
E Modulus of elasticity, lbf/in.^{2}
l Unbraced length of the column, in.
r Least radius of gyration of column, in.

Rafters Requirement

$$b = t \left(1.5 F_y / p \right)^{\frac{1}{2}} \le 84 \, \text{in.}$$

b Maximum allowable roof plate span
F_y Specified minimum yield strength of roof plate
t Corroded roof thickness
p Uniform pressure

Self-Supporting Cone Roofs

$$\text{Minimum Thickness} = \text{Greatest of } \frac{D}{400\sin\theta}\sqrt{\frac{T}{45}} + CA, \frac{D}{460\sin\theta}\sqrt{\frac{U}{45}} + CA, \text{ and } \frac{3}{16}\text{in.}$$

$$\text{Maximum Thickness} = \frac{1}{2}\text{in., exclusive of corrosion allowance}$$

D Nominal diameter of the tank shell, f
T Greater of load combinations with balanced snow load S_b, lbf/ft^2
U Greater of load combinations with unbalanced snow load S_u, lbf/ft^2
θ Angle cone elements to the horizontal, degree
CA Corrosion allowance

Self-Supporting Dome and Umbrella Roofs

$$\text{Minimum Thickness} = \text{Greatest of } \frac{r_r}{200}\sqrt{\frac{T}{45}} + CA, \frac{r_r}{230}\sqrt{\frac{U}{45}} + CA, \text{ and } \frac{3}{16}\text{in.}$$

$$\text{Maximum Thickness} = \frac{1}{2}\text{in., exclusive of corrosion allowance}$$

D Nominal diameter of the tank shell, ft
T Greater of load combinations with balanced snow load S_b, lbf/ft^2
U Greater of load combinations with unbalanced snow load S_u, lbf/ft^2
r_r Roof radius, ft

Liquid Weight at the Shell

$$w_L = 4.67 t_b \sqrt{F_{by}/H}$$

w_L Liquid weight, lbf/ft
F_{by} Minimum specified yield stress of the bottom plate under the shell, lbf/in.^{2}
H Design liquid height, ft
t_b Required thickness of the bottom plate under the shell, in.

Net Uplift Loads

Design Pressure

$$\left[\left(P - 8t_h\right) \times D^2 \times 4.08\right] - W_1$$

Test Pressure

$$\left[\left(P_t - 8t_h\right) \times D^2 \times 4.08\right] - W_1$$

Failure Pressure

$$\left[\left(1.5P_f - 8t_h\right) \times D^2 \times 4.08\right] - W_3$$

Wind Load

$$P_{WR} \times D^2 \times 4.08 + \left[4M_w / D\right] - W_2$$

Seismic Load

$$[4 \times M_s / D] - W_2 (1 - 0.4 A_V)$$

Design Pressure + Wind

$$\left[(0.4P + P_{WR} - 0.08t_h) \times D^2 \times 4.08\right] + [4M_{WH} / D] - W_1$$

Design Pressure + Seismic

$$\left[(0.4P - 0.08t_h) \times D^2 \times 4.08\right] + [4M_s / D] - W_1(1 - 0.4A_V)$$

Frangibility Pressure

$$\left[(3P_f - 8t_h) \times D^2\right] - W_3$$

A_V	Vertical earthquake acceleration coefficient, % g
D	Tank diameter, ft
H	Tank height, ft
M_{WH}	$= P_{WS} \times D \times H^2 / 2$, ft-lb
M_s	Seismic moment, ft-lb
P	Design pressure, in. of water column
P_f	Failure pressure, in. of water column
P_t	Test pressure, in. of water column
P_{WR}	Wind uplift pressure on roof, in. of water column
P_{WS}	Wind pressure on shell, lb/ft²
t_h	Roof plate thickness, in.
W_1	Dead load of shell minus any corrosion allowance and any dead load other than roof plate acting on the shell minus any corrosion allowance, lbf
W_2	Dead load of shell minus any corrosion allowance and any dead load including roof plate acting on the shell minus any corrosion allowance, lbf
W_3	Dead load of the shell using as-built thicknesses and any dead load other than roof plate acting on the shell using as-built thickness, lbf

Shell and Tube Heat Transfer

Basic Convention Heat Transfer Equation

$$Q = U A \Delta T_m$$

Q	Heat transferred, Btu/hr
U	Overall heat transfer coefficient, Btu / hr-ft² °F
A	Outside heat transfer surface of tubes, ft²
ΔT_m	Corrected mean temperature difference, °F

Log Mean Temperature Difference for Tube and Shell

$$LMTD = \frac{GTTD - LTTD}{2.3 \log_{10}(GTTD / LTTD)}$$

$LMTD$	Log mean temperature difference
$GTTD$	Wind pressure on shell, lb/ft²
$LTTD$	Wind pressure on shell, lb/ft²

Overall Heat Transfer Rate

$$U = \frac{1}{\sum r}$$

$$\sum r = r_{ft} + r_{fs} + r_m + r_{dt} + r_{ds}$$

$$r_m = \frac{t_w D_o}{12 k_m \left(D_o - 2t_w \right)}$$

r_{ft}, r_{fs}	Fouling resistance tube and shell-side respectively
r_{dt}, r_{ds}	Film resistance tube and shell-side respectively
r_m	Metal resistance
t_w	Tube wall thickness, in.
k_m	Tube metal thermal conductivity, Btu/hr-ft^2(°F/ft)
D_o	Metal resistance

Storage Pressure

$$\phi = P + \left[(\Delta - p)\frac{(T + 460)}{(t + 460)} \right] - A$$

ϕ	Required storage pressure, psig
P	Vapor pressure of liquid at maximum surface temperature, psia
p	Vapor pressure of liquid at minimum surface temperature, psia
Δ	Absolute pressure in tank at which vacuum vent opens, psia
T	Maximum average temperature of air-vapor mixture, °F
t	Minimum average temperature of air-vapor mixture, °F
A	Atmospheric pressure, = 14.7 psia

5.8 Electrical Systems

Ohm's Law

$$E = IR$$

E	Voltage, V
I	Current, Λ
R	Resistance, Ω

Voltage Loss in Conductor

$$R = \frac{\rho L}{A}$$

R	Resistance, Ω
ρ	Conductor resistivity, Ω-circular mil/ft
L	Conductor length, ft
A	Cross-sectional area of conductor, circular mil (A circular mil is the area of a circle with 1 mil diameter, and a mil = 0.001 in.)

Voltage Drop in Electrical Systems

Motor-Starting Voltage Drop (Off a Transformer)

$$\Delta E = \left(1 - \frac{Z_m}{Z_t} \right) 100$$

$$Z_m = \frac{1000 E_m^2}{P_m}$$

$$Z_t = Z + Z_c + Z_m$$

$$Z = \frac{10 Z_{tr} E_t^2}{P_t}$$

$$Z_c = \sqrt{3}\left(R\cos\theta + X\sin\theta\right)$$

$\triangle E$ Voltage drop, V
Z_m Motor starting impedance, Ω
Z_t Total impedance, Ω
Z_c The three-phase impedance of the cable between the transformer and the motor, Ω
Z Transformer impedance, Ω
Z_{tr} Transformer impedance, %
E_t Motor voltage, kV
E_m Transformer voltage, kV
P_t Transformer-rated kVA
P_m Motor-starting kVA
R Resistance, Ω
X Cable three-phase reactance, Ω
θ Power factor angle

Motor-Starting Voltage Drop (Off a Generator)

$$\Delta E = \left(1 - \frac{X_m}{X_m + X_g}\right)100$$

$$X_m = \frac{1000 E_m^2}{P_m}$$

$$X_g = \frac{10 X_d' E_g^2}{P_g}$$

$\triangle E$ Voltage drop, V
X_m Motor reactance during starting, Ω
X_g Generator reactance, Ω
X_d' Transient reactance of the generator, %
E_m Transformer voltage, kV
P_m Motor-starting kVA
E_g Generator voltage, kV
P_g Generator kVA

Power Factor

$$F_p = \cos\theta = \frac{P_a}{P_{ap}} = \frac{\text{kW}}{\text{kVA}}$$

F_p Power factor, $\cos\theta$
P_a Active power, kW
P_{ap} Apparent power, kVA
θ Power factor angle

Alternating-Current Motors

Synchronous Speed

$$N_s = \frac{120 f}{P}$$

N_s Synchronous speed, rev/min
f Frequency, Hz
P Number of poles

Slip

$$S = \frac{N_s - N}{N_s} 100$$

S Slip, %
N_s Synchronous speed, rev/min
N Rotor speed, rev/min

Motor Specifications

Power Formula for Single-Phase Motor

$$P_a = \frac{EIF_p}{1000}$$

Power Formula for Three-Phase Motor

$$P_a = \frac{EIF_p 1.732}{1000}$$

P_a Active power, kW
E Voltage, V
I Current, A
F_p Power factor, $\cos\theta$

Standard Motor Designs

$$H - \frac{TN_m}{5250}$$

H Horsepower
T Torque, lbf-ft
N_m Motor speed, rev/min

Electrical Formulas

Power for Alternating Current—Single Phase

$$P(Kilowatts) = \frac{\text{volts} \times \text{amps} \times PF}{1000}$$

Power for Alternating Current—Three Phase

$$P(Kilowatts) = \frac{1.732 \times \text{volts} \times \text{amps} \times PF}{1000}$$

Power for Direct Current

$$P(Kilowatts) = \frac{\text{volts} \times \text{amps}}{1000}$$

Power for Alternating Current—Single Phase

$$P(kVA) = \frac{\text{volts} \times \text{amps}}{1000}$$

Power for Alternating Current—Three Phase

$$P(kVA) = \frac{1.732 \times \text{volts} \times \text{amps}}{1000}$$

Reactive Power for Alternating Current—Single Phase

$$P(kVA) = \frac{\text{volts} \times \text{amps} \times \sqrt{1 - PF^2}}{1000}$$

Reactive Power for Alternating Current—Three Phase

$$P(kVA) = \frac{1.732 \times \text{volts} \times \text{amps} \times \sqrt{1 - PF^2}}{1000}$$

Power (Output) for Alternating Current—Single Phase

$$P(hp) = \frac{\text{volts} \times \text{amps} \times \mathit{eff} \times PF}{746 \times 100}$$

Power (Output) for Alternating Current—Three Phase

$$P(hp) = \frac{1.732 \times \text{volts} \times \text{amps} \times \mathit{eff} \times PF}{746 \times 100}$$

Power (Output) for Direct Current

$$P(hp) = \frac{\text{volts} \times \text{amps} \times \mathit{eff}}{746 \times 100}$$

Current [When P(horsepower) Is Known] for Alternating Current—Single Phase

$$I(\text{amps}) = \frac{Hp \times 746 \times 100}{\text{volts} \times \mathit{eff} \times PF}$$

Current [When P(horsepower) Is Known] for Alternating Current—Three Phase

$$I(\text{amps}) = \frac{Hp \times 746 \times 100}{1.732 \times \text{volts} \times \mathit{eff} \times PF}$$

Current [When P(horsepower) Is Known] for Direct Current

$$I(\text{amps}) = \frac{Hp \times 746 \times 100}{\text{volts} \times \mathit{eff}}$$

Current [When P(kilowatts) Is Known] for Alternating Current—Single Phase

$$I(\text{amps}) = \frac{\text{Kilowatts} \times 1000}{\text{volts} \times PF}$$

Current [When P(kilowatts) Is Known] for Alternating Current—Three Phase

$$I\left(\text{amps}\right) = \frac{\text{Kilowatts} \times 1000}{1.732 \times \text{volts} \times PF}$$

Current [When P(kilowatts) Is Known] for Direct Current

$$I\left(\text{amps}\right) = \frac{\text{Kilowatts} \times 1000}{\text{volts}}$$

Current [When P(kVA) Is Known] for Alternating Current—Single Phase

$$I\left(\text{amps}\right) = \frac{kVA \times 1000}{\text{volts}}$$

Current (When P(kVA) Is Known) for Alternating Current—Three Phase

$$I\left(\text{amps}\right) = \frac{kVA \times 1000}{1.732 \times \text{volts}}$$

PF   Power factor
eff   Efficiency
Hp   Horsepower

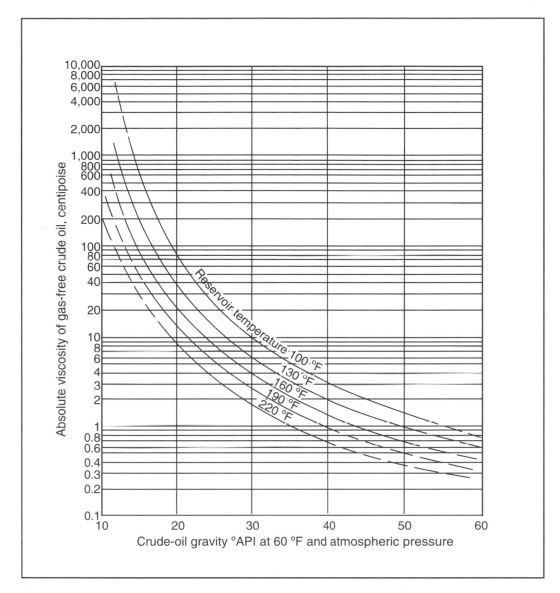

Fig. 5.1—Gas-free crude viscosity as a function of reservoir temperature and stock-tank crude gravity (from Beal 1946).

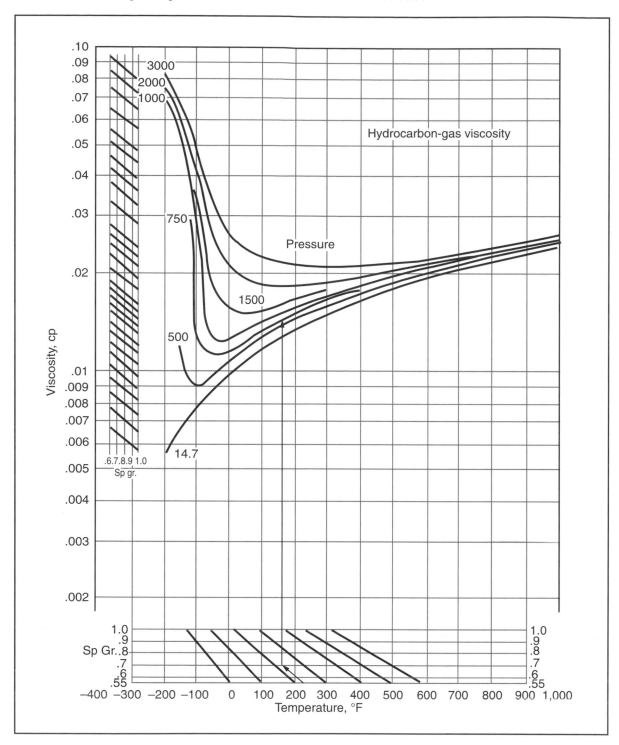

Fig. 5.2—Hydrocarbon-gas viscosity vs. temperature (Lake 2006). From the GPSA Engineering Data Book, 13th Edition, Fig. 23-23.

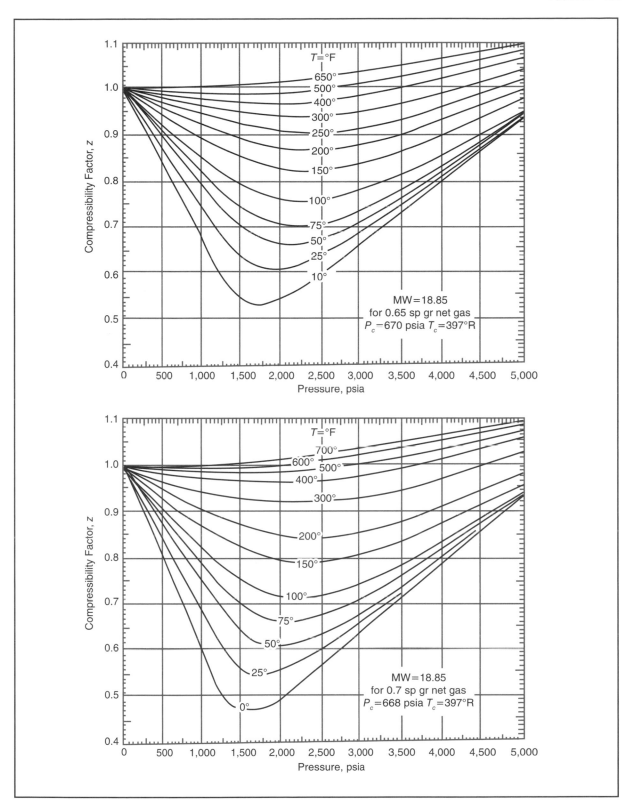

Fig. 5.3—Compressibility of low-molecular-weight natural gases (Lake 2006). Courtesy of Gas Processors Suppliers Association.

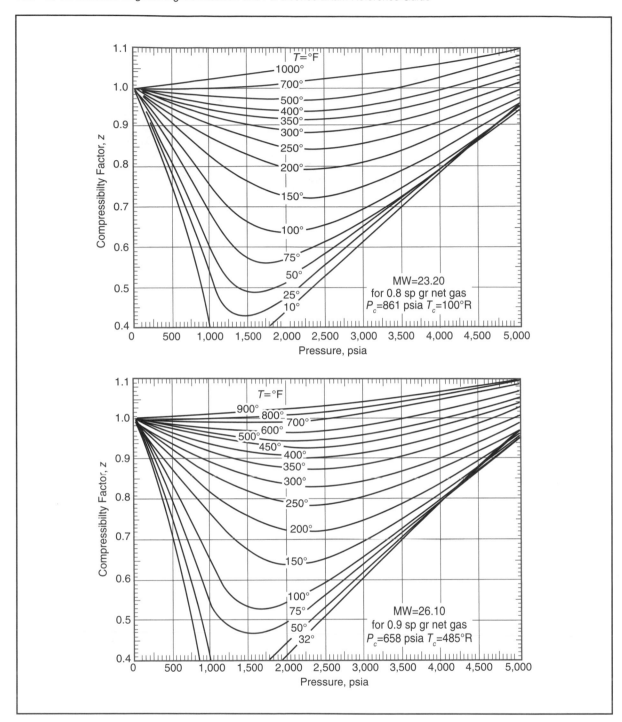

Fig. 5.3 (Continued)—Compressibility of low-molecular-weight natural gases (Lake 2006). Courtesy of Gas Processors Suppliers Association.

Chapter 6

Petroleum Economics

This chapter contains equations to study different aspects of petroleum economics, including estimating the valuation of oil and gas reserves by calculating parameters such as discounting, cost of capital, present and future value of lump sums, sinking funds, annuity, loans, leases, interest rates, etc. The fundamental concepts of reservoir management are also presented and include net cash flow, capital expenditures, operating expenditures, lifting cost, net profit, depreciation, depletion, and amortization. Also provided are the relationships for calculating such parameters as rate of return, ratio of profit to investment, and equity rate of return to analyze investment decision, net present value, and measuring risk by looking into risk adjusted capital, value of risk, and return on risk adjusted capital. The chapter also includes equations to represent investment decisions such as the calculations for a royalty-tax system, measures of dispersion, exploration risk analysis, and probability.

6.1 Valuation of Oil and Gas Reserves

Annual Discounting

$$D_f = \frac{1}{\left(1+r\right)^t}$$

Monthly Discounting

$$D_f = \frac{1}{\left(1+\dfrac{r}{12}\right)^{12t}}$$

Continuous Discounting

$$D_f = \frac{1}{e^{rt}}$$

D_f Discount factor for a specific point in time
r Annual rate of discount expressed as a fraction or present
t Time in years from the as of date to the point of reference for discounting

Weighted Average Cost of Capital

$$C_{at} = C_{bt} \times \left(1 - T_R\right)$$

C_{at} Weighted average cost of capital after federal income tax
C_{bt} Weighted average cost of capital before federal income tax
T_R Tax rate

Future Value of Lump Sum

$$F = P\left(1+i\right)^n$$

Present Value of Lump Sum

$$P = \frac{F}{\left(1+i\right)^{n}}$$

Sinking Fund

$$A = F\left[\frac{i}{\left(1+i\right)^{n}-1}\right]$$

Annuity (Loan)

$$A = P\left[\frac{i}{\left(1+i\right)^{n}-1}+1\right]$$

Annuity Due or Lease

$$B = P\left[\frac{i}{\left(1+i\right)^{n}-1}+\left(1+i\right)^{n-1}\right]$$

Modified Sinking Fund

$$B = F\left[\frac{i}{\left(1+i\right)^{n}-1}\bigg/\left(1+i\right)\right]$$

Nominal Interest Rates

$$i_{n} = i \times m$$

Effective Interest Rates

$$i_{e} = \left(1+i\right)^{m}-1$$

i The interest rate per period
n The total number of interest periods
m The total number of compounding periods
P A present lump sum of money
F A future lump sum of money (received n periods from now)
A An end-of-period payment or receipt in a uniform series continuing for n periods
B A beginning-of-period payment or receipt in a uniform series continuing for n periods
t The number of years

6.2 Reservoir Management

Net Cash Flow (NCF) = Net Annual Revenue − Net Annual Expenditure = Total Cash In − Total Cash Out

Capital Expenditures (CAPEX) =
Beginning Net Fixed Assets − Ending Net Fixed Assets − Depreciation Expense

Operating Expenditures (OPEX) =
Production Cost per Unit, USD/bbl × Production Volume, bbl

Or

Lifting Cost per Unit, USD/bbl =
(OPEX + Royalties + Exploration Expenses + Depreciation)/ Sales Volume

Net Profit =

Revenues – Costs = Cash Receipts – Cash Disbursement

Discount Cash Flow = Net Cash Flow × Discount Factor

Discount Cash Out (CAPEX+OPEX) = Cash Out × Discount Factor

Discounted Production, MM bbl = Daily Production × (365/1,000,000) × Discount Factor

Dividend Payout Ratio = Dividend per Share / Earnings per Share

Return On Investment (ROI) = Σ NCF / Investment

Return On Assets (ROA) = Average Net Income / Average Book Investment

Discounted Rate On Investment (DROI) = NPV / Present Value of Investment

Weighted Average Cost of Capital

$$C_{RW} = \frac{C_{RD}\left(1 - T_R\right)C_D + C_{RE}C_E + C_{RP}C_P}{C_D + C_E + C_P}$$

C_{RW} Weighted average cost of capital, %
C_{RD} Cost of debt, %
C_{RE} Cost of common stock equity, %
C_{RP} Cost of preferred stock, %
C_D Market value of debt
C_E Market value of common stock equity
C_P Market value of preferred stock
T_R Tax rate

Depreciation, Depletion, and Amortization Formulas (DD&A)

Straight Line Depreciation

$$C_{SL} = C/t_L$$

C Cost of tangible capital item
t_L Depreciation life

Sum-of-the-years Depreciation

$$SYD_n = \left[\frac{t_L - n + 1}{\left(\sum_{n=1}^{t_L} n\right)}\right] \times C$$

C Cost of tangible capital item
t_L Depreciation life
n Depreciation year

Declining Balance Depreciation

$$\sum_{i=1}^{n} DB_i = C\left\{1 - \left[1 - \left(M / t_L\right)\right]^n\right\}$$

C Cost of tangible capital item
t_L Depreciation life
M Multiplier (for double declining balance = 2)
n Number of years since start of depreciation

Switch From Declining Balance to Straight Line

$$N = t_L - \left(t_L / M\right) + 1$$

N Year to switch from declining balance to straight line
t_L Depreciation life
M Multiplier (for double declining balance = 2)

Unit-of-production Depreciation or Cost Depletion

$$UOP_n = C\left(Q_n / U\right) \qquad \text{or} \qquad UOP_n = \left[C - \sum_{i=1}^{n} UOP_i\right] \times \left(Q_n / R_n\right)$$

C Cost of tangible capital item or leasehold cost
Q_n Annual production (BOE) of year n
U Ultimate recovery, $= \sum_{n=1}^{t_L} = Q_n$
R_n Reserves at beginning of year n
n Depreciation year
t_L Producing life

6.3 Investment Decision Analysis

Accounting Rate of Return

$$ARR = \frac{NI}{\left(I - S\right)/2}$$

$$ARR = \frac{NI}{I}$$

ARR Accounting rate of return
NI Average financial income (after taxes) over the estimated life of the project
I Initial capital investment
S Salvage value

Net Present Value

$$NPV = \sum_{j=0}^{L} \frac{NCF_j}{\left(1+i\right)^j}$$

NPV Net present value discounted at rate i
NCF_j Net cash flow for period j
L Project life

Discounted Profit to Investment Ratio

$$\frac{P}{I} = \frac{\sum_{j=0}^{L} \dfrac{NCF_j}{\left(1+i_{op}\right)^j}}{\sum_{j=0}^{L} \dfrac{INV_j}{\left(1+i_{op}\right)^j}}$$

$$\frac{P}{I} = \frac{\sum_{j=1}^{L} \dfrac{NOI_j}{\left(1+i_{op}\right)^j}}{\sum_{j=0}^{L} \dfrac{INV_j}{\left(1+i_{op}\right)^j}}$$

Discounted Cash Flow Rate of Return (DCFROR)

$$\sum_{j=0}^{L} \frac{INV_j}{(1+i)^j} = \sum_{j=1}^{L} \frac{NOI_j}{(1+i)^j}$$

NOI_j Net operating income period j
NCF_j Net cash flow period j
INV_j Investment period j
i_{op} Average investment opportunity rate
i DCFROR
L Life of the project

Appreciation of Equity Rate of Return (AOEROR)

$$i = \left[\frac{\sum_{j=1}^{L} NOI_j \left(1+i_{op}\right)^{L-j}}{\sum_{j=0}^{L} \frac{INV_j}{\left(1+i_{op}\right)^j}} \right]^{\frac{1}{L}} - 1$$

NOI_j Net operating income period j
INV_j Investment period j
i_{op} Average investment opportunity rate
i AOEROR
L Terminal point

6.4 Risk Analysis

Measures of Risk
Risk Adjusted Capital (RAC):
Maximum amount of money that can be lost (with a certain confidence)

Value at Risk (VaR):
Difference between the mean and the maximum amount of money that can be lost (with a certain confidence)

Return on Risk Adjusted Capital (RORAC):
Relation between expected profit and the maximum amount of money that can be lost

Expected Value (EV) = Probability weighted value of all possible outcomes

Expected Monetary Value (EMV) = Expected value of the present values of the net cash flows = EV (NPV)

Or

$$EMV = \sum_{all\ i} P\left(outcome\ i\right) \times NPV_{outcome\ i}$$

$$Risked\ DROI = \frac{EMV}{EV\left(PV\ of\ Investment\right)}$$

Judging Probability of Recovery
P (wildcat discovery) = P(trap) × P(source) × P(porosity and permeability) × etc.

Profit or Net Cash Flow Calculations for a Royalty-Tax System
Gross Production – Shrinkage =
Gross Sales × Net Revenue Interest =
Net Sales × Price =
Gross Revenue – Share of State and Local Taxes – Share of Operating Costs =

Net Operating Income Before Income Taxes – Income Tax =
Net Operating Income After Income Taxes – Share of Investments =
Net Cash Flow After Income Tax

Measures of Dispersion

Population Variance

$$= \frac{1}{N} \sum (x_i - \bar{x})^2$$

Sample Variance

$$= \frac{1}{N-1} \sum (x_i - \bar{x})^2$$

Skewness

$$= \left[\frac{N}{(N-1) \times (N-2)} \right] \left(\frac{1}{s^3} \right) \sum (x_i - \bar{x})^3$$

Normal Distribution

$$f(x) = \frac{1}{\sqrt{2\pi\sigma^2}} \exp\left[-\frac{(x-\mu)}{2\sigma^2} \right]$$

Log-Normal Distribution

$$f(x) = \frac{1}{\sqrt{2\pi\sigma_1^2}} \exp\left[-\frac{(\ln x - \mu_1)}{2\sigma_1^2} \right] \qquad \mu_1 = \ln\left(\frac{\mu^2}{\sqrt{\sigma^2 + \mu^2}} \right) \qquad \sigma_1 = \sqrt{\ln\left(\frac{\sqrt{\sigma^2 + \mu^2}}{\mu^2} \right)}$$

μ Mean
σ Standard deviation

Probability Equations

Bayes' Rule

$$P(A_i | B) = \frac{P(B|A_i) \cdot P(A_i)}{\sum_{i=1}^{k} P(B|A_i) \cdot P(A_i)}$$

$P(A_i | B)$ Posterior probabilities
$P(A_i)$ Prior event probabilities

Binomial Distribution

$$P(x) = C_x^n \cdot p^x \cdot q^{n-x}$$

$$C_x^n = \frac{n!}{x!(n-x)!}$$

$P(x)$ Probability of obtaining exactly x successes in n trails
p Probability of success
q Probability of failure
n Number of trails considered
x Number of successes

Multinomial Distributions

$$P(S) = \frac{N!}{k_1!k_2!...k_m!} P_1^{k_1} P_2^{k_2} ... P_m^{k_m}$$

$P(S)$ Probability of the particular sample
P Probabilities of drawing types 1, 2, … m from population
N Size of sample, $= k_1 + k_2 + ... + m$
$k_1, k_2, ... k_m$ Total number of outcomes of type 1, 2, …, m
m Number of different types

Hypergeometric Distributions

$$P(x) = \frac{\binom{C}{x}\binom{N-C}{n-x}}{\binom{N}{n}}$$

$P(x)$ Probability of successes if trails are dependent and selected
N Number of items in the population
C Number of total successes in the population
n Number of trails (size of the sample)
x Number of successes observed in the sample

Poisson Distributions

$$P(x) = \frac{\lambda^x}{x!} e^{-\lambda}$$

$P(x)$ Probability of exactly x occurrences
λ Average number of occurrence per interval of time or space
x Number of occurrences per basic unit of measure

Normal Distributions

$$f(x) = \frac{1}{\sigma\sqrt{2\pi}} e^{-\frac{1}{2}\left(\frac{x-\mu}{\sigma}\right)^2}$$

$f(x)$ Probability density function
μ Mean
σ Standard deviation

Uniform Distributions

$$f(x) = \frac{1}{x_{max} - x_{min}}$$

Triangular Distributions

$$f(x) = \begin{cases} \left(\dfrac{X - X_{min}}{X_{mod} - X_{min}}\right)^2 \cdot \left(\dfrac{X_{mod} - X_{min}}{X_{max} - X_{min}}\right), & X_{min} \geq X \geq X_{mod} \\[2em] \left(\dfrac{X_{max} - X}{X_{max} - X_{mod}}\right)^2 \cdot \left(\dfrac{X_{max} - X_{mod}}{X_{max} - X_{min}}\right), & X_{mod} \geq X \geq X_{max} \end{cases}$$

Petroleum Exploration Risk Analysis

Probability of Wildcat Discovery =

$(\text{Probability of reservoir trap}) \times (\text{Probability that trap is in the position projected from seismic}) \times$

$(\text{Probability of pay thickness}) \times (\text{Probability of hydrocarbons in formation})$

Probability of $x_1, x_2, x_3, \ldots, x_r$ outcomes in a sample of n trials $= \dfrac{\left(C_{x_1}^{d_1}\right)\left(C_{x_2}^{d_2}\right)\left(C_{x_3}^{d_3}\right)\cdots\left(C_{x_r}^{d_r}\right)}{\left(C_n^N\right)}$

$d_1 + d_2 + d_3 + \ldots + d_r = N$

$x_1 + x_2 + x_3 + \ldots + x_r = n$

n	Number of trials (wells) in the multiple-well program
N	Total number of undrilled prospects in the basin or exploration area before the n wells are drilled
r	Number of possible outcomes on any trial
$d_1, d_2, d_3, \ldots, d_r$	Number of elements in the sample space designated as each outcome before the n wells is drilled
$x_1, x_2, x_3, \ldots, x_r$	Number of outcomes that occur in each of the r categories

Probability of x successes in n independent trials $= \left(C_x^n\right)(p)^x(1-p)^{n-x}$

n	Number of independent trials
x	Number of successes in the n trials $0 \le x \le n$
p	Probability of success on any given trial $0 \le p \le 1.0$
$\left(C_x^n\right)$	Combination of n things taken x at a time $= \dfrac{n!}{x!(n-x)!}$

Probability of $x_1, x_2, x_3, \ldots, x_r$ outcomes in n independent trials $= \dfrac{n!}{x_1! x_2! x_3! \cdots x_r!(n-x)!}(p_1)^{x_1}(p_2)^{x_2}(p_3)^{x_3}\cdots(p_r)^{x_r}$

$p_1 + p_2 + p_3 + \ldots + p_r = 1.0$

$x_1 + x_2 + x_3 + \ldots + x_r = n$

n	Total number of independent trials
r	The number of possible outcomes
$x_1, x_2, x_3, \ldots, x_r$	The number of times the outcomes occur in the trials
$p_1, p_2, p_3, \ldots, p_r$	Probability of occurrence of the outcomes on any given independent trial

Risk Analysis Using Simulation Techniques

$$EMV_A = \left[P(Dry) \times \left(\begin{array}{c}\text{Dry Hole} \\ \text{Expenses Plus} \\ \text{Write-offs}\end{array}\right) + P(Gas) \times \left(\begin{array}{c}\text{Conditional} \\ \text{Mean Value,} \\ \mu_{EMV(Gas)}\end{array}\right) + P(Oil) \times \left(\begin{array}{c}\text{Conditional} \\ \text{Mean Value,} \\ \mu_{EMV(Oil)}\end{array}\right) \right]$$

EMV_A	The expected value at chance node A
$P(Gas), P(Oil)$	Likelihood of occurrence of gas and oil

Chapter 7

Conversion Factors

Length
1 meter = 39.37 in.
1 inch = 2.54 cm
1 foot = 30.48 cm = 0.3048 m
1 mile = 5,280 ft = 1,720 yard = 1609.344 m
1 nautical mile = 6,076 ft

Mass
1 lbm = 453.6 g = 0.4536 kg = 7000 gr (grain)
1 Kg = 1000 g = 2.2046 lbm
1 slug = 1 lbf-sec^2/ft = 32.174 lbm
1 US ton = 2,000 lbm (also called short ton)
1 long ton = 2,240 lbm (also called British ton)
1 tonne = 1000 kg (also called metric ton) = 2204.6 lbm
1 kip = 1000 lb

Force
1 lbf = 4.448 N = 4.448 × 10^5 dynes
1 lbf = 32.174 poundals = 32.174 lbm-ft/sec^2

Gravitational Acceleration
g = 32.2 ft/sec^2 = 9.81 m/s^2

$$g_\lambda - 9.7803267714 \left(\frac{1+0.00193185138639 \sin^2 \lambda}{\sqrt{1-0.00669437999013 \sin^2 \lambda}} \right) m/s^2$$

λ The geographic latitude of the earth ellipsoid measured from the equator, degree

Pressure
1 atm   = 14.69595 psia = 2,118 lbf/ft^2
          = 29.92 in. Hg = 760 mm = 1.013 bars
          = 33.93 ft H$_2$O = 1.013 × 10 Pa = 101.3 kPa
1 Pa = 1 N/m^2 = 10^{-5} bars

Volume
1 ft^3 = 7.481 US gal = 6.31 Imperial gal = 28.316 L
1 m^3 = 1000 L = 10^6 cm^3 = 264.2 US gal = 35.31 ft^3 = 264.2 gal
1 bbl = 42 US gal = 5.61 ft^3
1 bbl = 9694.08 in.^{3}

Density
Water = 62.4 lbm/ft^3 = 1000 kg/m^3 = 1 g/cm^3 = 8.33 lbm/US gal

°API, 60°F = (141.5/SG, 60°F) − 131.5
SG, 60°F = 141.5/(°API, 60°F + 131.5)

Velocity
1 knot = 1 nautical mile/hr
60 mph = 88 ft/sec

$$\left(\frac{lb \times s^n}{ft^2} \right) = 0.002088543 \times eq.cp$$

Temperature
°F = 1.8 (°C) + 32
°R = °F + 459.67 = 1.8 (K)

Energy
1 J = 1 kg·m^2/s^2 = 10^7 dyne
1 Btu = 777 ft-lbf = 252 cal = 1055 J
1 hp hr = 2545 Btu
1 kW·hr = 3412 Btu = 1.341 hp hr

Power
1 hp = 550 ft-lbf/sec = 33,000 ft-lbf/min

Gas Constant
R   = 1.987 Btu/lb mol °R = 1.987 cal/g mol °K
         = 0.7302 atm ft^3/lb mol °R = 1545 ft-lbf/lb mol °R
         = 0.08206 L atm/g mol °K
         = 82.06 atm cm^3 mol °K
         = 8314 Pa m^3 mol °K ox. J/kg mol °K
         = 8.314 kJ/kg mol °K

Viscosity
1 cp   = 0.01 Poise = 0.01 g/cm·s = 0.01 dyne·s/cm
         = 0.001 kg/m·s = m·Pa·s = 0.001 N·s/m^2
         = 2.42 lbm/ft-hr = 0.0752 slug/ft-hr
         = 6.72 × 10^{-4} lbm/ft-sec
         = 2.09 × 10^{-5} lbf-sec/ft^2
1 Pa s   = 0.0209 lbf-sec/ft^2 = 0.672 lbm/ft-sec

$$\left(\frac{lb \times s^n}{ft^2} \right) = 0.002088543 \times eq.cp$$

$$\left(\frac{lb \times s}{ft^2} \right) = 4.79 \times 10^4 \ cp$$

References

1. Adams, N.J. and Charrier, T. 1985. *Drilling Engineering: A Complete Well Planning Approach*. Tulsa, Oklahoma: PennWell Publishing Company.
2. Ahmed, T. 2006. *Reservoir Engineering Handbook*, second edition. Burlington, Massachusetts: Gulf Professional Publishing/Elsevier.
3. Allen, T.O. and Roberts, A.P. 1978. *Production Operations: Well Completions, Workover, and Stimulation*. Tulsa, Oklahoma: Oil and Gas Consultants International.
4. ASME. 2005. *Drilling Fluids Processing Handbook*. Burlington, Massachusetts: Gulf Professional Publishing/Elsevier.
5. Baker, R.C. 2000. *Flow Measurement Handbook, Industrial Design, Operating Principles, Performance, and Application*. UK: Cambridge University Press.
6. Bassiouni, Z. 1994. *Theory, Measurement and Interpretation of Well Logs*. Richardson, Texas: Textbook Series, SPE.
7. Bateman, R.M. 1985. *Open-Hole Log Analysis and Formation Evaluation*. Boston, Massachusetts: International Human Resources Development Corporation.
8. Beal, C. 1946. The Viscosity of Air, Water, Natural Gas, Crude Oil and Its Associated Gases at Oil Field Temperatures and Pressures. In *Transactions of the Society of Petroleum Engineers*, Vol. 165, SPE-946094-G, 94-115. Richardson, Texas: Society of Petroleum Engineers.
9. Bell, W.T. and Sukup, R.A. 1995. *Perforating*. Richardson, Texas: Monograph Series, SPE.
10. Bourgoyne, A.T., Millheim, K.K., Chenevert, M.E. et al. 1986. *Applied Drilling Engineering*, Vol. 2. Richardson, Texas: Textbook Series, SPE.
11. Campbell, J.M. 1979. *Gas Conditioning and Processing*, fifth edition, Vol. I and II. Norman, Oklahoma: Campbell Petroleum Series.
12. Cholet, H. ed. 2000. *Well Production Handbook*. Paris, France: Editions Technip.
13. Clegg, J.D. ed. and Lake L.W. (Editor-in-Chief). 2006. *Petroleum Engineering Handbook, Volume 4: Production Operations Engineering*. Richardson, Texas: SPE.
14. Dake, L.P. 1978. *Fundamentals of Reservoir Engineering*, No. 8. Amsterdam: Developments in Petroleum Science, Elsevier Science BV.
15. Drillingformulas.com. 2012. Well Control Equations.
16. Economides, M.J. and Nolte K.G. 2000. *Reservoir Stimulation*, third edition.UK: Wiley & Sons Ltd.
17. Ezekwe, N. 2011. *Petroleum Reservoir Engineering Practice*. Boston Massachusetts: Pearson Education Inc.
18. Fanchi, J.R. ed. and Lake, L.W. (Editor-in-Chief). 2006. *Petroleum Engineering Handbook, Volume 1: General Engineering*. Richardson, Texas: SPE.
19. Gas Processors Supplier Association. 1979. *Engineering Data Book*, ninth edition, fourth version. Tulsa, Oklahoma: The association.
20. Helander, D.P. 1983. *Fundamentals of Formation Evaluation*. Tulsa, Oklahoma: OGCI Publications, Oil and Gas Consultants International Inc.
21. Holstein, E.D. ed. and Lake, L.W. (Editor-in-Chief). 2006. *Petroleum Engineering Handbook, Volume 5: Reservoir Engineering and Petrophysics*. Richardson, Texas: SPE.
22. Jensen, J.L. and Lake, L.W. 2000. *Statistics for Petroleum Engineers and Geoscientists*, second edition. Amsterdam, Netherlands: Elsevier.
23. Lake, L.W. (Editor-in-Chief). 2006. *Petroleum Engineering Handbook, Volume 7: Indexes and Standards*. Richardson, Texas: SPE.
24. Lake, L.W. (Edior-in-Chief). 2006. *Petroleum Engineering Handbook, Volume 3: Facilities and Construction Engineering*. Richardson, Texas: Society of Petroleum Engineers.

25. Lapeyrouse, N.J. 2002. *Calculations for Drilling, Production, and Workover*, second edition. Burlington, Massachusetts: Gulf Professional Publishing/Elsevier.

26. Mitchell, R.F. ed. and Lake, L.W. (Editor-in-Chief). 2006. *Petroleum Engineering Handbook, Volume 2: Drilling Engineering*. Richardson, Texas: SPE.

27. Newendorp, P. and Schuyler, J. 2000. *Decision Analysis for Petroleum Exploration*, second edition. Aurora, Colorado: Planning Press.

28. Penberthy, W.L. Jr. and Shaughnessy, C.M. 1992. *Sand Control*. Richardson, Texas: Monograph Series, SPE.

29. Rahman, S.S. and Chilingarian, G.V. 1995. *Casing Design, Theory and Practice*. Amsterdam, Netherlands: Elsevier Science B.V.

30. Samuel, R. 2010. *Formulas and Calculations for Drilling Operations*. Salem, Massachusetts: Scrivener Publishing LLC/Wiley & Sons.

31. Schlumberger Limited. 1969. *Log Interpretation Principles/Application*. New York: Schlumberger Limited.

32. Sperry-Sun. 1996–1998. Sperry-Sun Drilling Service Manual. Sperry-Sun: A Division of Dresser Industries Inc.

33. Thompson, R.S. and Wright, J.D. 1985. *Oil Property Evaluation*, second edition. Golden, Colorado: Thompson-Wright Associates.

34. Upp, E.L. and LaNasa, P.J. 2002. *Fluid Flow Measurements, A practical Guide to Accurate Flow Measurement,* second edition. Gulf Professional Publishing/Elsevier.

35. Warner, H.R. Jr. ed. and Lake, L.W. (Editor-in-Chief). 2006. *Petroleum Engineering Handbook, Volume 6: Emerging and Peripheral Technologies*. Richardson, Texas: SPE.

36. Wild Well Control. 2014. *Technical Data Book: A Quick Reference Book of Formulas, Charts and Tables*, http://www.wildwell.com/literature-on-demand/literature/technical-data-book.pdf (7 August 2014).

37. Willhite, G.P. 1986. *Waterflooding*, Vol. 3, 42. Richardson, Texas: Textbook Series, SPE.

38. Williams, B.B., Gidley, J.L., et al. 1979. *Acidizing Fundamentals*. Richardson, Texas: Monograph Series, SPE.